P9-APM-607

8⁹⁵

STRATEGY
AND
MARKET
STRUCTURE

NEW YORK · JOHN WILEY & SONS, INC.

London ·

STRATEGY AND MARKET STRUCTURE

Competition, Oligopoly, and the Theory of Games

MARTIN SHUBIK

SECOND PRINTING, AUGUST, 1960

Copyright © 1959, by John Wiley & Sons, Inc.

All Rights Reserved. This book or any part
thereof must not be reproduced in any form
without the written permission of the publisher.

Library of Congress Catalog Card Number: 58–14221

Printed in the United States of America

To my Parents and other Friends

FOREWORD

Some of the most important work in the development of economic theory is associated with the study of duopoly and oligopoly. Ever since these forms of market organization attracted the attention of Cournot, economic theorists have returned to the problems they offer, attempting to probe deeper and deeper into the behavior of firms under the strictly set conditions of these markets. Great ingenuity was displayed not only by Cournot but also by Edgeworth, Bertrand, and others. The revival of the interest in monopoly and monopolistic competition in the first half of this century is another step in this continued occupation of the best minds with the perplexing difficulties that have remained unsolved over the decades.

We now possess many proposals on how to deal with oligopoly and monopolistic competition. All have evolved from the general underlying principles of modern economic theory; but they have also shown that we are moving along the edges of the type of thinking that has led to the establishment of our present knowledge in these fields. This is clearly evidenced by the fact that all contemporary theory of oligopoly is piece-meal. There is an elaborate set-up of clever casuistry with seemingly endless additions of new and interesting cases. What is lacking is the central idea, the development of truly general principles. Without such unification, the individual cases discussed remain separated and singular. It is not even clear whether they have been properly focused and in their present form can ever be combined under a unifying principle. The desire to obtain a unifying view is naturally strong. It does not always succeed because it may require the stepping outside of the present framework of concepts and basic ideas which have led to the existing difficulties. When that situation arises a major step has to be taken, and fundamentally new notions must be introduced. Sometimes, in principle, this is impossible. Therefore it could be that the differences between free competition and oligopolistic behavior may never be overcome and that we will have to live with this dichotomy as best we can. But current theory has not shown that this situation has to be accepted, nor has it given any hints as to how an improvement could be made.

It is here that the theory of games of strategy assumes its fundamental role in economics. This theory, first shown in a comprehensive manner in 1944, gives a new turn to events. It opens the possibility of overcoming the above-named dichotomy and of unifying the numerous casuistic treatments of oligopolistic market forms. The theory of games provides a model for economic behavior no matter what the market structure is. The logico-mathematical properties of the model are well understood, and it is amenable to computation and numerical analysis. The basic feature of the theory is to show that in economics one is not confronted with maximum problems but with a conceptually different and, a fortiori, more difficult situation. This stems from the fact that the outcome of the behavior of firms and individuals does not depend on their own actions alone, nor on those combined with chance, but also on the actions of others who sometimes oppose, sometimes fortify, those of the former. Stating it differently: firms and individuals are not in control of all variables on which the result or "payoff" depends. This is most clearly seen when there are only a few in a market, as in an oligopoly. In such a case no maximum problem exists; indeed the notion of a maximum has no meaning. It is necessary to erect a new conceptual and, by necessity, mathematical edifice. This is precisely what has been accomplished by the theory of games. The next point of greatest importance is that economic activity is not always antagonistic but also requires co-operation. In this co-operative process side payments may or may not be offered in order for a player to be able to enter profitable arrangements with others. Hence big numbers of participants even in large markets do not always become effective; when there is an advantage in combining, coalitions will form, and the difficulties residing with small numbers will come again to the fore. The typical Lausanne situation of free competition, in which everyone faces fixed conditions, is merely a limiting case of not very great theoretical or practical importance. Economic theory must therefore deal centrally with what is typical from both these points of view. This means that oligopoly and related forms of market organization must be made the starting point of inquiries into the formation of prices, the optimal, rational behavior of firms, and the determination of their outputs rather than form appendices to a theory of general equilibrium which is neither based on a very realistic interpretation of the real world nor properly set up conceptually.

Since the appearance of the *Theory of Games and Economic Behavior*, over 1000 books and articles have been published in this new field. Most of these deal with the mathematical aspects of the theory which they expound and develop. It is natural that applications come later, especially to so difficult a matter as economics. Here further development of the theory and application are often inseparable. In some cases even the proper empirical background has to be provided for, since existing descriptions of market behavior are necessarily in terms of traditional concepts which are not always suited to capture the relevant elements and features of the situations to be analyzed. This, fortunately, makes it difficult merely to translate current views into a game theoretical terminology. Such translations would clearly not constitute true applications.

The present work by Martin Shubik illustrates all these points: it goes boldly after pivotal problems, some time-honored and associated with the finest names in economics. They are freshly formulated in a game theoretical manner, and the new solutions are carefully compared with earlier answers. Then new problems of market strategy are formulated and equally treated. Static and dynamic approaches are made, and from the whole emerge new insights into the optimal behavior of firms under conditions of duopoly, oligopoly, and monopolistic competition. Of particular significance is the widening of the scope of the traditional economic analysis: the problem of initial assets of a firm, the difficulty of entry into an oligopolistic market, the preservation or loss of the assets in a battle of economic ruin, the flow and cost of information about the market, all these introduce new and vital factors into the scope of the enquiry. This has two consequences of significance. First, it makes the analysis more realistic than the thin and pale schemes normally used, and, second, it advances the theory, i.e., game theory as well as economic theory. The latter could be carried forward only by introducing the interesting games of ruin which are extensively investigated. This double feature of a more realistic setting of the problem and a greater unity in theoretical analysis bespeaks the power of the theory of games. It will not surprise those who have become familiar with its main methods and results. It also shows the soundness of Dr. Shubik's approach and tells of the force and ingenuity of his investigation.

It is a test of the value and vigor of a theory that many other scholars are induced to take it up, to apply and develop it further. I have no doubt that the present work will cause many economists not only to study it carefully but to be inspired by the fruitfulness of the new approaches and the fresh ideas which it so abundantly displays.

OSKAR MORGENSTERN

Econometric Research Program
Princeton University
January 1959

PREFACE

The primary purpose of this work is to begin to develop a unified approach to the various theories of competition and markets. The main set of techniques employed to achieve this end are those of game theory.

Many economists and other social scientists have not been made aware of the uses of *Game Theory*. This is because little has been written that applies the new techniques to recognized substantive problems in their own disciplines. The first part of this book is presented to demonstrate their value by using these techniques to examine and compare many well-known approaches to the theory of oligopoly and to obtain some new results.

The second part lays the groundwork necessary for the construction of a dynamic theory. From my point of view, Chapters 10 and 11 are simultaneously the most satisfactory and the most unsatisfactory chapters in the book. A small start is made in the development of a dynamic theory by means of *Games of Economic Survival;* however, the exploration of the properties of the many models of the firm and its market environment has only begun. The roles of financial and technological strength and corporate form in influencing entry, survival, and market share are the type of phenomena which can be examined naturally by means of games of economic survival. In Sections 4, 6, and 9 of Chapter 10 examples are solved to illustrate some of the properties of the models, such as *conditional equilibria* (10.6.3).

The theory of market structure is in its infancy. The gap between economic theory, institutional studies, and the applied study of the functioning of firms and markets is great. In this book only limited attention is given to retailing and distribution systems, to the nature of corporate optimization, and to other substantive features of an economy which must be examined before a satisfactory theory of markets can be elaborated and tested. But even this brief treatment exceeds that found in many books of economic theory.

Although the audience for which the book is primarily designed consists of economists, the intent is that parts of it will be of interest to others. This includes behavioral scientists in general and those interested in management science, operations research, game theory, and law. In order to give this assertion more substance, we relate the contents of this book to the different disciplines mentioned.

Two apparently diverse topics are central to most of the work here. They are the concept of a theory of organization and the concept of a solution to an *n*-person game. The approach to the first topic adopted here consists of building a theory of market form based on the interaction of individual behaviors. The primitive concepts concern individual units from which organizations are derived. The postulation of a method for the solution of a *n*-person game amounts to suggesting a theory of organization for *n* separate (but usually interdependent) decision units.

To those interested in the yet-to-be-built general theory of organization this book represents an essay to construct part of a sub-theory, namely, a theory of market organization.

One of the greatest hindrances to the utilization of the apparatus of game theory by behavioral scientists has been a lack of understanding that the selection of a method of solution for an *n*-person game may pose a substantive problem. The concept of solution may be of only limited use in some particular science and not universally applicable. As Luce and Raiffa have already noted, there are many concepts of solution to an *n*-person game in existence. Some appear to be "reasonable" when used to explain some phenomena, and others, to explain others. Few, if any, have been tested.

The game theorists will find many problems formulated and solved. The economic background gives special properties to the problems which, in turn, lead to solutions of interest. An example of this is to be found in the convergence properties of the solutions to the non-co-operative market games in Chapter 6.

The operations researcher interested in problems of market competition will find that Chapters 1, 8, 9, and 12 and parts of 10 may help to connect in a useful manner some of the problems he is facing with work in economic theory. The developments in game theory and decision theory in my estimation have gone a long way toward providing us with the means by which we can construct refined and testable theories of markets. The development of econometrics, management science, operations research, and large-scale computing-machine technology provides the means for testing.

Eventually, digital computer simulation of the firm and market structures may help to do the empirical work that needs to be done before an applied science of market structures can advance much further.

Chapters 1, 12, 13, the last part of 11, and Appendix B are suggested for the interested lawyer. The meanings of co-operation, competition, "fair division," collusion, and so forth, are examined in the light of a game theoretic analysis. Emphasis is laid on the important distinctions between phenomena, such as market structure and market behavior.

The few sections in which the mathematical contents may require more than basic calculus and a little patience have been marked. If the reader is willing to accept the statements without following the proofs, little will be lost.

This work was done and this book was written during the years 1949 to 1956 when I was at Princeton University and, subsequently, at the Center for Advanced Study in Behavioral Sciences. I have since changed my employment and therefore desire to note here that this book was written before I made this affiliation. The views are entirely my own as they were developed at that time and do not represent the position or views of my present employer.

I am deeply indebted to Oskar Morgenstern and to Lloyd Shapley, with whom many stimulating conversations were held. A debt of gratitude is owed to Howard Raiffa, Roy Radner, and Richard Savage, my colleagues at the Center for Advanced Study in the Behavioral Sciences, as well as to Gerald Thompson, William Vickrey, Kenneth Arrow, Martin Beckmann, Morris Peston, and Edward Zabel. Part of this study was done while I was a member of the Economics Research Project directed by Professor Oskar Morgenstern and sponsored by the Office of Naval Research. Special thanks are due to Mrs. Thomas Marschak for her excellent research assistance and to Mrs. Robert Butow who fortunately is able to spell.

MARTIN SHUBIK

New York, N. Y.
January 1959

CONTENTS

Part I   The Background to Competition

Part II   The Dynamics of Oligopoly: Mathematical Institutional Economics

6 CONCLUSIONS   179

IX THE EXTENSIVE FORM OF A GAME: A
    PRELIMINARY TO DYNAMICS   182

    1 THE ECONOMIC MEANING OF THE EXTENSIVE FORM OF A GAME   182
    2 THE MATHEMATICAL DESCRIPTION OF THE EXTENSIVE FORM
       OF A GAME   186
    3 GAMES OF INDEFINITE LENGTH   198

X   A THEORY OF OLIGOPOLY (PART 1)   203

    1 INTRODUCTION. ENTRY, EARNINGS, ASSETS   203
    2 GAMES OF SURVIVAL   204
    3 GAMES OF ECONOMIC SURVIVAL   206
    4 SOLUTIONS TO A TWO-PERSON GAME OF ECONOMIC SURVIVAL   222
    5 A DYNAMIC DUOPOLY MODEL   232
    6 DIFFERENT TYPES OF TWO-PERSON GAMES OF
       ECONOMIC SURVIVAL   245
    7 ADVERTISING, STYLING, EFFICIENCY, INNOVATION, PRICE
       AND OTHER COMPETITION   249
    8 MONOPOLISTIC COMPETITION REVISITED   258
    9 ENTRY INTO COMPETITION   259

XI A THEORY OF OLIGOPOLY (PART 2)   268

    1 SOLUTIONS TO AN n-PERSON GAME OF ECONOMIC SURVIVAL   268
    2 MODELS OF AN OLIGOPOLISTIC MARKET   278
    3 THE STATE OF INFORMATION IN AN OLIGOPOLISTIC MARKET   280
    4 STRUCTURE OR BEHAVIOR?   282

XII THE STRUCTURE OF THE MARKETS   287

    1 INTRODUCTION   287
    2 THE STRUCTURE OF AMERICAN INDUSTRY   288
    3 MEASURES OF INTERDEPENDENCE   293
    4 THE AUTOMOBILE INDUSTRY   296
    5 THE TOBACCO INDUSTRY   309

XIII ECONOMIC ANALYSIS, SOCIAL POLICY,
      AND THE LAW   325

    1 PREAMBLE   325
    2 THE ANTITRUST LAWS   326
    3 ECONOMIC THEORY AND THE MARKET   329
    4 COMMENTS ON SOCIAL POLICY AND THE ECONOMIC
       ANALYSIS OF MARKETS   335

PART ONE

The Background to Competition

chapter I

TOWARD
A GENERAL THEORY
OF OLIGOPOLY

1. INTRODUCTION

There exist three bodies of economic theory to explain the action of firms under various market forms. They are the theories of pure competition, monopoly, and oligopoly. Chamberlin remarks that,

Economic literature affords a curious mixture, confusion and separation, of the ideas of competition and monopoly. On the one hand, analysis has revealed the differences between them and has led to the perfection and refinement of a separate body of theory for each.... On the other hand, the facts of intermixture in real life have subtly worked out against the complete theoretical distinction between competition and monopoly which is essential to a clear understanding of either.[1]

It is this intermixture which gives rise to the problems of oligopoly, and it is here that the crux of the difficulties in present theory lies. Pure competition and monopoly on the surface present very different aspects, yet economic models of such markets, from one very important conceptual viewpoint, have been treated in the same manner. The entrepreneur operating in a monopolistic or purely competitive situation acts against a mechanistic environment in the form of a demand curve or a price. Given information on costs, his way is plain: in both cases he maximizes certain well-defined quantities. In a market in which there is oligopolistic competition the entrepreneur can no longer work and act according to well-known laws of maximization in an environment portrayed as a simple mechanism, but he becomes a competitor, fighting against other human beings operating in a situation that affords them the opportunity to exercise their free will in a manner that will vitally influence him.

In a purely competitive situation, as usually portrayed, the individual cannot influence the market by himself. His strategic possibilities are so constrained that he usually has but one uniquely defined optimal action available to him. The pure monopolist has no competitors; hence he need not worry about the strategies of others. His strategy is defined as that which maximizes his profit, given the aggregate demand schedule.

The theory of oligopolistic competition offers no simple universal solution that gives rise to a unique determination of prices and distribution of goods. Fellner [2] and many others have pointed out that the problem of setting the price and production levels among a few competing firms can be made to yield a determinate solution if a conjecture concerning the behavior of the firms is specified. Early mathematical solutions offered for duopoly were of this variety. The reason for the rejection of Cournot's and Edgeworth's solutions is simply that the hypotheses regarding the actions of the competing firms seem to be unreasonable. The original mathematical models have been recognized as implausible if they are meant to mirror reality. The problems involved may be too complex to be capable of simple symbolic formulation. Yet certain basic aspects of oligopoly may be explored by the use of simplified abstract models.

Modern economic literature has dealt with leader-follower situations, with bargaining power, and with many other partially economic or extraeconomic phenomena. Even in the most nonmathematical discussion the concepts of move or strategy have been introduced. In this chapter these and several other concepts are formalized and the discussion of oligopoly is advanced from this viewpoint.

Where is one to define the boundaries between oligopoly, pure competition, or monopoly? Numbers play a very important role, but experience and observation tell us that fewness alone is not a sufficient criterion. Product differentiation certainly enters in, and the cross-elasticity of demand (see Chapter 2: 4.1) for the products of the various firms helps to define a market form; but again, this is not necessarily a sufficient criterion. Hotelling has introduced the factor of transportation costs. [3] This, as with the other two factors mentioned, helps to determine the strength of the entrepreneur vis-à-vis the rest of his competitors but does not provide a complete key to the basic problems of the nature of competition.

A market in which oligopolistic competition exists is one in which there is at least one entrepreneur whose possession of economic influence, as it is manifested in the many strategic possibilities available to him, has to be taken into consideration by at least one other firm when planning its market action.

The many types of special and mixed-market situations that exist in all economies have long defied simple classification. Market forms have been treated by patchwork theory, borrowing sometimes from competition, sometimes from monopoly, and sometimes from special institutional observation. That there exists a mechanics for the economics of an oligopolistic world which is as simple and powerful as that of the theory of pure competition is doubtful. The observations of institutional economists indicate no way to this Philosopher's Stone. Nevertheless, it is possible that beneath the welter of special cases and exceptions to the rule that make up the economics of oligopoly there lies a structure which, though not of such immediate and direct use as the structure of competition, will cast light on the general, if not the specific, form of the problem of cross-purpose maximization. By doing this, new insight may be gained into the deep and interesting problems concerning the nature of competition and collusion. It is the belief put forward here that the methods of game theory help us to find and examine this structure.

2. GAME THEORY: THE NECESSARY BACKGROUND

As noted in section 1, the object of this book is to explore the nature of oligopolistic competition by using the methods of game theory. In this section a bare sketch is given of the essential features of game theory which are relevant to the understanding of the first two chapters. In later chapters additional concepts and formalism are introduced as needed.

Although an attempt has been made to make the following exposition self-contained, references to more detailed treatments of the formal aspects of game theory are given for those who desire a more exhaustive description than is presented here. [4]

With the word *game* we can associate *rules, players, moves, strategies, payoffs,* some concepts of *competition* or *co-operation,* and some usually ill-defined notions about the nature and importance of *information* as it is manifested in bidding in bridge or bluffing in poker.

These words and ideas also have immediate intuitive meaning when they are associated with our conception of conflict in economic life, politics, and war.

Unfortunately, our everyday usage is often not precise, and the ambiguities which arise tend to confuse rather than clarify some of the problems that are faced in a study of competition or collusion between groups of individuals. Our first task is to clear up these ambiguities by formalizing the concepts associated with a game.

Consider a set of individuals involved in a competitive situation, be it poker or production in the economy. We identify this set as N and the number of *players* in the set as n. The word player is used to denote a separate decision-making unit in a society. A player wishes to maximize some goal and is in control of certain actions which influence the amounts that he and his competitors obtain. The player may not always be an individual. For instance, we may wish to regard a corporation as a single player in some market models. The important feature is that he or it is an autonomous decision-making unit with a goal and some power to influence events.

We call the competitive situation in which the players are involved a *game*. A game can be totally described in terms of its *rules*. In chess, for instance, these rules specify the field of play, i.e., the type of board to be used, and state how all pieces can be moved in all possible situations. Ideally, the rules for producing automobiles could be given in great detail in the same manner. We would have to specify the institutional background of the economy, establish a legitimate, feasible action for any player, and describe the outcome which results from every possible combination of actions taken by different players.

Given in the rules of a game are a description of what constitutes a player's *move*, his *state of information* prior to his *choice* of move from a *set of alternatives*, and his *payoff function*.

At the start of a chess game White selects his first move by making a choice from the set of twenty alternatives which can be selected according to the rules of chess (sixteen alternatives utilizing pawns and four utilizing knights). His state of information is such that before making his choice he knows the location of every chessman on the board and he knows what moves his opponent has made up to that time (in this case none).

At any point during the *play* of a game a player always knows where all the chessmen are located on the board and (at least if his memory is good or he has taken notes) he also knows exactly what sequence of moves has been made up until that time. In a game such as chess we say that a player possesses *perfect information*. In games such as "kriegspiel" or "double-blind chess," bridge, or poker this is not true. The player is not so well informed. After his opponent has chosen his move in kriegspiel the player is not informed of the choice; he can calculate that the move must have been one in a certain set of alternatives, but he does not know which one. During a poker game the move of a player may be to discard some cards. A player knows that his opponent has chosen his move when he sees him discard, but he does not know which cards have been discarded. This lack of information leads to the existence of such phenomena as bluffing in poker and signaling in bridge. A game of this type is said to be one of *imperfect information*.

In games of perfect or imperfect information players possess *complete information*. Complete information refers to the rules of the game. It implies that all payoff values are known. It means, for instance, that an entrepreneur knows the cost structure of his competitors and the market demand so that he is able to work out the value of any market situation not only to himself but to his competitors as well. (In a realistic theory of market action we must give up such an assumption and make allowances for ignorance and uncertainty; this is done in Chapter 8.) The knowledge that an opponent will win if he has a royal flush constitutes part of the complete information concerning the rules of the game of poker. Whether or not he has the royal flush depends upon the deal, and, since this is usually done face down, the individual player is incompletely informed about the actual cards dealt to the others.

What a move is has already been mentioned; however, a little elaboration is required. There are two types in a game. These are *personal* and *chance* moves. In bridge or poker the deal is a chance move. A machine could be placed in the middle of the table to deal the cards. The outcome of the game depends heavily upon how the cards are dealt; however, this is a random event beyond the control of the players (unless someone cheats).

The rules of a game specify when the game is over, who has won, and what the payoff is. Thus in chess the rules specify the positions which constitute a checkmate or stalemate. In tournaments the winner is awarded one point and the loser zero; in the case of a draw each obtains a half point. A simple duopoly model can be defined as one in which each player has a single move made by choosing from a set of alternative production rates. Given the costs of the firms, the demand of the market, and the market mechanism, the rules then specify a payoff to both players for every pair of production rates they can select.

The term play is used as an *ex post* concept. It is described by the sets of moves used by all the players from the start to the end of a game. Thus the write-up of a championship chess game or of a baseball game (if done with sufficient care) describes a particular play in chess or baseball. A description of the way in which two firms carried out negotiations, fixed production rates, divided a market, and worked out a joint pricing policy illustrates a play in a game formulation of a market situation. The description of the way the same two firms fought for the market and went into a price war in which one was finally driven out of business illustrates a different play of the same game.

We have sketched the description of a game and have illustrated the meaning of choice, move, and state of information. These deal with a game's microscopic aspects. However, by making use of the features described up to this point we are able to formalize the concept of a *strategy*. The everyday usage of the word strategy implies some sort of over-all plan which an army commander, a football team, or a corporation might employ in carrying out a program. Implicit in the meaning of strategy is a method for dealing with contingencies. An army commander might include several "if" clauses in his plan for action. It might state that a brigade would commence action by attacking the enemy's left flank; if the attack were successful, then the general attack on all sectors would begin; if the attack failed and the enemy followed a certain line of action then...and so on. In a business situation the strategy might contain contingent clauses which would depend upon the rivals following certain actions. Practically, the computation is too great to be carried out, but, theoretically, a strategy specifies the course of action that should be followed by a player for every possible set of moves or "conjectural variations" of his opponents. In the example of chess it would be a plan of the following sort:

If he opens with pawn to king four, then I will reply with pawn to king four; if he then replies with knight to king's bishop three, then I...; if, however, he opens with pawn to queen four, then....

A game can be discussed in two forms: the *extensive form* and the *normalized form*. In chess, for example, in order to describe how the game is played in extensive form we must examine the position of each player before every move, state the information conditions, specify the set of alternatives which are relevant to the choice at that position, and then state which move is to be chosen. The manner in which chess is usually played does this. A player moves after he has utilized all the information available to him at that time. After a series of moves the play of the game is terminated and each player receives his payoff. We can think of a different way in which chess could be played. Both players could write out their strategies before either of them approached the board. Then, simultaneously, they could present the referee with their books of instructions as to what they intended to do under all contingencies, leave the referee to work out the *play* of the game that would result from having employed these two strategies, and merely wait for their payoffs which they would obtain from the play of the game caused by the employment of their strategies. The strategies would involve millions of contingent statements and would be, at this time, practically impossible to examine, although we are able to think about them theoretically.

The notion of a strategy can be made clearer by means of a simple example. Consider a game in which each player has only one move. At his turn each player has to choose one of the numbers, 1 or 2. If both players pick the same number, then the first player wins a dollar and the second loses a dollar. If they pick different numbers, then the first loses a dollar and the second wins the same amount. Suppose that we make this a decidedly "unfair" game in the sense that we force the first player to move first and allow the second player to be informed of the move chosen by his opponent. It is obvious that the second player will always be able to win, and in this sense the game is unfair (as though when matching pennies one player were allowed to "peek" before calling). We can describe this game completely as one with perfect information: one choice for each player from a set of two alternatives, with the moves made in sequence, and four possible resulting plays of the game with payoffs to both players associated with each of these plays. Thus, although each player has a choice of two possible moves, the first player can choose one of *two* strategies, whereas the second player has *four* available strategies.

Suppose that the second player could not be bothered to wait around until the first had moved. He could submit to the referee one of four documents which would state

(1) If my opponent chooses the number 1, then I choose 1; if he chooses 2, then I choose 2.
(2) If he chooses 1, I choose 1; if he chooses 2, I choose 1.
(3) If he chooses 1, I choose 2; if he chooses 2, I choose 2.
(4) If he chooses 1, I choose 2; if he chooses 2, I choose 1.

The strategies of the first player are identical to his moves and involve no contingent statements. All that he can submit to the referee is one of two documents which would state

(1) I choose move 1.
(2) I choose move 2.

We can replace the original game in which there was perfect information and the players moved in sequence by a game in which both players move simultaneously and each does so by selecting a strategy which he gives to the referee. This *normalized* form of the other game makes use of all the information available in the other game but now enables us to represent all relevant features by a simple payoff table or *payoff matrix*:

Table 1

	(1, 1; 2, 1)	(1, 2; 2, 1)	(1, 2; 2, 2)	(1, 1; 2, 1)
(1)	1, −1	−1, 1	−1, 1	1, −1
(2)	−1, 1	−1, 1	1, −1	1, −1

The column of numbers on the extreme left lists the strategies available to the first player. The row of numbers above (each entry having four numbers) contains the strategies for the second player. The eight entries in the table, each consisting of a pair of numbers, are the payoffs resulting from any pair of strategies. For instance, if the first player picks his first strategy and the second player picks his third strategy, the resultant play of the extensive form game will be that the first chooses his first move and the second chooses his second move. In the payoff the first obtains minus one dollar and the second obtains plus one dollar. This shorthand notation completely describes everything that can happen in the original game.

By merely examining the structure of the table we can see that the second player will always choose his second strategy. This is his *optimal strategy*. It guarantees him one dollar under all contingencies.

What use to economic theory is the description of a game in the normalized form? The number of moves may be many and may involve production rates, the choice of prices, advertising expenditures, and many other economic variables. As a result of these complications, most economic models permit millions of strategies.

If, in answer to this question, we are able to evolve a method of describing relatively simple games in terms of strategies and are able to discuss the results of adopting certain types of strategies, we will be in a position to work out the more complicated cases without necessarily having to specify all the millions of new strategies that may enter into the picture. For instance, suppose we construct a simple model of a duopoly situation in which the two firms produce a single homogeneous product, with no advertising, product variation, or transportation costs. If we develop a theory of action, we can observe that the addition of extra moves, in which, for example, the firms specify advertising outlays, will enlarge the number of strategies and change the value of the payoffs. But, if we make use of our economic information, it will indicate the manner in which the number of strategies will be enlarged and the way in which the payoffs are affected. If we believe that the same theory of behavior holds true for the duopolists in this more complicated case, we may be able to state immediately the effect that these added complications will have. We will be able to obtain the solution to the new economic problem from our understanding of the solution to the old.

We shall see in the next five chapters that many of the problems discussed in the theory of oligopoly by Cournot, Bertrand, Edgeworth, Hotelling, Chamberlin, Mrs. Robinson, and others can be clarified and their results extended by making use of the normalized form of a game in the manner suggested.

Before we are in a position to apply our framework to economic problems, a few more features of game theory must be described.

For ease of exposition at this stage we limit ourselves to games involving only two players. Most of the complications of "cross-purposes" maximization and interdependence of action occur here, so for the moment this is not a serious restriction.

Each player in a two-person game possesses a set of strategies which we denote S_1 and S_2. The total number of strategies in the set S_1 is s_1 and the number in S_2 is s_2. We identify a particular strategy in S_1 by the letter i, and in S_2 by the letter j. Every pair of strategies, i from S_1 and j from S_2, will have two payoff values associated with it. We label these payoff functions $P_1(i, j)$ and $P_2(i, j)$. They indicate the amounts that the first and second players, respectively, receive after having employed strategies i and j.

A game is said to be *zero sum* if the amount that one player wins is always the same as the amount that the other player loses; in other words, if $P_1(i, j) = -P_2(i, j)$. Most card games are of this type, as are chess, checkers, and the Japanese game Go. A few military situations, such as duels to the death, may be regarded as zero sum. The pertinent property that a zero-sum game possesses is that it is one of *pure opposition*. It is a *strictly competitive* game. The game described in Table 1 is of this nature. If one player wins one dollar, the other loses it. There is no possibility for collusion because no jointly played strategy can improve the position of both.

In almost no economic situations is the zero-sum criterion satisfied. Generally, a group of firms or individuals can obtain more by co-operation or collusion than they can get by independent action. We call a game in which the payoffs do not sum to zero, i.e., in which the losses of one side are not necessarily equal to the gains of the other, a *nonzero-sum game.*

Economic usage has often failed to distinguish between the objective background of a market and the behavior of the participants which determines the market outcome. To rephrase this in terms of game theory, the rules of the game (such features as cost conditions, the nature of demand, and the relevant legal framework) are not carefully separated from the description of how the game is played. For instance, a purely competitive market in the sense employed by economists is not necessarily a market which has a physical background that will be represented by a strictly competitive game. If large groups of players band together, a purely competitive market may be transformed into a monopolistic one. In a strictly competitive game there is no motivation for any coalition to form. In any attempt to construct a measure for the degree of collusion present in a market there is a great need to separate carefully the objective background or rules of the game from the behavioristic assumptions concerning the method of play. Before we can know the degree of collusion present we must be able to explore the possibilities available to the players.

For the two-person, zero-sum game, game theory analysis provides not only a description but also suggests a method of play that the players should employ.

Consider the game represented by the matrix given in Table 2. This specifies the payoff function for player 1. We do not need to draw the payoff table for player 2, since we know that it is the negative of the one shown. Since each player has three strategies, there are nine payoff values, and, as this is a zero-sum game, we observe that the first player wishes to maximize the same number that the second player wishes to minimize. The first wishes to maximize his gains, whereas his opponent wants to minimize losses. (If we carried out this discussion, using the second player's payoff matrix, the roles of the two would be reversed; therefore, there is no asymmetry or unfairness introduced by assuming that the first player maximizes here.)

If the first player chooses his strategy 1, then the very worst that his opponent can do to him is to choose his strategy 3. In this

Table 2

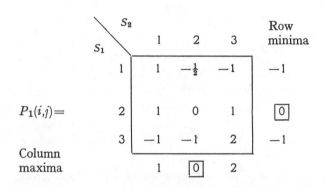

case the first player will lose 1. The column labeled "row minima" indicates the worst that can happen to the first player if he has chosen any one of his strategies. We now carry out this analysis for the second player. If he chooses his first strategy, the worst that can happen to him is the choice by the first player of his strategy 1 or 2, in which case the second player will lose 1. The row labeled "column maxima" indicates the worst that can happen to the second player if he has used any of his three strategies.

If player 1 chooses his strategy 2, at the very worst he will obtain 0. We observe that 0 is the maximum of the row minima (denoted *maxmin*). Similarly, if player 2 uses his strategy 2, at the very worst he will obtain 0. This is the minimum value of the row maxima (denoted *minmax*). In general, these two values need not be equal. However, here they are. Whenever this is so we say that the game is *strictly determined* and possesses a *saddle-point*. By employing strategy 2 the first player can guarantee himself a payoff greater than or equal to 0. By employing his strategy 2 the second player can guarantee himself an amount no less than 0. Writing this symbolically, we have

$$P_1(2, j) \geqslant 0 \quad \text{for } j = 1, 2, 3,$$
$$P_1(i, 2) \leqslant 0 \quad \text{for } i = 1, 2, 3.$$

We can also write

$$\text{maxmin } P_1(i, j) = P_1(2, 2) = 0 = P_1(2, 2) = \text{minmax } P_1(i, j).$$

Whenever this condition holds the value of minmax (in this case 0) is called the *value* of the game. It is the optimal amount that either player can guarantee for himself. A strategy which assures a player that he will obtain a payoff at least equal to this amount is an *optimal strategy*.

If a player employs an optimal strategy, then his opponent cannot benefit by knowing his intentions before, in turn, selecting his own strategy.

We have noted that not all games possess a saddle-point. Consider the following game, for instance:

Table 3

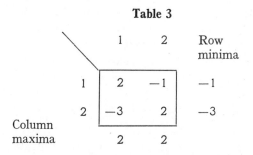

In Table 3 the minmax is 2, but the maxmin is -1. There is no naturally defined value such that the first player can guarantee that he will obtain at least this amount nor that the second can guarantee that he will lose at most the same amount.

Suppose that the first player does not wish to run the risk of having his income from this game fluctuate between -3 and 2. What is the expected value of the position of player 1 to an insurance company? In order to find out how much he should be paid in return for relinquishing his rights to receive the winnings or pay the losses resulting from a play of the game, we must introduce the concept of *mixed strategy*.

We allow a player more leeway than before. He is no longer restricted to a choice between his two pure strategies, the numbers 1 or 2, but may employ probability mixtures of them. We can explain this in a different manner. We have already described a game in which each player presented the referee with a strategy (which can be regarded as a book of instructions). Now we permit a player to give the referee more than one pure strategy and to tell him according to some random device or method involving probability how to select the one that is to be used. For instance, if player 1 in the example given uses his mixed strategy which combines pure strategy 1 with probability $\frac{1}{2}$ and pure strategy 2 with probability $\frac{1}{2}$, we can calculate his expected return if player 2 uses his pure strategy 1. In this case it is

$$\tfrac{1}{2}(2) + \tfrac{1}{2}(-3) = -\tfrac{1}{2}.$$

If player 2 uses his pure strategy 2, the expectation is

$$\tfrac{1}{2}(-1) + \tfrac{1}{2}(2) = \tfrac{1}{2}.$$

The worst that can happen to the first player by employing this strategy is an expectation of losing $\frac{1}{2}$. This is better than the pure strategy maxmin value of -1.

It can be proved that any zero-sum game with no saddle-point (maxmin = minmax when the players are restricted to using pure strategies) will have a saddle-point if the players are allowed to use mixed strategies. [5]

We denote a mixed strategy for a player by a set of numbers which has as many entries as the player has pure strategies. All these numbers sum to 1. For instance, the mixed strategy of the first player discussed is identified as $(\frac{1}{2}, \frac{1}{2})$. His pure strategy 1 becomes $(1, 0)$ in this notation. A general mixed strategy of player 1 can be indicated by $\zeta_1 = (\zeta_{1,1}, \zeta_{1,2})$. The symbol $\zeta_{1,2}$ stands for the second component of the first player's mixed strategy. We call the minimum expected value of the game to player 1, V'. He wishes to choose his strategy in such a manner that he will maximize this value. The conditions that an optimal strategy for player 1 must satisfy are

$$\zeta_{1,1}(2) + \zeta_{1,2}(-3) \geqslant V'$$

$$\zeta_{1,1}(-1) + \zeta_{1,2}(2) \geqslant V', \text{ subject to } \zeta_{1,1} + \zeta_{1,2} = 1.$$

Given these three relations (if we replace the "greater than or equal to" signs by "equals"), we can solve by simple algebra for $\zeta_{1,1}, \zeta_{1,2}$, and V'. We find that $\zeta_1 = (\frac{5}{8}, \frac{3}{8})$ and

$$V' = \tfrac{5}{8}(2) + \tfrac{3}{8}(-3) = \tfrac{5}{8}(-1) + \tfrac{3}{8}(2) = \tfrac{1}{8}.$$

In a similar manner we can solve for the optimal strategy for player 2. It is $\zeta_2 = (\frac{3}{8}, \frac{5}{8})$. It is interesting to note that this apparently "fair" game is biased in favor of the first player if he plays his optimal strategy.

The solution to a game in which each player has two pure strategies can be found in the simple diagram shown in Figure 1:

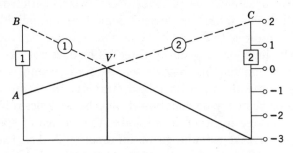

Figure 1

The lines marked $\boxed{1}$ and $\boxed{2}$ represent the use of these pure strategies by player 1. The lines marked ① and ② indicate the expected payoff to the first player, as he varies his mixed strategies, if the second player uses his pure strategy 1 and 2, respectively. For instance, the meaning of the point A is that when player 1 uses his first pure strategy and player 2 uses his second pure strategy the payoff to player 1 is -1. Point V' indicates that if player 1 uses his mixed strategy $(\frac{5}{8}, \frac{3}{8})$ he can obtain $\frac{1}{8}$ no matter what strategy is employed by player 2.

We call a game in which the saddle-point is obtained by the use of mixed strategies, a *generally strictly determined* game. By this we mean that it has an expected value V' which the players can always obtain by using their optimal strategies.

We can see immediately that a *constant-sum* game will also be strictly competitive. Suppose that we merely added the number 2 to every payoff for player 1 in Table 3. Strategically nothing has changed. The value of the game to player 1 will now be $2 + \frac{1}{8}$; player 2 will still obtain an expectation of $-\frac{1}{8}$.

There are some economic situations for which a constant-sum game model presents an adequate approximation. A battle between two firms selling in an almost saturated market in which most of the customers gained by one are customers lost by the other comes close to this, especially if the advertising expenses of the firms are approximately offset by the slight increase in market which might result from their policies. However, as already noted, most economic models require that we examine the general nonzero-sum game which is not necessarily constant-sum.

The concept of mixed strategy at first seems rather hard to accept. Do, or should, people ever decide which action to choose by actually using a random device? Sometimes an individual may flip a coin in order to decide between two actions, but more often than not he flips for "two out of three" if he does not like the first result. Even though this may be so, there are examples in which it is easy to see the use of a mixed strategy. In an open market operation or currency devaluation it may be very desirable to use a mixed strategy in order to minimize the chance of speculators being able to take advantage of information leaks. The use of bluffing in poker helps to emphasize the rationale behind a mixed strategy in a generally strictly determined game. Oswald Jacoby in his book on poker [6] suggests that a good method of play to follow in draw poker is to hold a "kicker" (i.e., a third, nonmatching card, usually an ace or king) about one time out of three when drawing to a pair. This has not been worked out rigorously and may not even be true. Yet the implication is plain to any poker player. One cannot afford to be completely predictable in poker.

Most of the analysis in this book does not depend on the use of mixed strategies. There have been several criticisms of the minimax strategy as a sensible method of play in a two-person, zero-sum game. There is objection to calling it *the* rational way to play. This objection may be sustained if one regards as too pessimistic the assumption of each player that his opponent is rational. In a world in which scoundrels play against fools the scoundrels may do better than minimax if they understand the psychology of the fools. However, if the scoundrel is playing a scoundrel, or *homo sapiens* suspects that he is faced by *homo sapiens*, then he is well advised to play minimax. It is possible to modify a two-person, zero-sum game to account for known irrationality on the part of a player. This may eventually lead to models, which are not games at all, in which one player merely keeps statistics on the actions of the other and discovers by empirical test that it is legitimate to regard his opponent as a predictable mechanism against which he maximizes.

The word *rational* has already appeared. By this no value judgment is implied as to what a "rational" being should prefer. All that is intimated is that given his desires as known his actions are consistent with them. This assumption can be given up later when we take into account the imperfections that are usually present.

Another and more cogent criticism of the minimax solution is that it may involve the use of mixed strategies, and they imply that individuals assign an actuarial value to situations involving risk. This is a criticism aimed at the method of evaluating the worth of the expected return from the employment of such a strategy rather than at its employment. Actually it is not true that game theory uses this assumption. An adequate answer to this criticism leads us into the area of utility theory, discussion of which is presented in Appendix A. In some cases the assumption that corporations use the actuarial value in risks which do not involve the possibility of ruin is made implicitly. Modification of this assumption does not vitiate the analysis presented here.

We have described the nature of *move, strategy, play,* and *payoff*. A further distinction concerning the objective features of a game which is far more important to economic analysis than it is to game theory must be made. We must distinguish between *prospects*, [7] the evaluation of prospects, and the payoff which results from some play. An example is given to clarify this. We construct a very simple model of a duopoly, almost the same as the one noted before. We define a strategy for an individual as the naming of two production rates, one for each of two periods. Once both players have named their production rates a market mechanism determines the price that prevails in each period and a simple computation gives the profits of both players. The prospect resulting from the play of the game determined by the strategies selected by each player is some pair of profits. It is a well-defined physical entity. The value of that prospect to each player depends upon the utility each has for money, and the valuation involves us in the type of utility problem already noted. The same prospect may be obtained from the employment of many different pairs of strategies. In Table 3, if both players use their first pure strategies or their second pure strategies, the prospect they obtain is the same. The payoff function has the same value for both pairs of strategies. We can now consider a slightly more sophisticated model of duopoly.

Let the cost-and-demand conditions be the same as before. However, we now define a strategy as the naming of a production rate combined with a statement as to what the firm intends to do in the next period, depending upon the production rate named by its opponent in this period. This model allows each player to have many more strategies than the previous model, and its payoff matrices will be much larger. However, the prospects attainable in both cases are the same.

The importance of this distinction is made clearer when we investigate the conditions of oligopolistic demand and the work of Sweezy, Stigler, and others on the "kink" in oligopolistic demand functions.

Game theory provides us with tools to construct useful models of competitive situations. In the case of two-person, zero- or constant-sum games it also provides a normative theory as to how to play. By doing so it is able to define a *value* for such games. This is not so for general nonzero-sum games or for zero-sum games with more than two players. There are many theories concerning the solution of these games. Some appear to be reasonable when applied to one set of phenomena but not to another. The two main distinctions made are between *co-operative* and *non-co-operative theories*. The first type of theory tends to deal with joint maximization, co-operation or collusion, open communication, and side payments. The second usually examines situations with limited or no communication, individual unsynchronized action, and no side payments. A distinction between co-operative and non-co-operative solutions to a game is not always easy or desirable to make. This observation is amplified in the last chapters of the book.

The three theories of solution used here for the most part are the von Neumann and Morgenstern theory for co-operative games, [8] the Nash theory for non-co-operative games, [9] and a theory developed here to apply to dynamic market models.

3. OUTLINE OF CONTENTS

The book is divided into two parts. Part One is employed to give the essentials of game theory and to construct game models of non-co-operative markets. Emphasis is placed upon problems of formulation, especially those dealing with the distinction between behavioristic and technological features of market action and between statics and dynamics.

Part Two is given over to dynamics. A discussion of some of the problems of incomplete information is given, the extensive form of a game is explained, and a class of games called Games of Economic Survival is constructed and used in the analysis of oligopoly. The title of Part Two uses the phrase "Mathematical Institutional Economics" because the examination of dynamic models indicates that financial structure, time lags, entry costs, liquidation values, a host of other empirically observable factors, and information on trade associations and social and legal factors must play a role in any successful theory of oligopoly.

Chapter 2 contains a brief discussion and critique of some of the existing writings on oligopoly and monopolistic competition. This is not intended as an exegesis, but it serves to integrate the previous studies with the work in this book.

In Chapter 3 we commence with the examination of simple oligopoly models in a static situation. Monopoly and bilateral monopoly are dealt with. Game-theory models yield the usual economic analysis if monopoly is regarded as a one-person, nonzero-sum game. Several models of bilateral monopoly are examined. The importance of asset structure and financial conditions in interfirm bargaining is noted, and observations are made concerning the allocation of resources between bilateral monopolists. The notion of *threat* is introduced and examined.

Chapter 4 is devoted to a study of quantity-variation duopoly models. A non-co-operative solution to a game is defined, and the meaning of *equilibrium point* is explained. The equilibrium-point solution to a game coincides with many of the equilibrium theories present in economic analysis, in particular the Cournot duopoly and pure competition analyses. Several co-operative and non-co-operative solutions to a duopoly are given. The meaning of threat is discussed in more detail than in Chapter 3, and the existence of a threat curve related to the Pareto optimal surface is shown. The problems of explicit and implicit collusion are dealt with.

Duopoly models involving price variation and price-quantity variation are investigated in Chapter 5. By the latter we mean models in which the strategy for an individual firm is to name both a price and a production rate simultaneously. This calls for explicit consideration of the risk of unfavorable inventory positions. Before it is possible to construct the duopoly models in this chapter, the problem of oligopolistic demand must be dealt with. This is done in detail for the duopolistic market. The more general treatment is left until Chapter 7. The non-co-operative models here are closely related to the work of Bertrand, Edgeworth, Chamberlin, Mrs. Robinson, and others, although the relation to the more modern theories becomes more transparent after Chapter 7.

Chapter 6 is more technical than the other five. The basic models from the preceding two chapters are utilized, and it is shown that as the size of the individual firm decreases and the number of firms grows the solutions to non-co-operative market models using the behavioristic assumptions of quantity, price, or price-quantity variation converge to the pure competition solution, even though they give rise to different solutions for small numbers. Entry into and exit from competition are considered. Models involving excess capacity and the influence of a dominant firm are examined.

Previous to Chapter 7, product variation, transportation costs, and other market imperfections are not discussed. They are introduced here with the general problem of demand conditions in an oligopolistic market. This work, combined with other chapters on non-co-operative games, enables us to relate the papers of Sweezy, Stigler, and others to our analysis. We are able to show that the Chamberlinian and Robinsonian analyses can be described and handled by non-co-operative game theory and that behavioristically they are not very different from the models of Cournot, Bertrand, and Edgeworth.

In the chapters preceding Chapter 8 there is an implicit assumption that the individual firms possess *complete* information in the sense defined in game theory. Chapter 8 is devoted to an examination of information conditions in a market. Action under low information conditions is discussed, and *games against nature* are investigated as a means of obtaining a theory of action under uncertainty and ignorance.

The remainder of the book is devoted to a dynamic theory of oligopoly. Chapter 9 contains a detailed exposition of the extensive form of a game.

Chapters 10 and 11 are used to define and discuss *games of survival and games of economic survival.* The latter give rise to dynamic models of competition in which the role of asset structure, the financial factors, and corporate features of a firm are of great importance. The concept of solution to a dynamic game is developed and is applied to several models. The relevance of the type of analysis presented by Berle and Means is shown here. The game models are neither co-operative nor non-co-operative, in the sense previously used, but are semi-co-operative to greater or lesser degrees, depending upon technological features, information conditions, and/or the degree of organization present between the competitors. The effect of corporate structure on the form of competition and the goals of maximization is emphasized in these chapters. Chapter 12 presents a sketch of the structure of competition in industry in the United States.

Chapter 13 is given over to a short statement of conclusions.

Appendix A deals briefly with utility theory. If we wish to consider chance and uncertainty, then it is no longer adequate to assume that the individual entrepreneur wishes to maximize money income.

Appendix B is devoted to problems of "fair division." Although this topic is more closely related to welfare economics, it poses many problems concerning the allocation of gains obtained by collusion.

Appendix C is used to present mathematical comments and proofs not included directly in the text or footnotes.

NOTES

[1] Edward H. Chamberlin, *The Theory of Monopolistic Competition* (Cambridge: Harvard University Press, 6th ed., 1950), p. 3.

[2] William Fellner, *Competition among the Few* (New York: Knopf, 1949), pp. 51, 53.

[3] H. Hotelling, "Stability in Competition," *The Economic Journal*, **XXXXI** (March 1929), p. 41.

[4] J. von Neumann and O. Morgenstern, *Theory of Games and Economic Behavior* (Princeton: Princeton University Press, 3rd ed., 1953), Chapters I, II, V, VI; Chapter III, pp. 85–112, and Chapter IV, pp. 169–186; also J. C. C. McKinsey, *Introduction to the Theory of Games* (New York: McGraw-Hill, 1952), especially Chapters 1, 2, 5, 6, 15, 16, 17, and 18. A comprehensive discussion of many aspects of game theory is to be found in R. D. Luce and H.

Raiffa, *Games and Decisions, Introduction and Critical Survey* (New York: Wiley, 1957.)

[5] J. C. C. McKinsey, *op. cit.*, Chapter 2, Section 1.

[6] O. Jacoby, *Poker* (New York: Doubleday, rev. ed., 1948), p. 42.

[7] J. Marschak, "Rational Behavior, Uncertain Prospects and Measurable Utility," *Econometrica*, **XVIII** (April 1950), p. 114.

[8] J. von Neumann and O. Morgenstern, *op. cit.*, Chapter V.

[9] J. F. Nash, "Non-Cooperative Games," *Annals of Mathematics*, **LIV** (September 1951), pp. 286–295.

CURRENT THEORIES OF MONOPOLISTIC COMPETITION

1. THE PROBLEM OF MONOPOLISTIC COMPETITION

In this chapter a brief discussion of some of the current theories of competition is offered in order to compare and contrast their main features with the analysis given in this book. No attempt has been made to provide a complete exegesis of the works discussed.

In the recent literature much emphasis has been laid upon the inadequacy of theories based on price and quantity, the traditional economic variables, to explain price formation and market equilibria under oligopolistic conditions. Consideration has been given to product and quality variation, to advertising, location, and special services. All these are, no doubt, important, and some of them may be even more important than price as a variable in certain markets. However, it will be shown that they all merely serve to change the nature and number of strategies available to the entrepreneur. The extra variables do not, per se, offer a deterministic theory of entrepreneurial behavior, although they may put severe limits upon such behavior. In all the theories under discussion the authors have advanced the study of monopolistic competition by introducing objective factors which they deem to be important; however, in order to describe the final state of the market, the power relations, and the imputation or division of resources, they have, for the most part, assumed that the entrepreneurs follow behavior patterns which lead to the eventual establishment of certain forms of equilibria.

Our criticisms deal with the objective features of the previous theories and assumptions concerning equilibrating behavior.

2. CHAMBERLIN'S THEORY OF MONOPOLISTIC COMPETITION

Chamberlin stresses product differentiation [1] and selling costs, [2] pointing out that most entrepreneurs have a market at least partially distinct from their competitors. [3] He says that,

Monopolistic competition is a challenge to the traditional viewpoint of economics that competition and monopoly are alternatives and that individual prices are to be explained in terms of either the one or the other. By contrast it is held that most economic situations are composites of both competition and monopoly and that wherever this is the case a false view is given by neglecting either one of the two forces and regarding the situation as made up entirely (even though imperfectly) of the other. [4]

With the aid of the new variables introduced, he is able to point out that the demand for the product of an entrepreneur is neither completely elastic, as in pure competition, nor independent of the supply of others, as would be the case in a pure monopoly. He develops an equilibrium theory for small and large groups of firms in monopolistic competition under conditions of price cutting, product variation, and advertising and under the possibility of the entry of new firms into competition.

Chamberlin's major emphasis is laid upon features in the market which increase the autonomy of competitors. Product differentiation and selling costs do precisely this to the sets of variables controlled by each entrepreneur. By splitting up demand, each player is able to wield a considerable amount of control in the market. Chamberlin's analysis enlarges the strategy space under the control of each competitor from one in which only quantity and/or price enter to one which includes selling costs and product differentiation. An attempt is made in his book [5] to devise graphical methods for handling the complications introduced by adding new dimensions of strategy. As we shall see in Chapters 4, 5, 6, and 7, this approach can be characterized as a non-co-operative game in which each player may have as much as a four-dimensional strategy and entry is possible. A strategy may involve the naming of four numbers: one of m possible products (product differentiation); an amount s to be spent on advertising; a quantity q of the product to be produced; and a price p to be charged for it. Pure competition is a limiting case of this non-co-operative game, in which only the quantity and/or price (see Chapter 6) elements of a strategy remain important.

In his discussion of equilibrium under monopolistic competition [6] Chamberlin outlines a graphical method whereby the group adjustment can be examined. He makes use of three theoretical constructs: individual equilibrium, [7] large group equilibrium, [8] and small group equilibrium. [9] The first is merely the usual maximization of an individual monopolist facing a demand curve with

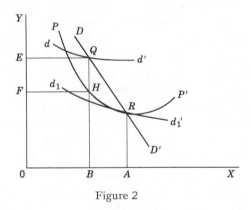

Figure 2

finite elasticity. The second and third may be explained with the aid of the diagram given in Figure 2. Chamberlin makes the assumption [10] that costs and demand are identical for all firms, but this does not change the nature of the analysis. DD' "shows the demand for the product of any one seller at various prices on the assumption that his competitors' prices are always identical with his"; [11] dd' shows "the increased sales which any one producer may enjoy

by lowering his price, provided the others hold theirs fast at
BQ." [12] *PP'* is the supply curve of one of the entrepreneurs. For
the large group Chamberlin argues that one of the producers will
cut his prices because he believes that his action will not be sufficient
to disturb the rest of the market, thereby increasing his demand
along *dd'*. However, by a similar argument, the others will soon
follow him, with the result that he will find himself proceeding
along the demand curve *DD'* until equilibrium is reached at *R*,
where the new *dd'* is tangent to *PP'* and *DD'* intersects *PP'* at
this point of tangency. [13] This graphical demonstration is used to
show how an equilibrium is finally reached. An alternative path
of adjustment to equilibrium is given by assuming that when the
price is high, in the neighbourhood of *BQ*, more firms come into
competition until *DD'* moves to the left, remaining parallel to its
original position until it becomes tangent with *PP'*. This will be
an unstable equilibrium, for some competitor will cut prices and
"war" will continue until some firms are driven out of competition.
Chamberlin suggests that if competitors are few in number each
will take into account the possible retaliation of the others and
that the price will settle somewhere in the range given by *BQ*
and *AR*. An alternative solution [14] may come about if more firms
enter the field. As in large numbers, the demand curve *DD'* moves
to the left until it is tangent with *PP'*. However, this equilibrium
with excess capacity is stable because each competitor realizes that
if he cuts prices he will cause an unfavorable reaction.

There are three areas of criticism of the Chamberlinian theory:
first, the logical consistency of the models developed; second,
the relevance and realism of the behavioristic assumptions made;
and third, the relevance, realism, and completeness of the set of
variables used in the construction of the theory.

All of the diagrams used by Chamberlin in the three equilibrium
constructs noted make use of demand curves which are defined
specially for oligopolistic competition and purport to portray the
demand faced by a firm under two objectively defined sets of
contingent conditions or restraints placed on the actions of all
other firms in competition. The curve *DD'* describes the demand
conditions faced by a firm if all others charge the same price as it
does (Figure 14 of Chamberlin, reproduced here as Figure 2). The
demand curve *dd'* describes the contingent demand of a firm when

the prices of its competitors are fixed at the price BQ. Unfortunately, if we accept the theory of individual consumer choice, this contingent demand curve will not, in general, have the shape given to it by Chamberlin. It may have a kink, "wiggle," or discontinuity, depending explicitly upon the number of competitors and the cross-elasticities between their products. If the number of competitors is large and cross-elasticities are low, then the dd' curves drawn in Figure 2 may be adequate for the purposes of Chamberlin. When the number of competitors is small and they are selling close substitutes, the true shape of the dd' curve must, in some cases, be such that there will be profit maxima to be obtained both by cutting and raising price. The substantiation of this criticism requires a detailed examination of demand conditions under oligopolistic competition. This is given in Chapters 5 and 7 where the general shape of *contingent demand functions* is investigated. From our investigation of contingent demand we are able to show that the possible range of price fluctuation in an oligopolistic market given by Chamberlin [15] is not correct (see Chapter 5).

This criticism may seem to be somewhat picayune. After all, Chamberlin implies [16] that if the products are differentiated violent price fluctuation is not very important; and to the best of our knowledge this is not observed in fact. However, the other two criticisms are more to the point. Suppose, for the moment, that we ignore all problems of cost of entry, liquidity, financial structure, inventories, interest rates, money markets, and corporate structure. Let us make the sweeping assumption that these are minor imperfections that a student of oligopolistic competition can afford to relegate to a secondary place in his analysis of oligopoly. Having done this, we observe that at some point (when a "small group" becomes a "large group") the Chamberlinian oligopolists cease to pay attention to their effect upon each other. They indulge in price cutting which finally leads to an equilibrium either after the existing firms' aggregate repeated misconception of their strategic interlinkage has brought them down to a non-co-operatve equilibrium point or after a war, in which outside firms laboring under an even larger misconception have come in and fought until some firms have been ruined. This picture of the large group may be an accurate description of some trades (whether it is or not must be verified empirically). However, even if it is true, the problem of the economic theorist becomes one of finding out what defines a "small group" and a "large group." Many markets appear to have two to several hundred major firms. Where does the transition take place, and what happens in the "twilight zone"? This problem is not dealt with. Suppose that it does not matter. Let us examine Chamberlin's small group equilibrium. The same firms whose owners or managers are sufficiently wise to take account of each other's reactions and therefore do not indulge in price cutting or major economic wars between themselves in a cavalier fashion are at the same time assumed to be utterly insensitive to the possibility of new entry. This results in new firms coming into competition, and a non-co-operative equilibrium is established with the presence of considerable overcapacity. It is the opinion of this writer that a cursory glance at the structure of industry indicates that if the group of competitors is small (say the major steel producers) and sufficiently intelligent to take each other's actions into account it is also intelligent enough to consider the possibility of new entries. If entry is not blocked by institutional means (such as licenses) or by the need of prohibitively large amounts of capital, the active competitors may still be able, by an occasional price war, threat of price war, or control of factor markets, to indicate that new entry is risky and unwelcome.

The second criticism leads directly into the third. Although the Chamberlinian analysis may be regarded as static, a more accurate description is "partial or semidynamic." As such, it cannot afford not to deal explicitly with entry conditions, financial structure, and the other features noted. Chapters 10, 11, and 12 of this book are devoted to an examination of some of these factors and the role they must play in determining the nature of competition. A theory of monopolistic competition that is to be more than a mental exercise must be able to offer some insight into the nature, meaning, and cause of the myriad market forms which exist with a "medium sized group" of competitors. [17]

3. MRS. ROBINSON'S ECONOMICS OF IMPERFECT COMPETITION

The type of solution which Mrs. Robinson looks for in her theory is the same as that sought by Chamberlin; namely, a non-co-operative game equilibrium point. Like Chamberlin, Mrs. Robinson does not integrate the study of collusion and co-operation among firms into her study of imperfect competition.

Triffin [18] has already noted that Mrs. Robinson manages to throw away the central core of difficulty in any theory of oligopolistic competition, namely, interdependence, by the simple device of ignoring it. She states: [19]

> The demand curve for the individual firm may be conceived to show the full effect upon the sales of that firm which results from any change in the price which it charges, whether it causes a change in the prices charged by others or not. It is not our purpose to consider this question in detail. Once the demand curve for the firm has been drawn, the technique of analysis can be brought into play, whatever the assumptions on which the demand curve was drawn up.

Once the above is done we are left with a straightforward maximization problem, and the real difficulties in imperfect competition theory have been side-stepped. The reaction of the other firms upon the individual firm's environment is bypassed. The strategic interlinkage of firms in competition is dismissed as being of only incidental importance to a theory of imperfect competition, and the book then returns to the study of a simple maximization problem of the firm facing a sloping "individual" demand curve. It is not surprising that this central aspect of imperfect competition should be overlooked in a book which mentions neither the work of Cournot nor of Edgeworth on limited competition.

That Mrs. Robinson may be referring to the subjective aspects rather than the objective aspects of the demand facing a firm (the latter being described by a function involving at least $2n$ variables if there are n firms in competition) has been pointed out by Triffin. [20] If this is so, then we must assume that she is suggesting a method of action for her entrepreneurs which may lead to and/or maintain an equilibrium. In this case she may be sketching a dynamic theory of adjustment, although her demand assumptions indicate that she has assumed away this problem as well. Thus Chamberlin at least distinguishes between the equilibrating process for large and small groups of firms, [21] but Mrs. Robinson because of her demand assumptions ignores the difference completely. [22]

The third criticism of Chamberlin's work, the failure to consider many of the relevant variables, applies with equal force to Mrs. Robinson's.

4.   OTHER WORKS ON MONOPOLISTIC COMPETITION

4.1.   TRIFFIN'S MONOPOLISTIC COMPETITION AND GENERAL EQUILIBRIUM THEORY

The crux of Triffin's addition to the theory of monopolistic competition, as developed by Chamberlin and Mrs. Robinson, comes in his use of cross-elasticities by which he hopes to give a general equilibrium analysis of competitive groups of firms. He considers only price competition between firms in his discussion of interdependence. The definition of cross-elasticity is given as

$$e_{ij} = \frac{d\,(\log q_i)}{d\,(\log p_j)} = \frac{p_j\,dq_i}{q_i\,dp_j}.$$

We see that it is a measure of the change upon i's sales caused by a change in price by j. Triffin states that three categories of competition can be distinguished by examining the size of this coefficient. They are (see Note 2, Chapter 3)

(1) Isolated selling (the limiting case being pure monopoly) for $e_{ij} = 0$.

(2) Heterogeneous competition when e_{ij} takes a finite value.

(3) Homogeneous competition when $e_{ij} = \infty$.

There are two criticisms of the use of cross-elasticity by Triffin and others which are noted here. First, the definition of the cross-elasticity measure is ambiguous; and second, how useful is it as an index or measure of the type of competition between firms?

The first criticism is mainly formalistic and not of central importance to his work. However, by stopping short of considering the multivariate aspects of his problem, Triffin has left some gaps in his use of cross-elasticity. If we consider that there are n firms in a competitive situation, each capable of offering a certain amount of goods to the market and naming a price, then the demand for the ith firm is

$$q_i = \phi_i(p_j, q_j) \qquad \text{for the prices } p_j,\ j = 1, \ldots, n,$$

and for quantities produced q_j, $j = 1, \ldots, i - 1, i + 1, \ldots, n$. By measuring the cross-elasticity between any two firms, *assuming that the prices of the others are fixed*, we can get an estimate of their relative effect upon each other. Triffin does not stress that the value of a cross-elasticity index depends upon the values assigned to the prices charged and quantities being produced by the firms not explicitly being examined (this condition is implicitly satisfied if cross-elasticity is used only to examine equilibria). It is easily seen when we realize that the cross-elasticity between firms i and j in a market with n firms is

$$\frac{\partial \log q_i}{\partial \log p_j} = \frac{\partial \log \phi_i(p_1, p_2, \ldots, p_n, q_1, q_2, \ldots, q_{i-1}, q_{i+1}, \ldots, q_n)}{\partial \log p_j}.$$

The value of this expression usually depends upon the actions of firms other than i and j. For example, if a third firm undercut both i and j and supplied the whole market (assuming homogeneous product), the cross-elasticity between i and j would be zero because the actions of one would have no effect on the other, for both could sell nothing in the neighbourhood of their present prices; if the third firm "priced itself out of the market" and was barely selling anything, then j would certainly feel the effect of i's price change.

If we view a market as an n-person game, the interpretation of cross-elasticity is easy. If the strategy space consists of $2n$ dimensions (n price and n quantities), a cross-elasticity between any two firms is a measure of their strategic interdependence in a neighborhood of a two-dimensional subspace of the strategy space. In other words, it measures the interlinkage between the actions of two firms, given the actions of all other firms as fixed.

Another trouble with the concept of cross-elasticity, as used by Triffin, is that it may not be single-valued at the point where we wish to examine it. Previous work [23] and our study of contingent demand in Chapters 5 and 7 indicate that there may be a kink or a discontinuity in the demand for the product of one firm caused by a small change in the price charged by another firm. [24]

From the empirical viewpoint cross-elasticities appear to be a useful guide to the interrelatedness of market demand for products and as such constitute part of the information necessary to the study of a market form. However, this does not make them useful as a description of the nature of competition in the market. Suppose that we were able to measure cross-elasticities with a fair degree of accuracy and had been able to solve all the vexing time-period problems which arise whenever an attempt is made to do so. We would then have a set of numbers which would serve one purpose and one purpose only. It would give us necessary empirical information about the structure of market demand between certain firms, groups of firms, or products.

At this point we must be careful to make an important distinction between *market form* in the sense of a description of technical, legal, and political relations of a group of firms to their environment and the *behavior* displayed by these firms. In game theory terminology this is the difference between the payoff functions and a description of a play of a game. The expressions monopoly, oligopolistic market, market with many sellers, a homogeneous product, and free entry are clearly descriptions of market forms. Terms such as monopolistic competition, heterogeneous competition, and pure competition are often used to imply not only the market form but also the behavioristic pattern of the competitors. Thus Chamberlin's use of the word "competition" implies non-co-operative behavior.

Triffin's use of cross-elasticity measures serves to supply part of the information needed for market description. If we are willing to make Chamberlin's behavioristic assumptions, forget asset structure, leave out dynamics, and ignore coalitions and institutional imperfections, then cross-elasticities would also indicate the form that would be taken by the market behavior of the competitors. If we are unwilling to make these heroic assumptions, then cross-elasticities supply a necessary, but by no means sufficient, part of the information needed to describe the objective features of market forms. Asset structure, corporate structure, and entry and exit conditions must be included if a market-form classification is constructed for any applied purpose. When this has been done we are ready to examine the behavior of businessmen in a market.

In the last few pages of his book Triffin devotes a section to the modern corporation and control. He notes that theoretical economics has paid little or no attention to the problems raised by the corporate structure of the economy.

4.2. BREMS' PRODUCT EQUILIBRIUM UNDER MONOPOLISTIC COMPETITION

Brems pays great attention to the development of Chamberlin's observations on the importance of product variation and advertising competition. He devotes the first seven chapters of his book to a discussion of these features of monopolistic competition. He then turns to an explicit examination of the firm in multiperiod planning. Here he notes the importance of the theory of investment to a theory of monopolistic competition and mentions the literature on this topic. After a discussion of some observed features of action in the market, such as buyer's inertia, some comments are made on the nature of uncertainty. In the rest of his book Brems discusses duopoly in a dynamic situation. It is to part of this work that we address our major criticism.

The failure by both Chamberlin and Mrs. Robinson to discuss collusion is noted by Brems at the beginning of his discussion of theories of noncollusive and collusive duopoly. Here the author misinterprets much of the work done in game theory. [25]

The interesting thing about von Neumann and Morgenstern's treatment of zero-sum, two-person games is that expectations about the rival's behavior are largely irrelevant to the problem. This proposition is so revolutionary and so contrary to everything said by duopoly theorists that we shall examine it more closely.

There are two features of this quotation that merit attention. The first is that Brems is incorrect in his statement that conjectures about the opponent's behavior are irrelevant. The player assumes very specifically that he is playing an intelligent maximizing opponent. If he were guaranteed that he were playing an individual with a fixed set of biases, then a von Neumann-Morgenstern two-person, zero-sum game model could be reformulated to take care of the biases. The second and far more important criticism is that Brems has set up a straw man. Nowhere in their book do von Neumann and Morgenstern claim that the two-person, zero-sum game is a model for duopoly. In fact, the opposite is explained. A duopoly model falls naturally under the classification of a two-person, *nonzero-sum game*, which is treated by von Neumann and Morgenstern as a co-operative game, *not* as a *noncollusive* situation, as Brems seems to believe. The only noncollusive game treatment of duopoly or any other market comes in the use of Nash's work on non-co-operative games, [26] a subject which is not touched by von Neumann and Morgenstern and which also deals with a non-zero-sum model.

Brems also observes that "von Neumann and Morgenstern assume that players want to maximize the mathematical expectation of the outcome of the play." [27] He objects to this on the grounds of reaction to uncertainty. This involves a lack of understanding of the axiom systems concerning utility. (The axioms are given in Appendix A.) Marschak pays special attention to this problem. [28] If Brems wishes to raise objections, the proper place to do so is at the axiom system.

In order to complete his argument Brems points out that most duopoly situations are not games with perfect information, [29] hence do not have a pure strategy solution. He then says that,

We expect entrepreneurs to attempt to find out each other's strategies rather than choose chance coefficients and afterwards throw dice.[30]

Both of these comments are good solid statements of common sense and go against nothing that has been said in any game model of duopoly. Yet for some reason Brems believes that they are relevant criticisms. They would be if anyone had treated duopoly as a two-person, zero-sum game with perfect information. No one has done so.

4.3.   FELLNER'S COMPETITION AMONG THE FEW

Fellner's [31] treatment of oligopoly emphasizes the role of quasi-agreements and limited action for joint profit maximization. [32] The central theme of his book differs considerably from those previously mentioned (except Brems) inasmuch as he lays stress on the semi-co-operative aspects of oligopolistic markets rather than on the non-co-operative and equilibrium features. His analysis consists more in the listing and discussion of many observable features of modern oligopoly struggles than in the erection of a theoretical framework of a general nature. Fellner, as well as Triffin, includes a brief discussion of the possible effect of corporate structure on the competitive economy. [33] Unfortunately, there is no explicit discussion of the role of financial conditions, although the importance of a firm's ability to make and withstand threats is noted.

These very brief remarks on Fellner's work are by no means intended as an adequate review. They are made in order to call attention to the contrast between the approach put forth here and in the other books discussed. Fellner points to the welter of market forms which have to be accounted for. His work, in the opinion of this writer, represents a necessary and early step in the direction of the description and specification required before the formalization of a satisfactory theory of oligopoly.

NOTES

[1] Edward H. Chamberlin, *The Theory of Monopolistic Competition* (Cambridge: Harvard University Press, 6th ed., 1950), Chapter IV.

[2] *Ibid.*, Chapter VI.

[3] *Ibid.*, p. 10.

[4] *Ibid.*, p. 204.

[5] *Ibid.*, p. 98.

[6] *Ibid.*, pp. 89–94.

[7] *Ibid.*, pp. 74–81.

[8] *Ibid.*, pp. 81–100.

[9] *Ibid.*, pp. 100–110.

[10] *Ibid.*, p. 82.

[11] *Ibid.*, p. 90.

[12] *Ibid.*, p. 91.

[13] *Ibid.*, p. 92, Figure 15.

[14] *Ibid.*, pp. 104–105.

[15] *Ibid.*, p. 44, 52, 101.

[16] *Ibid.*, p. 101.

[17] It seems strange that a book on oligopolistic competition which is now in its sixth edition has not found room for a single reference to Berle and Means or work of a similar nature.

[18] R. Triffin, *Monopolistic Competition and General Equilibrium Theory* (Cambridge: Harvard University Press, 1940), pp. 45, 67–68.

[19] Joan Robinson, *The Economics of Imperfect Competition* (London: Macmillan, 1950), p. 21.

[20] R. Triffin, *op. cit.*, pp. 67 and 68.

[21] Edward H. Chamberlin, *op. cit.*, pp. 81–94 and 100–104.

[22] J. Robinson, *op. cit.*, p. 21.

[23] Paul M. Sweezy, "Demand under Conditions of Oligopoly," *Journal of Political Economy*, **XLVII** (1939), 568–573. See also: George J. Stigler,

"The Kinky Oligopoly Demand Curve and Rigid Prices," *The Journal of Political Economy*, **IV** (October 1947), pp. 432–449.

[24] Bishop has noted in his critique on the use of cross-elasticity that there also exists a cross-elasticity measure in which the quantity of one firm is regarded as the independent variable. This is not noted in Triffin's analysis, although the quantity cross-elasticity has the happy property of being continuous and single-valued for many conditions. R. L. Bishop, "Elasticities and Market Relationships," *American Economic Review*, **XLII** (December 1952), pp. 779–803.

[25] H. Brems, *Product Equilibrium under Monopolistic Competition* (Cambridge: Harvard University Press, 1951), p. 166.

[26] J. P. Mayberry, J. F. Nash Jr., and M. Shubik, "A Comparison of Treatments of a Duopoly Situation," *Econometrica*, **XXI** (January 1953), pp. 141–154.

[27] H. Brems, *op. cit.*, p. 168.

[28] J. Marschak, "Rational Behavior, Uncertain Prospects and Measurable Utility," *Econometrica*, **XVIII** (April 1950), p. 138.

[29] H. Brems, *op. cit.*, p. 172.

[30] *Ibid.*, p. 173.

[31] William Fellner, *Competition among the Few* (New York: Knopf, 1949), p. 53.

[32] *Ibid.*, p. 51.

[33] *Ibid.*, pp. 169–174.

chapter 3

THE FIRM IN AN OLIGOPOLISTIC MARKET: MONOPOLY AND BILATERAL MONOPOLY

1. INTRODUCTION

1.1 PLAN AND MOTIVATION

The plan in this book is to divide up the difficulties faced in the formulation of an adequate theory of oligopoly, analyze them separately, and then attempt to construct a theory which handles all major aspects of oligopolistic competition at the same time.

In order to carry out this plan this and Chapters 4 and 5 are devoted to the study of monopoly, bilateral monopoly, and duopoly models in a static setting. We are limiting ourselves to the two traditional economic variables, price and production or quantity. As we are considering only one period, in the game models we are limited to the very simple behavioristic assumptions that a strategy consists of naming a price, a production rate, or both. Some non-static models are given, such as a modified version of Edgeworth's duopoly problem. When this is done the behavioral assumptions are specified explicitly. All of the behavioristic assumptions made in Chapters 3, 4, and 5 are for the most part too simple or are false in the opinion of this writer, as even casual empiricism will quickly demonstrate. However, they serve as an excellent medium through which we are able to illustrate certain objective features of the nature of oligopolistic competition. By this we mean the nature of the prospects which can be attained by the firms, the technical possibilities of collusive action, the amount of damage that one firm can inflict upon another, and the cost of doing damage. In game theoretic terms we are primarily interested in carrying out an exhaustive examination of all prospects, strategies, and payoffs. When we have done this we will be in a position to introduce complications in the form of product variation, transportation costs, and other imperfections. An extension can then be made which carries the analysis into dynamics. At that point our interest must be more concerned with the realism of our behavioristic assumptions than it is here. Until then we will devote ourselves, for the most part, to the exploration of the problems of oligopoly, making use of different behavioristic assumptions more as means to help illustrate certain features rather than as ends or methods for providing solutions which are to be believed.

In line with this program we are postponing a general discussion of the use of conjectural variation hypotheses in the study of oligopoly until later in the book. We are able there to point out that this procedure has been for the most part ill defined and hazy.

Chapters 4 and 5 contain several diagrams unfamiliar to the usual diagrammatic representations of the economics of duopoly. They are used to indicate every technologically feasible position of competition and implicit or explicit collusion which can be attained by two firms. Most of the results obtained in these three chapters come more from the successful formulation of certain oligopoly problems and the isolation of relevant, yet previously obscured, features than from the specialized concepts of solution which are given.

1.2. A Formulation of Market Conditions

A firm is assumed to be an independent entity owned and run by a single entrepreneur; hence the firm's maximization problem will coincide with that of the owner (detailed consideration of the effect of different corporate and financial structures is delayed until Chapter 10).

In general, the models are formulated as n-person, nonzero-sum games in the normalized form. This means that for the most part we will study games of the following type: There is a set N of n competitors, each in control of a set of strategies. The number of pure strategies controlled by the ith player is denoted by s_i. If we represent a mixed strategy of the ith player by ζ_i, then we can write down n payoff functions, one for each player, so that $H_i(\zeta_1, \zeta_2, \ldots \zeta_n)$ [1] specifies the amount that the ith player receives as a function of the strategies employed by all the players. Each player is assumed to know the rules of the game and the payoff functions; this is sometimes termed complete information.

An economic interpretation of complete information can be given immediately. There are n firms, each having control over its own production. Every firm is assumed to know the possible production range and costs of the other firms. In other words, any firm can compute not only the profits it can itself obtain from any market action but also the profits of others (this assumption can be weakened, but for the sake of clarity and specificity we use it here).

In general, it is also assumed in this book that consumers do not form co-operatives or participate in joint action but merely react to the price structure individually in a manner that maximizes their individual goals. Thus when we analyze quantity-variation competition between firms selling a homogeneous product we are able to define the aggregate demand curve for their product. As soon as we attempt to deal with price-variation models, even with a homogeneous product, we meet with the difficult problems raised by demand under oligopoly conditions. These are solved by formalizing the concept of *contingent demand* (see Chapter 5: 2). The family of contingent demand functions which we will construct consists of every possible "imagined demand curve" of Kaldor [2] and can be used to derive and explain the nature and size of the "kinks" or discontinuities postulated by Sweezy [3] and elaborated by Stigler. [4]

It is assumed that not only are there no transportation costs, product differentiation, or other market imperfections but that conferences, negotiations, telephone calls, and all other activities of organization are both costless and timeless. This assumption is made specifically in order to separate and call attention to a very important factor in oligopolistic markets. One of the major features that may keep a certain level of competition in a market, at least in the short run, is that the costs of collusion are too great when compared with their returns.

2. MONOPOLY

The limiting case of competition which can be called pure monopoly occurs when the cross-elasticities (Chapter 2: 4.1) of demand between a firm's product and the products of any other firm or group of firms approaches zero. Practically, this amounts to saying that the effects of other firms' actions on the monopolist are so small that they can be ignored with little loss in accuracy in describing the monopolist's market. Another way of stating this is that the *strategic interlinkage* between a monopolist and any other firm or group of firms is very small.

A monopolistic market can be described as a one-person, non-zero-sum game; i.e., the monopolist is the only player with strategic possibilities. He will be rewarded according to the action he takes. We assume that he knows the demand for his product or at least has an estimated demand forecast.

We can construct our model in terms of price, quantity, or both price and quantity simultaneously, as the independent variables. Conforming to our previous notation, the symbol P_1 is used to represent the payoff function of the monopolist. This tells him his payoff for any pure strategy (see Note 1 for a description of the payoff evaluation for mixed strategies). We must distinguish between the type of pure strategies we wish to consider. If we allow the monopolist to select any price or production rate within some specified range, then we use the symbols p_1 and q_1 to represent a price or a production strategy. A particular p_1 or q_1 can be represented by a number in the ranges $0 \leqslant p_1 \leqslant \bar{p}$ and $0 \leqslant q_1 \leqslant \bar{q}$, where $\bar{p}$ and $\bar{q}$ are the highest price and production rate, respectively, that we wish to consider. The payoff function for any pure strategy can then be written as $P_1(q_1)$, $P_1(p_1)$, or $P_1(p_1, q_1)$ where a pure strategy is interpreted to be, respectively, the selection of a production rate, a price, or both simultaneously. If we wish to limit the monopolist to producing and pricing only in discrete units (indivisibilities may be such that it is possible to produce five or six units of some item, but not five and a half), then we use the notations $q_{1,j}$ and $p_{1,j}$, respectively, in which the first subscript stands for the "name" or number of the player (since we have only one player here we do not need this subscript, but generally we do for two or more), and the second is the number of the pure strategy. The symbols above are, respectively, the jth production rate and the jth price of the first player. The payoff function is now expressed as $P_1(q_{1,j})$, $P_1(p_{1,j})$, or $P_1(p_{1,j}, q_{1,j})$.

Conforming to the usual practice in economic theory, we will treat price and quantity as though they were continuous variables. Denoting the demand function for the product of the monopolist as $p = \phi(q)$ and his total costs as $C_1(q)$, then for any production rate q_1 his profit will be $P_1(q_1) = q_1\phi(q_1) - C_1(q_1)$. This is his payoff function regarding his strategy as the selection of a production rate. The monopolist, in order to maximize, must solve a simple maximization problem. His payoff function involves only one variable, and he controls that variable. The standard economic conditions for maximization by a monopolist are obtained. He selects a production rate in a manner that *marginal revenue* equals *marginal cost*.

It is possible to write the payoff as a function of price. The strategy for a monopolist is then the selection of the price which maximizes revenue. Once the price has been determined he can calculate his production rate at that price. This method gives precisely the same solution as before.

Von Neumann and Morgenstern [5] treat monopoly and monopsony as an n-person game is which the many buyers or sellers are considered as players. By studying the properties of the von Neumann and Morgenstern solutions to games in which n players have the characteristics of buyers and m have the characteristics of sellers the classical monopoly and monopsony solutions can be obtained. The cases occur for $n = 1$, $m \to \infty$ and $n \to \infty$, $m = 1$, respectively (under certain conditions when both m and $n \to \infty$ together the pure competition solution is obtained). This approach is not followed further here, but it is considered elsewhere. [6]

3. BILATERAL MONOPOLY

3.1. GENERAL REMARKS

As soon as an economic situation involves more than one decision maker whose actions influence the outcome to others, game theoretic complications arise in full force. In our brief discussion of monopoly we did not treat the purchasers as though they were players in any strategic sense, i.e., we assumed that they acted independently, each in turn assuming that he had no effect on the market price. Thus only one decision maker had to be considered, and the strategic difficulties encountered in games of more than one player were avoided. As soon as we deal with bilateral monopoly or bargaining, no simplification is possible, and the influence of both the buyer and seller must be considered.

Discussion, understandings, and agreements are vital to bilateral trading. By the very nature of the situation, co-operation is called for. Without some degree of co-operation either side can block trading and thus reduce individual gain to zero. We see that bilateral monopoly and bargaining are amenable to treatment as two-person, nonzero-sum games. Four formalizations of bilateral monopoly are presented here and compared. They are those of Edgeworth, von Neumann and Morgenstern, the Nash solution with side payments, and the treatment of bilateral monopoly by a price-parameter model.

3.2. THE VON NEUMANN AND MORGENSTERN SOLUTION

We do not intend to enter into a detailed discussion of the von Neumann and Morgenstern definition of solution for an n-person game. However, a very brief sketch of the nature of this solution when applied to a two-person, nonzero-sum game is given here.

It is assumed that the two players agree to maximize their joint return and then settle between themselves by means of a side payment. For instance, if two firms are competing for a market which can yield a profit to only one of them, barring interference by the other, then the solution which will achieve joint maximization is such that one firm stays out and the other pays its part of the profits as a side payment.

No firm is expected to enter into a collusive arrangement if it is offered an amount that is less than the amount it can obtain by itself, regardless of the actions taken by the others.

A game is called *essential* if the amount which can be obtained by all players acting together is greater than the sum of the amounts they can obtain by individual action. If this is not the case, then there is no motivation for co-operation or collusion, and the game is said to be *inessential*. All two-person, zero- and constant-sum games are obviously inessential. If trading at some prices will yield a gain to both parties, then it is evident that a bilateral monopoly will be portrayed by an essential game.

We may state the condition for essentiality in the following manner: Let $v(\{1\})$ and $v(\{2\})$ represent the amounts that players 1 and 2 can guarantee for themselves without co-operation (in a bilateral monopoly this would be the amount obtained by not trading and in most cases would be assigned the value zero, although not always, as noted in subsection 3.6). Let $v(\{1, 2\})$ represent the amount of joint gain they can obtain by trading; then

$$v(\{1, 2\}) > v(\{1\}) + v(\{2\}).$$

Since von Neumann and Morgenstern assume that individual utilities are comparable, there would, in general, be only one point on the contract curve of bargains (see subsection 3.3) which would be jointly maximal (the point corresponds to Edgeworth's utilitarian point; see subsection 3.3 immediately following). According to the theory, this bargain would be selected, and it would then be possible that a side payment of money or "utility" would be made.

This bargaining model requires us to treat the money payment made by the buyer as though it were a transfer of a number of units of a measurable utility. Sometimes, to do so may appear quite unreasonable. However, if the traders are bilateral monopolists, the first trader being a primary producer selling to the second, who, in turn, sells his product to the market, an interesting interpretation of the solution can be given. The monopsonist determines the best pricing and production policies for his final product on the assumption that he can buy from the monopolist at marginal cost. The two firms then set their outputs to maximize the revenue of the monopsonist from the final market. After this they settle up between themselves by a side payment. Hence the outputs of both goods and the market price of the consumer good sold by the second firm are all determinate, but the actual price paid for the monopolist's good must be bargained for.

This may hold true of a labor-management negotiation between a corporation with market control and a union in control of labor supply. Their interests may diverge concerning the division of their joint profit, but they may coincide in wishing to make their joint profit maximal. [7]

In order to describe the von Neumann and Morgenstern solution completely, we must explain the meaning of *imputation*. In a two-person game an imputation is a set of numbers $\alpha = (a_1, a_2)$ such that $a_1 + a_2 = v(\{1, 2\})$ and $a_i \geqslant v(\{i\})$. a_1 is the amount that the first player obtains after the game has been played co-operatively and side payments have been made. Similarly a_2 is the amount that the second player obtains. The two amounts add up to the joint maximum.

A von Neumann and Morgenstern solution to this two-person game consists of the set of imputations which *dominate* all others but do not dominate each other. In this case all the imputations will be of the form $\alpha = (a_1, a_2)$, where $a_1 \geqslant 0$ and $a_2 \geqslant 0$. An imputation will dominate another imputation if there is a set of players in a position to obtain the first imputation and all members of that set obtain more from the first imputation than from the second. In this two-person example this condition is equivalent to Pareto optimality, [8] i.e., the condition used to reject any point which does not lie on the contract curve (see subsection 3.3). Any imputation in which the sum of the components is maximal cannot dominate another imputation with this property because both players cannot simultaneously improve their position by changing from one to the other.

At this point one might well ask what has been gained by setting up all this special notation in order to arrive at a solution which says that the players jointly maximize and split the profits in such a manner that each gets at least as much as he could have obtained by himself. In the two-person, nonzero-sum example the answer is not very much. The major difficulties, new ideas, and contributions of the von Neumann and Morgenstern theory of solution to a general n-person game come when there are three or more players. This is noted elsewhere. [9]

3.3. THE EDGEWORTH SOLUTION

Edgeworth's solution for a two-person, two-commodity bargain [10] has been demonstrated for many years by the use of the simple box diagram shown in Figure 3. Traders 1 and 2 start with a given quantity A and B of their product. The upper left corner of the box is the initial point at which trader 1 has A (as measured from the upper right corner) and trader 2 has B (as measured from the lower left corner). The curves which are convex when viewed

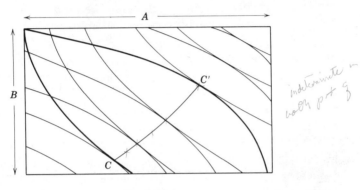

Figure 3

from the upper right corner are the indifference curves for the second trader; the curves which are convex when viewed from the lower left corner are the indifference curves of the first trader. Edgeworth notes that trading will be carried on until a point on the contract curve cc' is reached. The contract curve is a solution to the bargaining problem in the game theory sense. It consists of a set of imputations [11] which do not dominate each other. Any point lying off the contract curve is not jointly optimal. This means that for any distribution off the contract curve there exists at least one imputation on the curve that will be preferable to both bargainers.

Under the Edgeworth assumptions, a multi-imputation solution is obtained. This solution to the bargaining problem has been called "indeterminate." The meaning of solution in an economic situation needs stressing. Of course, the actual result of any bilateral bargain will be a single imputation, but the economic assumptions made are usually not strong enough to enable the economist to forecast the specific imputation that will be chosen. Often all that he can do is to indicate a range in which the outcome must fall. In that case the specification of this range constitutes the solution in the sense that it fully utilizes the economic information. In order to single out an imputation within this range, dynamic sociological and psychological information may be needed.

Edgeworth believed in the measurability of utility and in the possibility of making interpersonal comparisons. Consistent with this belief was his observation that there would be one imputation on the contract curve that would have the property of joint maximality which would make it more desirable than all others. This, he called the "utilitarian point." If $P_1(x, y)$ and $P_2(x, y)$ are the utilities to the two bargainers, respectively, for the amounts x of the first good and y of the second, then the maximum of $P_1(x, y) + P_2(x, y)$ would be the utilitarian point and would have extra ethical significance. He did not advocate that this would necessarily be the solution to a bargain because such a distribution might be most disadvantageous to one side. This can be explained by noting that Edgeworth did not consider the possibility of side payments. In a bargaining situation, with goods and money or "utils" available, it would be possible for the participants to exchange goods in such a manner as to maximize jointly their utility in the exchange and then settle up by a side payment of money. This is the mode of solution employed by von Neumann and Morgenstern and also the type of solution that comes about when companies in a cartel make side payments (sometimes even to the extent of paying their more inefficient members money for closing down their plants).

3.4. THE PRICE-PARAMETER SOLUTION

We observed that in the von Neumann and Morgenstern solution the two firms jointly maximized their profits and then settled up by side payment. Suppose that the two firms were run by one management which wished to maximize its profit. For purposes of internal cost accounting and resource allocation it could set up a system of "shadow prices." These are obtained by solving the two-plant system as though the manager of each made his own production decisions, treating the internal price as if it were a parameter over which he had no control. Suppose that the total cost function for the first factory were $C_1(q_1)$. It sells its product to the second factory which uses this input (and possibly others) to manufacture an article which is sold to the consumers. We identify the quantity of the consumer good produced as q. The production function for q is such that

$$q = \Psi(q_1, q_2, \ldots, q_n)$$

where the q_i for $i = 2, 3, \ldots, n$ are inputs other than those obtained from the first factory. Suppose that there were supply functions given for all inputs except the first. Let them be $p_i = \phi_i(q_i)$ for $i = 2, 3, \ldots, n$. Let the demand function for the final product be $p = \phi(q)$. Then the corporation wishes to maximize its total profit $P_1 + P_2$, where P_1 stands for the profit imputed to the first factory it owns and P_2 stands for the profit imputed to the second factory.

$$P_1 + P_2 = q\phi(q) - C_1(q_1) - \sum_{i=2}^{n} p_i q_i.$$

In order to maximize the joint profit from both factories we must have

$$\frac{d(P_1 + P_2)}{dq} = 0.$$

This can be stated as the condition in which the marginal cost of the production of the final product to the corporation as a whole equals its marginal revenue.

If we set up a shadow-pricing system in which, possibly for internal bookkeeping purposes, the first factory charges the other a price for its product, then the two factories may be regarded as attempting to maximize individually the following payoffs:

$$P_1 = p_1 q_1 - C_1(q_1),$$

$$P_2 = q\phi(q) - p_1 q_1 - \sum_{i=2}^{n} p_i q_i.$$

If we add these together, we get the same equation as before. The way in which we were able to define the two separate payoffs was by adding the $p_1 q_1$ term to the first factory as revenue and subtracting it from the second as extra cost. The individual maximizing actions of both factories give us the relations

$$\frac{dP_1}{dq_1} = 0 \qquad \frac{\partial P_2}{\partial q_1} = 0.$$

The first amounts to a statement that the first factory will sell its product to the second at a price equal to its marginal cost, whereas the second condition states that the other factory is willing to pay a price to the first equal to the marginal value productivity of the factor being supplied.

We note that if a corporation uses this accounting method it will ensure the maximization of its net revenue, but it may impute a loss to some of its branches. For instance, in the case given, suppose that the first factory had a high overhead but was producing a factor for the second factory for which there were no substitute. Allocation of income to the first factory by the shadow-price system might not cover the overhead costs of the first factory. Yet when we consider the corporation as a whole it may be making a large profit. The paradox in this situation is easily resolved when we observe that the problem posed here is essentially one of joint production; hence there is no inherent logic in assigning all of the overhead cost faced by the first factory to it alone because in essence it is a joint overhead.

If the two factories in the example were actually different firms, then, of course, we would have to assign each its own overhead. In that case, if marginal cost pricing were used, the producer of the factor would be running at a loss which would force him to close down and sell out to the other firm. (If we assume that the factor has no alternative use, then the other firm would be the only one interested in buying the first as an operating concern.)

3.5. THE NASH SOLUTION

Economic indeterminacy has already been encountered with only two competitors in the market. In the von Neumann-Morgenstern solution the quantity to be traded was determined, but no price within a range could be determined. In the price-parameter solution no indeterminacy is encountered, but it is unreasonable to expect that bilateral monopolists would adopt such a device to decide upon a bargain. Is there any reasonable manner in which a pricing agreement between the firms might be determined, or should we merely say that all outcomes within some range depend upon some complex of "bargaining abilities"? The Nash solution to the bargaining problem [12] suggests a method of fair division." The best way to look at the motivation behind this method is that it is normative. It suggests a way of dividing joint profits that is "fair" in the sense that the referee or judge in a cartel board "should" follow such a procedure if called upon to settle a division between two corporations. Nash's division method and the validity of some of the assumptions he makes may be questioned; however, even with this qualification his formulation of the problem and investigation of the role of "threats" advances our understanding of bilateral monopoly.

Nash differs from von Neumann and Morgenstern in that he brings out explicitly the role of threats in bargaining situations. To show their importance, consider the following two bargaining games. In both games player 1 has one unit of a good a, and player 2 has one unit of a good b. In the first game player 1 has a utility function such that $u(a) = 1$, $u(b) = 50$. Player 2 has his utility function $w(a) = 50$, $w(b) = 1$. In the second case $u(a) = 1$, $u(b) = 2$, $w(a) = 98$, and $w(b) = 1$. Let us suppose that each player has the choice of trading, which we denote by T; or not trading, which we denote by N. We may draw up a table of the following sort for each game:

	Game 1			Game 2	
	T	N		T	N
T	50, 50	1, 1	T	2, 98	1, 1
N	1, 1	1, 1	N	1, 1	1, 1

where, for instance, 50, 50 stands for a utility of 50 for player 1 and a utility of 50 for player 2, realized by both having decided to trade as indicated by the pair of strategies T, T.

According to von Neumann and Morgenstern the players will jointly maximize; hence they will agree to trade and will be able to obtain $a_1 + a_2 = 100$ between them in both games. In both games neither player will accept having to make a side payment which will leave him with less than 1 because he can get this without trading. Thus we have the conditions $a_1 \geqslant 1$ and $a_2 \geqslant 1$. These, together with the condition that $a_1 + a_2 = 100$, are all the restraints put on by von Neumann and Morgenstern; and the same range is offered as the solution in both cases.

Nash points out in the first case that if 1 carries out a threat not to bargain then he and player 2 are hurt equally. In the second case player 1's threat causes him to give up a possible gain which is far smaller than the gain of player 2. The Nash solution takes into account the different threat positions of the participants; thus in the second case the side payment from player 2 to player 1 would be larger than in the first.

In essence the Nash two-person co-operative [13] game solution, which we use for both bilateral monopoly and duopoly problems, can be characterized in the following manner: The two entrepreneurs inform each other through their lawyers or a trade board of the threat action they are prepared to take if they are unable to obtain at least the amount each claims as his share of the proceedings due to co-operation. The profits (or losses) which would be caused by using the threats are computed. This pair of profits is used as the base from which the "fair division" is then calculated. Nash claims that each player should be willing to accept this division scheme which takes into account both the amount they can obtain by co-operation and the damage they could do to each other if they decided to fight.

The threat action available to a player is evaluated both in terms of the costs to the threatener and the damage done to the opponent. For instance, suppose that against an action taken by an opposing firm a businessman has a set of alternatives which yield him the same final profit but which have different effects on the profits of his opponent. The action which gives his opponent the smallest profit will be the best threat in this case.

The object of stating the threats is to enable each player to attempt to make the initial point from which he will use some method of fair division as favorable to himself as possible. Thus each businessman will pick from threats involving a given cost to himself the one which guarantees the largest amount of damage to his opponent, no matter what action this opponent may take. If we assume that both opponents have the same evaluation of money, it can be shown that the appropriate threat actions can be determined by a simple criterion: the first player will try to maximize the quantity $P_1 - P_2$, and the second will attempt to minimize $P_1 - P_2$, where P_1 and P_2 are the profits made by players 1 and 2, respectively. The optimal threat strategies to each player will be determined by those actions which satisfy

$$\min_1 \max_2 (P_1 - P_2) = \max_2 \min_1 (P_1 - P_2).$$

For many bilateral monopoly situations the only effective threat that can be carried out by one of the players unilaterally is simply to refuse all trade. In this manner each firm can guarantee that the other will lose at least its overhead costs no matter what it does (assuming no flexibility of plant use). The selection of threats when several are available is considerably more complicated; such choice arises in the duopoly model, and the method of selection is discussed in Chapter 4: 3.6.

The "no-trade" strategies have the minimax properties of optimal strategies used in a zero-sum game (see Chapter 4: 3.6). The minimum return that any player can be forced to accept is that obtained by no trade, but this is also the maximum return that he can guarantee for himself.

The fair-division method employed by Nash is discussed in detail in Appendix B. In the simple case in which two individuals with the same preference functions for money must share a sum of money the Nash method, using the values of the no-trade position as a basis, gives each participant an equal gain from his no-trade position.

3.6. SOME BILATERAL MONOPOLY MODELS

In this comparative study of proposed solutions to bilateral monopoly we include an example computed in order to illustrate the different methods.

For simplicity we consider two factories, one of which is the producer of a primary product which it sells to the second. The second factory processes this factor and sells the resultant product to the market. Let the average cost functions of the two factories be

$$\gamma_1 = \frac{4}{q} + 4 - 0.99(q - q^2),$$

$$\gamma_2 = 5 - 0.01(q - q^2).$$

We take the final market demand for the product of the second firm to be

$$\phi(q) = p = 20 - q.$$

The nature of the average cost functions chosen implies that there is a one-to-one relation between the factor supplied by the first factory and the final output of the second factory. This simplification is solely for convenience in computing an example; the general formulation is given in subsection 3.4.

3.6.1. THE VON NEUMANN AND MORGENSTERN SOLUTION. When both firms collude against the market they jointly maximize the quantity

$$P_1 + P_2 = pq - q(\gamma_1 + \gamma_2),$$

where p is the price of the final product sold to the consumers. If the firms refuse to trade with each other, then because of the overhead-cost structure the first firm obtains -4 and the second firm obtains 0. The von Neumann and Morgenstern solution consists of the production rates which maximize joint profit (in this case 11.34) and then any division of profit which gives each firm at least as much as it could get if no trade took place. The resultant values are tabulated in subsection 3.7.

3.6.2. THE PRICE-PARAMETER OR PSEUDOCOMPETITIVE SOLUTION. If each firm determines output so as to maximize profit, taking the transfer price as given, and the transfer price is fixed so as to equalize the resulting outputs, the results are as follows:

The profit of the first firm is given by

$$P_1 = p_1 q - q\gamma_1(q) = p_1 q - 4 - 4q + 0.99(q^2 - q^3).$$

The profit of the second firm is given by

$$P_2 = q\Psi(q) - q\gamma_2(q) - p_1 q = q(20 - q)$$
$$- 5q + 0.01(q^2 - q^3) - p_1 q.$$

The solution is obtained by setting

$$\frac{dP_1}{dq} = 0, \qquad \frac{dP_2}{dq} = 0,$$

so that

$$p_1 = 4 - 0.99(2q - 3q^2)$$

and

$$p_1 = 15 - 2q + 0.01(2q - 3q^2),$$

where p_1 is the "shadow price" charged between the two factories. From the foregoing we obtain $11 - 3q^2 = 0$ and $q = \left(\dfrac{11}{3}\right)^{\frac{1}{2}}$ as in the preceding case.

3.6.3. THE NASH SOLUTION. As in the previous cases the firms will jointly maximize against the final market; however, the division of profit will depend upon the relative situation of the firms if no trade takes place. In this example, in the event of no trade, the raw material firm will suffer a loss of 4, which represents its heavy fixed costs. The other firm has no fixed costs (or at least negligibly small ones); hence it would be reduced to a loss of zero by not trading. Using the point $(-4, 0)$ as the initial point for the division, the Nash solution for this bilateral monopoly can be represented on a diagram, as indicated in Figure 4. The line ab

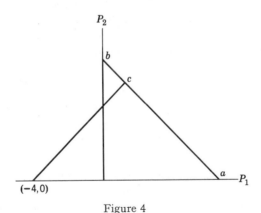

Figure 4

represents every possible division of the revenue obtained by joint maximization. The co-ordinates P_1 and P_2 are the profits of the two firms. Using the point $(-4, 0)$ as the base point for the fair division we draw a 45-degree line which cuts ab at c. This is the "fair division" point; it splits the profit evenly between the two firms in the sense that each obtains the same gain when it compares its share of the profits with the amount it would get if there were no trading.

3.6.4. THREATS, ASSET STRUCTURE, AND VULNERABILITY. In the von Neumann-Morgenstern and Nash models we assumed implicitly that if one firm decided not to trade both firms would lose at least their overhead costs (leaving out the possibility of inventories). This is not necessarily so. Even in these essentially static models we can introduce liquidity and asset-structure conditions which enable us to obtain a more faithful portrayal of the strength of the firms if agreement fails. For instance, it may pay a firm to liquidate rather than remain closed down for a protracted length of time. The financial criterion for the decision to liquidate can be obtained by comparing overhead costs with the income stream obtained by re-employing the net funds obtained from liquidation.

For the purpose of exposition we present an actual example of a bilateral monopoly in which capital structure is considered. We use the same average cost functions as in previous examples. Let us imagine that the assets and liabilities of the second firm are negligible; there is no alternative employment of resources to be accounted for, and, as there is next to no overhead, a trade embargo by the other firm reduces its maximum profit under threat to zero. We give the first firm a simple balance sheet:

Assets		Liabilities	
Plant, etc.	200	Common stock	150
		Bonds	50
	200		200

In order to compute its liquidation position we assume that it can obtain 150 for all physical assets, that it has to redeem its bonds, but can retain the remaining capital for reinvestment (this could happen if the common stock were held in a family corporation). We assume that capital can earn 5 per cent in a venture with similar risk features. If the second firm threatens not to trade, we can compare two situations that are available to the first firm. It can stop production and maintain its plant at a cost of 4 per annum. In other words, its income is —4 per annum. Alternatively, it can liquidate its plant and use the proceeds for reinvestment.

This results in a loss of 50 in assets but gives an income of 5 per annum due to reinvestment of funds. This is equivalent to a steady annual income of 2.5. Hence the threat position of the firm with the high overhead is actually quite good. The fair division is indicated in Figure 5 at c. The range of divisions for the von Neumann-Morgenstern solution in this case becomes ad.

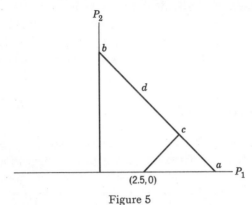

Figure 5

We note that the introduction of financial considerations changed the Nash solution and changed the range for the von Neumann-Morgenstern solution because it assigned new values to the amount that an individual could obtain without co-operation. No change was needed in the price-parameter solution, which depends purely upon the physical features of the productive process. In the other solutions financial power played a role in the determination of the division of profits, but production rates and efficient intrafactory allocation of resources were the same as in the price-parameter solution.

3.7. A COMPARISON OF THE RESULTS FOR BILATERAL MONOPOLY MODELS

Table 4

	q	P_1	P_2	$P_1 + P_2$	p_1	p
von Neumann-Morgenstern	1.915	...	...	11.34	...	18.09
Price-parameter	1.915	7.86	3.48	11.34	11.10	18.09
Nash	1.915	3.67	7.67	11.34	8.91	18.09
Fair division with asset structure	1.915	6.92	4.42	11.34	10.61	18.09

P_1 and P_2 are the profits of firms one and two, p is the price charged to the consumers for the final product, p_1 is the price paid by the second firm to the first for the factor, and q is the output, both of the factor and final product.

All these solutions are collusive in the sense that the greatest joint profit is obtained from the consumers. Except in the price-parameter case, the individual firms do not use the final factor price to determine trade between them; they jointly maximize and settle up by side payment. We can translate this side payment into a price, but this price does not enter into any production plans.

3.8. "Fair Settlements"

The Nash solutions were of a normative nature. They assumed away such features as bargaining ability. As a suggestion for policy it might be desirable to be rid of such aspects of economic life as bargaining and "toughness," in which case a bilateral monopoly which has been involved in threats and counter-threats might be advised to recognize the Nash or some other arbitration solution as a "peculiarly reasonable" settlement.

The literature on bilateral monopoly, bartering, and bargaining is considerable. Some interesting suggestions have been made by Jannaccone, who offers several division conventions for bargainers, [14] Zeuthen has constructed a dynamic scheme to deal with wage problems, [15] and Raiffa [16] considers bargaining situations under many different assumptions concerning individual utilities, thus deriving several "fair" arbitration schemes (akin to some of those mentioned in Appendix B). If we assume with Nash that individual utilities are not comparable, then part of Raiffa's work leads to the same "fair" division as Nash.

The extensive writings on union-management negotiations, international agreements, and legal arguments all deal with the dynamics of settlements, taking into account lack of knowledge, negotiation skills, psychological factors, and other realistic complications. The purpose of this section on bilateral monopoly was more limited than this. We wished to explore the economic background for dealings between two firms. The features of major interest have been the nature and magnitude of threats, the role of side payments, and the two different roles played by production and financial considerations.

NOTES

[1] An example serves to illustrate the difference between P_i and H_i. In the simple two-person, zero-sum game given by Table 3 in Chapter 1 the table $P_1(i, j)$ represents the payoff values to player 1 for all combinations of pure strategies. It does not indicate the payoff for mixed strategies. Suppose that the first player used his mixed strategy $(\frac{1}{2}, \frac{1}{2})$, and the second player also used $(\frac{1}{2}, \frac{1}{2})$. In this case there is a probability of $\frac{1}{4}$ that any pair of pure strategies will occur, and the expected payoff to player 1 is 0. In general, if we denote the expected payoff to player 1 for all mixed strategies by $H_1(\zeta_1, \zeta_2)$ then we can also write

$$H_1(\zeta_1, \zeta_2) = \sum_{i=1}^{s_1} \sum_{j=1}^{s_2} \zeta_{1,i} P_1(i, j) \zeta_{2,j},$$

which indicates that it is derived by calculating the expected values of the payoffs in P_1; the expectations being determined by the mixed strategies.

[2] N. Kaldor, "Mrs. Joan Robinson's Economics of Imperfect Competition" (review), *Economica* (new series), **I** (August 1934), pp. 335–341.

[3] P. M. Sweezy, "Demand under Conditions of Oligopoly," *Journal of Political Economy*, **XLVII** (1939), pp. 568–573.

[4] G. J. Stigler, "The Kinky Oligopoly Demand Curve and Rigid Prices," *Journal of Political Economy*, **LV** (October 1947), pp. 432–449.

[5] J. von Neumann and O. Morgenstern, *Theory of Games and Economic Behavior* (Princeton: Princeton University Press, 3rd ed., 1953), pp. 384–586.

[6] M. Shubik, "Edgeworth Market Games," R. D. Luce and A. W. Tucker, eds, *Contributions to the Theory of Games*, **IV** (Princeton: Princeton University Press, 1958).

[7] — —, "A Business Cycle Model with Organized Labor Considered," *Econometrica*, **XX** (April 1952), pp. 234–294.

[8] R. D. Luce and H. Raiffa, *Games and Decisions* (New York: Wiley, 1957).

[9] V. Pareto, *Manuel D'Économie Politique* (Paris: Girard, 2nd ed., 1927), Chapter VI.

[10] F. Y. Edgeworth, *Mathematical Psychics* (London: C. Kegan Paul, 1881), pp. 20–25.

[11] We must interpret the meaning of imputation more broadly then von Neumann and Morgenstern do, if utility is not comparable. In the Edgeworth model an imputation is any distribution that gives both players at least as much as they can obtain for themselves without co-operation *and* is jointly maximal in the sense that there is no other distribution with which both can be made better off.

[12] J. F. Nash, Jr., "The Bargaining Problem," *Econometrica*, **XVIII** (April 1950), pp. 155–162.

[13] — —, "Two-Person Cooperative Games," *Econometrica*, **XXI** (January 1953), pp. 128–140.

[14] P. Jannaccone, *Prezzi e Mercati* (Torino: Einaudi, 1951), Chapters I and II.

[15] F. Zeuthen, "Undeterminierte Lohnprobleme," *Archiv für Socialwissenschaft und Sozialpolitik*, **62** (1929).

[16] H. Raiffa, "Arbitration Schemes for Generalized Two-Person Games," *in Contributions to the Theory of Games*, **II**, H. W. Kuhn and A. W. Tucker, eds. (Princeton: Princeton University Press, 1953), pp. 361–387.

chapter 4

THE FIRM IN AN OLIGOPOLISTIC MARKET: DUOPOLY (PART 1)

1. INTRODUCTION

The same method of approach employed for bilateral monopoly is adopted here. Many solutions are presented in general form, after which specific examples are given for illustrative purpose. In this first chapter on duopoly we restrict ourselves to models in which the producers are limited to quantity adjustment. In other words, the quantity of production of each producer is taken to be his strategic variable. The market price is determined by a demand mechanism which assures that the market is cleared of whatever quantities the duopolists offer. We examine the efficient point or price-parameter solution, the solutions of Cournot, von Neumann and Morgenstern, and the Nash co-operative game with and without side payments.

We stress here once more that although these models are highly simplified they are capable of handling most complications that would bring them closer to "reality." Specifically, advertising, product differentiation, transportation costs, and the effect of various taxation schemes can be taken into account without substantially changing the nature of the models. The major effect of introducing these complications is added computation. The complications are dealt with specifically in Chapter 7.

The study of oligopoly involves an examination of "fine structures." Miniscule details which can be glossed over in a study of pure competition cannot be ignored. The "unreal" single period models presented here in detail serve only as a necessary preliminary to the development of a more realistic theory in Part 2.

2.   EQUILIBRIUM SOLUTIONS TO NON-CO-OPERATIVE GAMES

The type of solution suggested for a nonzero-sum game which is closely related to many of the noncollusive theories of price formation is given by Nash in his theory of non-co-operative games [1].

The relevant properties of a non-co-operative game solution are cited and illustrated with examples.

Consider a simple two-person, nonzero-sum game of the following sort:

$$
\begin{array}{ccc}
 & H & L \\
H & 3,3 & -1,4 \\
L & 4,-1 & 1,1
\end{array}
$$

The two payoff matrices of the players have been combined; thus the entry 3, 3 states that if player 1 and player 2 both use strategy H (which may stand for a restricted production rate in the market) both will make a profit of 3. If 1 uses H and 2 uses L, the first player will make a profit of -1 and the second, 4.

The co-operative solution to this game is such that both players select strategy H and make a joint profit of 6, which can be divided between them in some manner to give both more than either is able to obtain individually. In the non-co-operative solution both play strategy L and each obtains a profit of 1.

The pair of strategies (L, L) defines an *equilibrium* point. If player 1 were informed that player 2 had chosen his strategy L, then the maximizing action for the first player would be to choose his strategy L, and vice versa. This point has the same type of circular stability as the Cournot or pure competition equilibrium. Given the market price or the production rates of the opponents, no firm is motivated to change its strategy from the equilibrium.

The game

$$
\begin{array}{ccc}
 & H & L \\
H & 3, 3 & -1, 4 \\
L & 4, -1 & -3, -3
\end{array}
$$

differs from the first example in that the pair of strategies (L, L) no longer forms an equilibrium point. This game has three different equilibrium points. The pairs of strategies (H, L) and (L, H) are two of them. If player 1 knew that player 2 had decided to play L, then he would maximize by playing H, whereas if player 2 knew that the first player going to play H, he would maximize by playing L. The same argument applies to the pair of strategies (L, H). The economic interpretation of this model and the equilibria is that of a market with overcapacity. If both firms produce a large output, they both lose; if one were to produce less, leaving the major part of the market to its competitor, it would still lose, but not so much. If both were able to trust each other and co-operate, they could make a monopoly profit.

There is another equilibrium point at which each player has an expected profit of $\frac{5}{3}$. This is a *mixed strategy equilibrium*, which occurs if each player uses his strategy H with the probability of $\frac{2}{3}$ and strategy L with probability of $\frac{1}{3}$.

Suppose that the second player were informed that the first player intended to randomize in such a way that a $\frac{2}{3}$ chance of H and a $\frac{1}{3}$ chance of L existed. If he used his strategy H, his expected payoff would be $\frac{2}{3}(3) + \frac{1}{3}(-1) = \frac{5}{3}$. If he used his strategy L, then his expected payoff would be

$$
\tfrac{2}{3}(4) + \tfrac{1}{3}(-3) = \tfrac{5}{3}.
$$

Thus, given this mixed strategy of player 1, player 2 is indifferent to the choice of strategies because they yield him the same payoff. In particular, if he were to use his strategy H with $\frac{2}{3}$ chance and his strategy L with $\frac{1}{3}$ chance and player 1 were to find this out, player 2 would have no motivation to change his own strategy. However, if player 2 used any other strategy, player 1 would be motivated to shift.

The economic interpretation of a mixed strategy equilibrium is hard to give, especially in a static "one-shot" model of a market which is such a vast oversimplification of economic life. However, before we discuss dynamic models (Chapters 10, 11, and 12), a rationale can be supplied. In a market of the type described by the payoff matrix neither firm can afford to trust the other completely if there is no communication or enforcement of agreements. Cutthroat competition damages both severely. The mixed strategy consists of two components, one in which a firm cuts back production, the other in which it floods the market. The latter component, even though on occasion it may cause some loss to the firm, serves to keep the other firm "in line." Each firm is willing to show its occasional willingness to fight.

The method of solving a mixed strategy equilibrium point in two-person games in which both sides have two strategies is given in Appendix C.

We present the general definition of an equilibrium point. Consider an n-person game which consists of a set N of n players, each with a (finite) set of pure strategies. To each player i there is associated a payoff function H_i (his expected profit, see Note 1, Chapter 3). If ζ_i is a mixed strategy of player i, then the payoff function H_i which is defined for all strategies has the value

$$H_i(\zeta_1, \zeta_2, \ldots, \zeta_n).$$

Denote the n-tuple [2] of strategies $(\zeta_1, \zeta_2, \ldots, \zeta_n)$ by S. We introduce the substitution notation $(S; \eta_i)$ to stand for the n-tuple $(\zeta_1, \zeta_2, \ldots, \zeta_{i-1}, \eta_i, \zeta_{i+1}, \ldots, \zeta_n)$ where η_i is a strategy of player i different from ζ_i. An n-tuple S is an equilibrium point if and only if for every i

$$H_i(S) \geqslant \max_{\text{all } \eta_i} H_i(S; \eta_i).$$

Thus, an equilibrium point is an n-tuple such that each player's strategy maximizes his expected payoff if the strategies of the others are held fixed. Hence each player's strategy is optimal against those of the others. [3]

We reiterate that the Cournot equilibrium assumes that if one duopolist's strategy is known and happens to be the output at equilibrium then the other duopolist, if he maximizes on the basis of this information, will produce his equilibrium output. If a competitive market is in equilibrium, then the output of the individual, if he assumes the price to be given, is such that the quantity he produces will not affect it. These are examples of non-co-operative game equilibria. [4,5]

3. DUOPOLY (PART 1) [6]

3.1. THE COURNOT SOLUTION

Cournot assumes that the producers sell an undifferentiated product and compete through quantity adjustment. Each producer acts under the assumption that his opponent will keep his rate of production constant, no matter what output changes he himself makes. If this belief is maintained, then, given certain conditions on the shapes of the demand and production functions, a unique equilibrium point will be reached. [7,8]

Cournot stresses his assumption of independent action by the producers.

We say *each independently* and this restriction is very essential, as will soon appear; for, if they should come to an agreement so as to obtain for each the greatest possible income, the results would be entirely different and would not differ, so far as consumers are concerned, from those obtained in treating of a monopoly. [9]

Thus he rules out explicit or implicit collusion.

His model can be given both dynamic and static interpretations. Cournot's original writings seem to imply that he had a dynamic process in mind in which each producer adjusts to the other over a period of time, possibly taking five or ten production periods before the neighborhood of an equilibrium point is reached. Stackelberg's treatment of quantity variation is of this nature. [10] It is also possible to regard Cournot's problem as static; we can interpret the equilibrium point as being such that if the duopolists were at such a point neither would be motivated to change his rate of production. This does not explain how or why the individuals move to this point. It merely specifies the equilibrium property once it has been attained.

The equilibrium point can be obtained (it may not be unique) by solving the simultaneous equations

$$\frac{\partial P_i}{\partial q_i} = 0 \qquad (i = 1, 2), \qquad P_i \geqslant 0,$$

where P_i is the profit of the ith firm: $P_i = q_i p - q_i \gamma_i$, γ_i is the average cost of production for the ith firm, and $p = p(q_1 + q_2)$ is the market price.

A simple diagram is given in Figure 6 to demonstrate a path of adjustment to an equilibrium point. q_1 and q_2 are the production rates of the duopolists; $q_1 = f(q_2)$ and $q_2 = h(q_1)$ are, respectively, there action function of the first duopolist, given the production of the second, and the reaction of the second, given the production of the first. If the first duopolist produces the amount a on the assumption that the second produces b, the second will retaliate with a production of b'; the first will readjust to a', the second to b'', and so on until an equilibrium is reached at c.

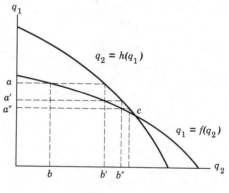

Figure 6

Possibly the major contribution of Cournot's analysis is that it explicitly recognizes the nature of strategic interdependence and attempts to provide a mechanism to deal with such a problem. Reference to Chapter 2 will show that the Chamberlinian analysis is closely connected to the type of equilibrium adjustment used by Cournot. In Figure 2 Chamberlin's dd' and DD' play the roles of the reaction functions for the first oligopolist and for the rest of the market, respectively. Chamberlin introduces market entry conditions explicitly into his equilibrium system; Cournot does not, although a simple direct extension of the Cournot analysis can be made to do this, as shown in Chapter 6: 2.

A study of the foregoing equations and reference to section 2 will show that the Cournot equilibrium conditions satisfy and are a special case of a Nash non-co-operative equilibrium point.

If we regard the Cournot duopoly model as describing a dynamic adjustment path to equilibrium, with each iteration as a production period, two problems must be dealt with. The first involves the difference between statics and dynamics. An equilibrium point defined for a static model may not be stable dynamically, as is shown by such phenomena as the hog cycle. The second concerns asset and financial conditions. A producer engaged in the successive errors and adjustments outlined in a Cournot or Chamberlinian model may be bankrupt before he reaches equilibrium. In analyzing a modern corporate economy, or even an economy of individual entrepreneurs with limited finances, many of the important problems of competition will be hidden by failure to deal explicitly with asset conditions. For the most part, economic theorists have discussed competition in terms of firms concerned primarily with the arrangement of their real asset structure, the pricing mechanism, and the allocation of physical resources in the market. With this must go the problems of financial structure. An implicit assumption that the firm operates in a financial environment of complete liquidity is not sufficient. Such an assumption ignores one of the most important features of an oligopolistic market. When we include the financial features in our analysis we remove the straight jacket from the theory. We are in a position to discuss many economic problems of oligopoly such as those that arise when corporate competitors may initially be only financial entities with no fixed assets at all. For instance, they may be financial syndicates interested in buying up firms engaged in production for reorganization or for liquidation. However, before we can deal with the financial aspects of competition, it is important that we explore fully some simpler models. We first limit ourselves to exploring the strategic possibilities open to two firms in one period in a market in which they compete through their individual control over the supply of goods, the market price, or both. The remainder of this and the next chapter are devoted to this study.

3.2. THE EFFICIENT POINT OR PRICE-PARAMETER SOLUTION

The assumption behind this solution is that the firms aim to maximize "efficiency" or total social product. In order to do this instead of pursuing their own immediate interests the producers act as though impelled by altruistic motives but constrained not to operate their plants at a loss. They maximize production subject to the condition that marginal cost must not exceed price and that total profit must be nonnegative (i.e., they must not operate at a loss). The condition that no firm operate at a loss is actually an entry condition which states that if a firm cannot cover costs it should cease production and allocate its resources elsewhere. (This implicitly assumes complete liquidity, i.e., a perfect market for all physical assets.)

The precise meaning of efficient production and the criteria for it have been studied under various names, such as activity analysis, by T. C. Koopmans [11] and others. [12] In order to reconcile the duopoly model with this efficiency theory we might suppose that the two firms are units in a centralized economy which uses money and marginal cost pricing as an accounting device to allocate resources. The price function represents the reaction of the rest of the economy to these prices. We may then specify the rules that the two firms must follow in terms of their price and cost functions alone. The criterion, in economic terms, is that each producer should behave as if the selling price were constant and attempt to maximize his profit under that assumption. Thus, at equilibrium, his marginal cost of production will equal his selling price.

$$\frac{d(q_i\gamma_i)}{dq_i} = p \ (i = 1, 2), \qquad \text{for } P_i = q_i p - q_i\gamma_i(q_i) \geqslant 0.$$

These equations will in general have a unique solution for a positive market price if the average cost curves are "U-shaped," the market demand is downward sloping to the right, there is no "overcapacity" present, and certain elasticity conditions hold. There will be overcapacity present if for every price at which neither firm makes a loss, the production of the firms oversaturates the market demand at that price. Specific reference is made again to overcapacity in Chapter 6.

These conditions, of course, are the same as those which exist if production is carried out under conditions of pure competition. Our example can be given the interpretation that an organized economy may be able to achieve efficient production, while leaving certain aspects of decision making decentralized, if the central authority were to issue a set of "shadow prices" and let each plant manager attempt to maximize his plant's income, assuming these prices to be fixed. [13]

3.3. THE VON NEUMANN AND MORGENSTERN SOLUTION

The market situation is treated as a two-person, nonzero-sum, co-operative game. It is assumed that the two firms will co-operate in such a manner as to maximize joint profits. After this has been done they will settle between themselves by means of side payments. The amount of the payment is not determinate (in general) but is limited by the amounts which the firms can obtain for themselves, regardless of the competitors' actions. (The limit for a firm can be obtained only if we can measure its ability to withstand cutthroat competition; this value certainly will not be lower than its sunk costs, which must be paid if the firm ceases production.)

The production rates must satisfy

$$\frac{\partial}{\partial q_i}(qp - q_1\gamma_1 - q_2\gamma_2) = 0 \qquad (i = 1, 2),$$

where p is the market price, $q = q_1 + q_2$, and γ_1 and γ_2 the average cost of production to the first and second producer, respectively. Equation 1 expresses the condition for joint maximization. The production levels determined by solving the foregoing equation must lie on a maximal boundary of joint profits which will play the same role between the duopolists as the Edgeworth contract curve in bilateral monopoly. The condition that a point be on the maximal boundary curve is that it is impossible for both players to improve their situations simultaneously. This can be characterized by the Jacobian [14]

$$\begin{vmatrix} \dfrac{\partial P_1}{\partial q_1} & \dfrac{\partial P_2}{\partial q_1} \\[2ex] \dfrac{\partial P_1}{\partial q_2} & \dfrac{\partial P_2}{\partial q_2} \end{vmatrix} = 0$$

The boundary curve is the Pareto optimal surface for the duopolists. There are several ways by which we can see that this condition must be satisfied. The most direct is by means of a diagram. In

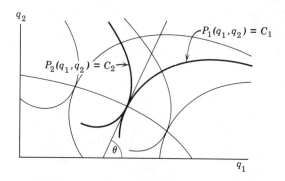

Figure 7

Figure 7 the axes are the rates of production of the duopolists. We can draw two sets of isoprofit curves. The curve through the points of tangency of these isoprofit curves will be the Pareto optimal surface. It is impossible for both players to improve their profits simultaneously, once they are at any point on this curve. The condition for two isoprofit curves to have a point of common tangency is

$$\frac{\partial P_1 / \partial q_1}{\partial P_1 / \partial q_2} = \tan \theta = \frac{\partial P_2 / \partial q_1}{\partial P_2 / \partial q_2} \, ,$$

as can be seen immediately from Figure 7. This pair of conditions is directly equivalent to the Jacobian condition. A different way of establishing the result is as follows:

Suppose we restrain one of the duopolists, say the second one, to making a fixed profit $P_2(q_1, q_2) = C_2$ (where C_2 is between the amount he could obtain as a monopolist and the amount he would obtain if he shut down his plant). Then if we wished to calculate the profit $P_1(q_1, q_2)$ so that the pair of profits (P_1, P_2) would be Pareto optimal, we could do so by solving

$$\max_{q_1} \max_{q_2} P_1(q_1, q_2), \text{ subject to } P_2(q_1, q_2) = C_2.$$

A necessary condition for this is that

$$dP_1(q_1, q_2) = 0 = \frac{\partial P_1}{\partial q_1}(q_1, q_2)\, dq_1 + \frac{\partial P_1}{\partial q_2}(q_1, q_2)\, dq_2.$$

However, the condition that $P_2(q_1, q_2) = C$ gives us an expression in which q_1 is implicitly defined as a function of q_2. [15] Differentiating this we obtain

$$\frac{\partial P_2}{\partial q_1}(q_1, q_2)\, dq_1 + \frac{\partial P_2}{\partial q_2}(q_1, q_2)\, dq_2 = 0,$$

from which we obtain

$$\frac{dq_1}{dq_2} = \frac{\partial P_2(q_1, q_2)/\partial q_2}{\partial P_2(q_1, q_2)/\partial q_1},$$

and using equation 2 we obtain the Jacobian condition as before.

3.4. The Nash Co-operative Game with Side Payments

The same rates of production used in subsection 3.3 are used here as the duopolists jointly maximize against the market. However, the side payments are now determined by evaluating the threats of the duopolists in order to determine a point from which they should agree to work out a "fair division" of profits. In the example of bilateral monopoly the threats consisted of refusing to trade (thus bringing about a state that benefited neither the firms nor the consumers). Here the threats consist of large production rates, which may damage the firms but help the consumer.

Before beginning our discussion of the evaluation of optimal threats, which is given in subsections 3.6, we note the salient features of collusion without side payments. An understanding of subsections 3.4, 3.5, and 3.6 is aided considerably by the examination of Figures 9 and 10, which appear and are explained in section 3.7.

3.5. The Nash Co-operative Game without Side Payments

If it is not possible (perhaps for legal reasons) for the producers to make side payments, this does not prevent collusion. However, instead of being able to obtain the absolute joint maximum (as indicated by the point J. M. in Figure 9, which shows production rates, and Figure 10, which shows profits), they can collude only by adjusting production rates along the Pareto optimal surface.

When the firms have identical cost structures they can jointly maximize against the market without having to resort to side payments. This is because of the symmetry of their cost structure. When they maximize joint revenue they do so by each producing an equal amount; hence they can split the proceeds of complete collusion without having to use the side-payment mechanism. The point of joint maximization (marked J. M. in Figures 9 and 10) will be symmetrically situated if the firms have the same costs. Optimal collusion between firms with different cost structures calls for side payments. The greater the difference in cost structure, the greater the need for side payments if optimal collusion is to take place. This is because in general the maximizing condition which calls for an equal marginal cost of production in all plants will require that one firm produce for most of the market. In this case the other firm must be rewarded for its action in restricting its output. The reward is the side payment.

When no side payments are permitted, production will be higher and price lower in general, if one firm has lower average costs than the other, than when open collusion with side payments is possible. This is because the firms can adjust accounts between themselves only by altering their rates of production. Such action calls for an "uneconomic allocation" of production, since they will pick some point on the Pareto optimal surface at which the marginal costs of production in both plants will not be equal. However, the more efficient firm (see Chapter 6: 2.2.) is in a better position to obtain larger profits under implicit collusion than with open collusion. A priori considerations might lead one to think that anything which facilitates collusion should improve the position of both firms. An example serves to show this to be false. Suppose that A and B could obtain 10,000 and 100 dollars, respectively, by collaboration and nothing if they did not co-operate, but that they could not make side payments. In this situation it is clear that they would co-operate and B would be happy to take the 100 dollars in preference to nothing. If side payments could be made, then B would surely demand that A give him part of the 10,000 dollars in return for collaboration; hence A would be better off when side payments were forbidden. This example magnifies a phenomenon of restricted competition. The efficient producer is intrinsically more capable of making profits than his rival. However, the inefficient firm's threat to ruin profits by increasing his production serves as blackmail to extract a side payment from his efficient competitor. The force of the blackmail is weakened as it becomes more difficult to make side payments.

3.6. ATTRITION, OPTIMAL THREATS, AND THE MAXIMIN SURFACE

3.6.1. THE OPTIMAL THREAT CURVE OR MAXIMIN SURFACE.   The consideration of threats is far more natural in a dynamic analysis than here. For instance, it is possible that a firm which has a stronger capital structure but less efficient plant than another may be in a better threat position than its more efficient competitor because it has more resources to withstand any projected attack. The reason to consider threats is that they may be utilized to enforce a market division over the course of time. However, before we introduce dynamics we can study the production and profit features of a market war in a single period.

Suppose that one firm wished to damage another. Perhaps the second firm in a duopoly would like to reduce the profits of the first. If both firms knew this, then the worst profit that the second could inflict upon the first is given by the quantity

$$\max_{q_1} \min_{q_2} P_1(q_1, q_2).$$

This quantity is not completely defined until we place some restrictions on the second firm's production rate. For instance, the production rate required of the second firm in order to force the first to cease production and lose overhead costs rather than have its goods swamped in the flooded market may be so high that it is prohibitively expensive or impossible (in the short run). In order to evaluate a threat not only the damage done to the opponent but the cost incurred by the threatener has to be considered. Suppose the owner of the second firm wished to reduce the profits of the first but that he was restrained from making a fixed profit $P_2(q_1, q_2) = C_2$. In order to calculate his action and his opponent's action we must solve

$$\max_{q_1} \min_{q_2} P_1(q_1, q_2), \text{ subject to } P_2(q_1, q_2) = C_2.$$

A necessary condition for this is that

$$dP_1(q_1, q_2) = 0 = \frac{\partial P_1}{\partial q_1}(q_1, q_2) \, dq_1 + \frac{\partial P_1}{\partial q_2}(q_1, q_2) \, dq_2.$$

We note that this gives rise to precisely the same two equations that were obtained in conditions 2 and 3 of subsection 3.3 for the Pareto optimal surface (although the second-degree conditions will be different). The meaning of the result achieved is that the Jacobian condition given in subsection 3.3 is satisfied by two surfaces. The first is the Pareto optimal surface (when there are only two firms the surface is a curve) as shown in Figures 9 and 10 by $M_1 M_2$, and the second is the optimal threat curve or maximin surface. This is also shown in Figures 9 and 10 by $E_1 E_2$. Any point on this curve has the property which recognises that for a given expense this represents the greatest harm that can be done to an opponent who wishes to maximize his profits.

Another way in which the property of the maximin surface can be understood is to observe that the points of common tangency between the isoprofit curves of both firms give rise to two different curves. Several isoprofit curves are drawn in Figure 9 to illustrate this.

3.6.2. THREATS IN THE CO-OPERATIVE GAME. In the Nash analysis a single pair of threats is selected as *the* optimal threats to be used in bargaining before collusion with side payments. A different pair of threats is selected when side payments are not permitted. Both of these lie on the optimal threat curve, but we must know how to find them.

We noted in Chapter 3: 3.5, 3.6.3, and 3.6.4 that when a given sum of money is to be divided between two individuals the Nash fair division amounts to an even split, regarding the initial position as $(0, 0)$ to both. Geometrically, once the initial point is given, a 45-degree line drawn from it to the optimal surface defines the division point (if side payments are permitted, the surface is a straight line on which the co-ordinates of any point sum to the joint maximum). In Figure 8 a series of parallel lines with slope of 45 degrees is drawn to the optimal surface. The axes of the diagram are, respectively, the profits to firm 1 and firm 2. Each line has the property that $P_1 - P_2$ is constant. If, for instance, the initial point from which bargaining starts is B, determined by the threats, the solution will be point N. It is evident that it is to the advantage

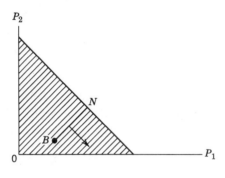

Figure 8

of the first player to have the initial point (which is determined by his and the other player's threats) lie as far downward to the right as possible. This is indicated by the arrow in Figure 8. The second player wants the initial point to be as far upward to the left as possible. Their selection of threats can be regarded as involving the playing of a *strictly competitive game* (see Chapter 1: 2) in which the interests of the players are diametrically opposed in an attempt to establish an initial point from which to carry out their fair division.

In order to obtain as favorable a position as possible the first firm will use as its threat the strategy which maximizes $P_1 - P_2$ against any strategy of its opponent; the second firm will attempt to maximize $P_2 - P_1$ or equivalently to minimize $P_1 - P_2$. This is the same as selecting optimal strategies in the zero-sum game which has a value of $(P_1 - P_2)$ to the first and $-(P_1 - P_2)$ to the second. Given that the firms are using their best threats, this value v will be

$$v = \max_{q_1} \min_{q_2} (P_1 - P_2).$$

It is easy to check that the resultant production rates and profits associated with these threat strategies lie on the optimal threat curve or maximin surface.

The method for computing the optimal threat and the Nash solution when side payments are forbidden is given in Appendix C. The understanding of this procedure depends heavily upon the understanding of the Nash bargaining model given in Appendix B. [16,17]

3.7. A COMPARISON OF THE RESULTS ON QUANTITY-VARIATION DUOPOLY

The duopoly models discussed in subsections 3.1 to 3.6 are further illuminated by the examination of a specific example of each. We take as our data two firms with average costs functions:

$$\gamma_1 = 4 - q_1 + q_1^2$$
$$\gamma_2 = 5 - q_2 + q_2^2,$$

where q_1 and q_2 are the amounts produced by firms 1 and 2, respectively, in each production period. Assuming that they are producing the identical product, we can take as the demand function

$$p = 10 - 2(\sum_i q_i) = 10 - 2q, \qquad i = 1, 2,$$

where p is the price when total production is $q = \sum_i q_i$.

The demand function is linear and the average cost functions are U-shaped, each with minimum average costs at $q = \frac{1}{2}$. The average costs of the second firm are always higher than those of the first.

The computation of the solutions was done by substituting the foregoing cost-and-demand information into the general equations presented with each of the models and then solving the resultant systems. [18] These solutions are displayed in Table 5.

We stress that the previous general discussion has been limited only to the extent that the firms were assumed to have U-shaped cost curves, the demand function sloped downward to the right, and the firms had increasing marginal costs at the efficient production point (i.e., when their marginal costs equaled market price). The specific examples calculated here are merely for illustration. Although Figures 9 and 10 are drawn for the specific examples, similar diagrams exist for all duopoly models fulfilling the general conditions given.

Table 5

	q_1	q_2	P_1	P_2	$P_1 + P_2$	p
Efficient point	1.1716	0.9411	1.8437	0.7812	2.6249	5.7747
Cournot	0.9386	0.7400	2.5346	1.3581	3.8927	6.6428
No side payment	0.7182	0.5187	2.6913	1.4644	4.1557	7.2742
N. S. P. threat	1.1708	0.9419	1.8436	0.7811	2.6247	5.8873
Side payment	0.9161	0.4125	2.6299	1.5692	4.1991	7.3428
S. P. threat	1.1196	1.0000	1.8214	0.7607	2.5821	5.7607
von Neumann-Morgenstern	0.9161	0.4125	...	...	4.1991	7.3428

P_1 and P_2 are the profits of firms 1 and 2, q_1 and q_2, their rates of production, $P_1 + P_2$, the joint profit, and p, the final market price for their product.

The division of profits is indeterminate in the von Neumann-Morgenstern example. In the side payment example the amount of the side payment is 0.5208, which is paid by firm 1 to firm 2.

Figures 9 and 10 are two representations of the static features relevant to a duopoly model. Figure 9 portrays the "production space" (this is the strategy space for a quantity-variation game). The·two axes measure the production rates of the firms. Figure 10 portrays the "profit space" (this is the payoff space for a game). Every pair of profits can be represented on this diagram. There is a transformation which carries every point in one diagram to points in the other. Unfortunately, this is not a simple one-to-one transformation. In other words, with every pair of production rates in Figure 9 there will be associated a pair of profits in Figure 10; however, more than one pair of production rates can give rise to the same pair of profits. In order to illustrate this we consider what happens to an isoprofit and an isoquant line for the first firm when we map or transform them into curves on the production and profit

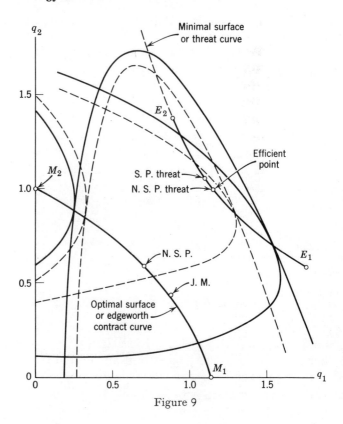

Figure 9

diagrams, respectively:

Profit Space		Production Space

isoprofit $P_1 = 1$ $\longrightarrow$ $q_1^3 + 2q_1q_2 + q_1^2 - 6q_1 + 1 = 0$

$P_1^3 - 14P_1^2 + 76P_1 - 8P_2 - 48 = 0$ $\leftarrow$ isoquant, $q_1 = 1$.

We see that a straight line on one diagram changes into a curve in the other.

The optimal surface M_1M_2 in Figure 10 was derived by substituting the information on costs and demand into the Jacobian equation given in subsection 3.3 in order to obtain the explicit equation for the curve. Then a few points were plotted on this curve. The equation is

$$6q_1^3 + (9q_2^2 + 6q_2 - 11)q_1^2 + (6q_2^2 + 4q_2 - 22)q_1$$
$$+ (6q_2^3 - 14q_2^2 - 22q_2 + 30) = 0.$$

Using the same equation, the Pareto minimal surface or threat curve E_1E_2 was drawn by plotting a few points on the other branch of this curve.

When we draw the production rates which correspond to the Pareto optimal or minimal profits, we get two curves in Figure 10 marked M_1M_2 and E_1E_2, respectively. The cusp on the curve E_1E_2 does not appear to have any particular economic significance. (If, however, the duopoly happens to be symmetric, i.e., the cost functions of both firms are the same, then the threat points, the efficient point, and the cusp will all coincide.)

The efficient point lies on the threat curve, as can be seen in Figures 9 and 10. This will always hold true if the average cost and demand functions are differentiable; γ_1 depends on q_1 only, γ_2 depends on q_2 only, and p depends upon q (the proof consists of showing that the conditions for the efficient point satisfy the Jacobian).

The side-payment and no-side-payment threat points are marked on the threat curve in Figures 9 and 10. The side-payment threat can be given direct economic meaning. At this point the marginal cost to either player of inflicting further diminution of profit on the other equals the decrement of profit, i.e., the marginal loss

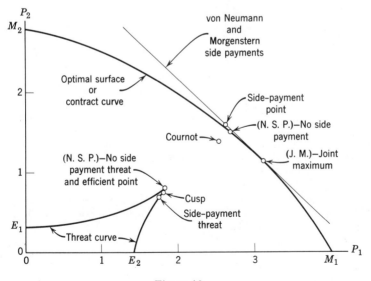

Figure 10

inflicted. In the price-variation models discussed in Chapter 5 a further connection between the efficient point and optimal threats is noted. The von Neumann and Morgenstern side-payment line is drawn through the point of joint maximal profit in Figure 10.

The marked effect of collusion upon production rates can be seen in Table 5. We observe that the Cournot solution neither maximizes social product nor does it maximize profits. It lies, in general, above the efficient point but below the optimal surface. [19]

The threat curve illustrates the structure of cutthroat competition. It plays a far more important role in dynamic models in which the exhaustion of the assets of a firm and its ruin are brought about through cutthroat competition. Some of the problems faced in the measurement of collusion are brought out even in these simplified static examples. Side payments are a sufficient but not a necessary criterion for collusion, as seen in 3.5.

Among our examples we computed the Nash side-payment and no-side-payment solutions. We re-emphasise that these are of a normative nature, developed from concepts of symmetry and "fairness." The major purpose in presenting these and the other solutions was not necessarily to advocate that they are "reasonable" solutions of a normative or predictive nature but to use them as a medium to illustrate the scope and meaning of the strategies available and economic structure present in the simple model of static quantity-variation duopoly.

NOTES

[1] J. F. Nash, "The Bargaining Problem," *Econometrica*, **XVIII** (April 1950), pp. 155–162.

[2] An "*n*-tuple" is an array of *n* numbers; here the *i*th number represents the strategy used by the *i*th player, $i = 1, 2, \ldots, n$.

[3] J. F. Nash, *op. cit.*, p. 287.

[4] *Ibid.* Nash proves the existence of equilibrium points for all finite games.

[5] Glicksberg has extended this result to games with continuous payoff functions. I. L. Glicksberg, "A Further Generalization of the Kakutani Fixed Point Theorem, with Application to Nash Equilibrium Points," *Proceedings of the American Mathematical Society*, **III** (February 1952), pp. 170–174. This extension covers all Cournot games which have continuous cost-and-demand functions.

[6] Much of the material in this section is reproduced from a joint paper

written by the author with J. F. Nash, Jr., and J. P. Mayberry. J. P. Mayberry, J. F. Nash, Jr., and M. Shubik, "A Comparison of Treatments of a Duopoly Situation," *Econometrica*, **XXI** (January 1953), pp. 141–154.

[7] See Abraham Wald, "On Some Systems of Equations of Mathematical Economics" (translation), *Econometrica*, **XIX** (October 1951), pp. 368–403.

[8] Most of our examples deal with production and demand functions which are assumed to be twice differentiable. This is an undesirable restriction from some points of view. A careful mathematical exploration of the weakest conditions which are necessary and sufficient for the existence of the solutions discussed is desirable but will not be pursued further at this time.

[9] A. Augustin Cournot, *Researches into the Mathematical Principles of the Theory of Wealth* (New York: Macmillan, 1897), pp. 79–80.

[10] H. von Stackelberg, *Marktform und Gleichgewicht* (Berlin: Julius Springer: 1934), pp. 134.

[11] T. C. Koopmans, "Efficient Allocation of Resources," *Econometrica*, **XIX** (October 1951), pp. 455–465.

[12] Oscar Lange, *On the Economic Theory of Socialism* (Minneapolis: University of Minnesota Press, 1938).

[13] This method of decentralized decision making implicitly assumes that the plant managers will find it in their interests to maximize their factories' profits and that the central planning board has a method of setting "shadow prices" which maximizes social welfare. Neither of these assumptions may be fulfilled.

[14] See R. Courant, *Differential and Integral Calculus*, I (London: Blackie & Son, 2nd ed., 1942), p. 479.

[15] *Loc. cit.*

[16] J. F. Nash, *loc. cit.*

[17] — — —, "Two-Person Cooperative Games," *Econometrica*, **XXI** (January 1953), pp. 128–140.

[18] For more detail see J. P. Mayberry, J. F. Nash, Jr., and M. Shubik, *op. cit.*, pp. 141–154.

[19] From the conditions given for the efficient point, the Cournot equilibrium, and joint maximization, it is easy to see that in some special cases some or all of these solutions could coincide. One trivial case for which all three coincide is when the elasticity of demand for the product is infinite.

chapter 5

THE FIRM IN AN OLOGOPOLISTIC MARKET: DUOPOLY (PART 2)

1. INTRODUCTION: PRICE-VARIATION DUOPOLY

Bertrand [1] objected to Cournot's analysis of the duopoly problem in terms of quantity as the strategic variable. He suggested a solution that depends upon price variation. As with Cournot's model, the method offered was apparently dynamic, although it can be cast in static terms. Bertrand considered two producers with no costs of production and wished to demonstrate that the profits of both would be wiped out by their competition. He purported to show that the two competitors would keep on under-cutting each other until they reached the competitive equilibrium.

Edgeworth [2] offered a modification of the Bertrand analysis. He indicated that price adjustment would yield a solution consisting of a price fluctuation between the monopoly or collusion price and a price equal to the marginal cost (assuming that the producers have the same cost functions). He demonstrated his solution by means of the diagram given in Figure 11.

He assumed the market to be evenly divided between both firms; hence RC and RC' are the two demand curves for the product.

80

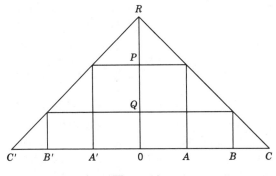

Figure 11

OB and OB' give the maximum output of each firm. OP is the
monopoly price. Edgeworth's argument was of a dynamic nature.
Producer 1 sets his price at OP to start, then producer 2 undercuts
him and steals some of his customers. The undercutting continues
until OQ is reached. At the price OQ, whichever firm puts its
supply on the market sells out and the other firm is able to raise
its prices against the remaining customers. Here we have some of
the difficulties of price-variation duopoly emphasized. Time
lags have been introduced, the market has been divided in a quite
arbitrary manner, and inventory fluctuations have been implicitly
excluded.

In fact, in price-variation models we are faced with basic economic difficulties which do not exist in the Cournot or other
quantity-variation models until product differentiation is considered
(Chapter 7: 3.1). These difficulties include the problem of *demand
in an oligopolistic market* with multiple pricing and the problem of
inventories. Both occur even in an analysis of a two-person market
in which the firms trade in an absolutely homogeneous product.

Suppose the two duopolists were charging different prices. If
the firm charging the lower price were unable or unwilling to supply
the whole market at that price, there would be some demand left
over for the higher priced firm.

Given that we have a method for computing such a "contingent
demand," it is possible that the production rate of the higher
priced firm would exceed this demand, thus leaving it with inventories. In order to construct an accurate model of this situation we
must attach inventory evaluation functions to the firms' payoff

or net revenue functions to take account of the danger that their strategies might involve "being stuck" with inventories.

2. CONTINGENT DEMAND FUNCTIONS

Considerable confusion on the topic of demand in an oligopolistic market, one of the major problems of oligopoly theory, permeates economic literature because of the failure of those writing on the subject to distinguish between the objective and subjective aspects of interdependent demand. Mrs. Robinson treats this issue by ignoring it, Chamberlin deals with it by means of his *DD'* and *dd'* curves, which have already been discussed, [3] and Sweezy, [4] Bronfenbrenner, [5] Stigler, [6] and others who have dealt with the subject of kinked demand curves fail to separate their behavioristic assumptions and dynamics from the objective background.

Edgeworth was aware of the difficulty of calculating contingent demand, but his method for handling the problem was not very satisfactory. An analysis reveals that there are three major types of theoretical difficulties and a host of empirical ones. R. D. G. Allen has noted that the points on an individual demand curve are a series of simultaneous alternative maximum bids for quantities associated with each price. [7,8]

This sets up the first problem. How should the individual consumer act when confronted by the same commodity (or a group of substitutes) offered at different prices in limited quantities? The second problem follows immediately. If a group of consumers has been left unsatisfied by its purchases, what does the new aggregate demand relation look like? The third problem, how quickly do consumers react to market changes in price, styling, and information, cannot be dealt with for the moment, as it is essentially dynamic and involves uncertainty, ignorance, and market frictions. It is left until Chapters 7 and 11.

2.1. INDIVIDUAL DEMAND FOR A MULTIPRICED COMMODITY

If we assume that an individual prefers to buy from the cheapest source of supply when faced with identical products, there is a natural way in which we can compute his *contingent demand* for the product of a duopolist whose price differs from that of his competitor. This demand depends upon the price charged and production offered by the competitor as well as the price charged by the duopolist. For every price and quantity pair of his opponent there will be a different contingent demand function. Suppose that an individual were able to purchase a commodity in unrestricted quantities at a single price. By the familiar method of rotating a price line through his indifference map for the commodity and money we are able to obtain his "offer curve" as the locus of points

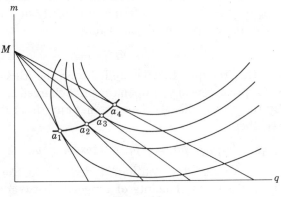

Figure 12

of tangency between the price lines and his indifference map. This is the curve $a_1 a_2 a_3 a_4$ in Figure 12, where M is his initial amount of money. Call this curve $q = \phi(p)$. We can represent the

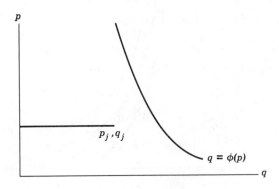

Figure 13

demand as in Figure 13. Suppose that one trader offered a quantity q_j of the commodity at the price p_j. If the other trader wished to charge a price p_i, what is the demand for his good? If the first had offered enough to satisfy the customer, there would be no demand if the second trader charged a higher price. If he charged a lower price his demand would be given by $q = \phi(p)$. Suppose that he charged a price higher than p_j and the other trader did not satisfy the demand. This amounts to stating that the price line of the first trader would have a point of tangency with the indifference map of the consumer at a point which called for a larger quantity of the commodity than he was offering. Figures 13 and 14 indicate this. We write the contingent demand function as

$$q_i = \Psi(p_i|q_j, p_j),$$

which states that the quantity demanded from the ith supplier is a function of his price, contingent upon the price charged and quantity supplied by the jth supplier. If the customer buys from the cheaper supply first, then

$$q_i = \Psi(p_i|q_j, p_j) = \phi(p_i) \qquad \text{for } p_i < p_j.$$

When $p_i > p_j$ we find the contingent demand in the following manner: It is the locus of points of tangency between the indifference map of the consumer and the family of price lines drawn through the point $(M - p_j q_j, q_j)$ where M is the initial amount of money possessed by the consumer and 0 is the initial amount

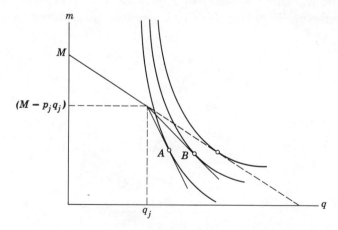

Figure 14

of the commodity. After he has bought from the lower-priced supplier, if his demand is not saturated, he will possess the amount of money $M - p_jq_j$ and q_j units of the good. As the price of the second supplier is varied, we obtain the new demand function. This is illustrated in Figure 14, in which points A and B are on the new demand curve.

It is evident that if the second supplier were unable to supply the residual market, the consumer would be willing to buy from a third supplier, and so on. Given the appropriate restrictions on the quantity of goods offered by an individual supplier, it would be possible to have the consumer buy from an indefinite number, all charging different prices. [9,10]

2.2. Aggregate Contingent Demand in a Duopolistic Market

It seems unlikely, except in some pathological cases, that the demand of an individual consumer would fail to be satisfied by his purchases from one supplier (although this might happen when he is buying a commodity that he expects may be rationed in the near future). There is a reasonable chance that some customers will be completely satisfied and others will fail to obtain anything at the lower price. This often happens in sales. If it happens in a duopolistic market, we must know how the market splits in order to compute the demand. In this chapter we are dealing only with competition between sellers of a homogeneous product (see Chapter 7 for the general case). Abstracting from all frictions and imperfections, we make the assumption that consumers prefer to buy a homogeneous commodity from the lower-priced seller if they are able to do so. We now define $q = \phi(p)$ to be the *aggregate market demand* function for a commodity, obtained by summing all individual demands. Figure 13 may now be regarded as representing the aggregate demand picture with p_j and q_j, the price charged and quantity offered by the jth seller. We use the notation $q_i = \Psi(p_i|q_j, p_j)$ to denote the aggregate contingent demand for the ith supplier, given the price p_j and production q_j of the jth supplier. As before, when i offers a lower price than j there is no problem in obtaining the relevant section of his aggregate contingent demand function. It will be a section of the aggregate demand function of the market as a whole. If i charges a price which is

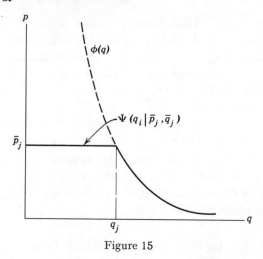

Figure 15

higher than that of j, then customers will prefer to buy from j. If j can satisfy the whole market demand, there will be nothing left for i, whose contingent demand function in this case will have the shape indicated in Figure 15. If j does not satisfy the whole market, then there will still be some demand left for i at higher prices, but this demand will depend specifically upon which customers were satisfied by j. Edgeworth tried to resolve this problem by arbitrarily splitting the market in two, as indicated in Figure 11. We suggest here three "neutral" general conventions for dealing with this problem.

Given the individual demand schedules, we can assume the following:

Convention 1.   The customers are chosen randomly (i.e., if there are k customers, the probability that an individual is served first is $\frac{1}{k}$).

Convention 2.   Individuals are weighted proportionate to the amount of the good they desire at each price. In other words, if one purchaser wishes to buy N units at price p, he is given N ballots at that price. The sales are made by choosing randomly from all the ballots.

Convention 3.   The customers are allocated in a manner to maximize effective demand in the contingent demand curve (i.e., demand against the price asked by the second firm.)

The first two conventions amount to symmetry assumptions, and, for the purpose of constructing a complete model without putting in special conditions which would imply a knowledge of a specific society's trading methods, they appear to be the most reasonable statements that can be made in order to provide us with a "norm." The third convention is the one that would be followed if the marketing board wanted to maximize trade. It would be undesirable on almost ony criterion for a marketing board to act so as to maximize trade in this manner: a stock market specialist is specifically forbidden to do so. In the actual study of a market the method of trading would have to be evaluated empirically and is, no doubt, closely related to information conditions and social and spacial factors which cause customers to choose between suppliers. Such Veblenesque conventions as having customers prefer trading with a higher, priced firm might easily fit the market for some luxury goods better than the three conventions noted.

We have not described the contingent demand conditions for a seller whose competitor is charging the same price as he is. The way the market is split in such a situation will, no doubt, depend upon features such as "customer loyalty," state of information, and the minor differentiations which are always present. Formally, in order to be able to specify completely the payoff functions for every pair of strategies that can be used in a price-variation duopoly model we should state a convention to determine market division at equal price. However, we leave this until subsection 4.4.1.

The general method for constructing contingent aggregate demand functions in an oligopolistic market has been described. In practice, the computation of families of contingent demand functions is complicated and requires more information than is usually available. However, for the purposes of the theory of price-variation duopoly the important feature of contingent demand functions is that they are rarely convex (i.e., they have discontinuities, wiggles, kinks, or scallops.) This lack of convexity causes secondary maxima in the revenue functions of the firms. A simple example of a family of contingent demand functions which is easy to compute serves to illustrate the general features caused by the nonconvexity of these curves.

2.3. CONTINGENT DEMAND IN A DUOPOLISTIC MARKET FOR A HOMOGENEOUS PRODUCT

In this section we carry out the computation for the family of contingent demand functions in a very simple model. The model is selected in order to minimize mathematical difficulties and yet illustrate the general properties of demand.

Let the aggregate demand, i.e., the collective demand schedule, be $p = 10 - 2q$. In order to be able to calculate the contingent demand whenever the market has been only partially saturated we need to know not only the collective demand schedule but also the individual schedules and the manner in which customers are served in case of insufficient supply at some prices.

As we wish to simplify the calculations as much as possible, let us consider the individual demand schedules to be such that one customer is willing to buy one unit at the price 10 or lower, but never more than one unit; the next customer is willing to buy one unit at price $10 - \epsilon$ or lower, and so on, as illustrated in Figure 16. The demand schedules might be a fairly good approximation of the demand for a newspaper (I will buy one for a certain sum or less, but no more, regardless of the price, and none if the price is too high). Although the demand example picked is peculiar, it must be stressed again that all phenomena discussed in the

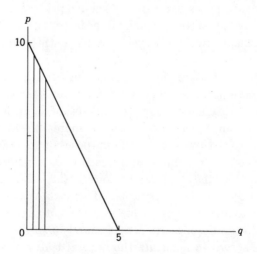

Figure 16

succeeding pages depend neither upon the peculiarities of the individual demand functions nor the absolute homogeneity of the products sold (see the discussion in Chapter 7).

With individual demand functions as given, conventions 1 and 2 of subsection 2.2 become the same and can be given a geometric interpretation (see Figure 17). Suppose that the first duopolist offered his goods at a lower price than the second. If he offered the quantity $\bar{q}_1$ which did not saturate the market and if the price charged by the second firm were p_2, the latter would be able to sell the amount indicated by q_2 in Figure 17. Actually, this amount is the expected demand if the customers are selected randomly. This construction is easy to understand when we realize that because of random selection (if at the price $\bar{p}_1$ a certain percentage of the market were satisfied) the same percentage of

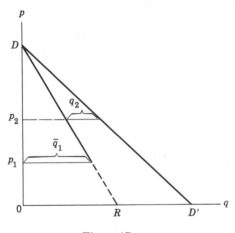

Figure 17

customers drawn from any price level will have been satisfied.

In Figure 18 we present the family of contingent demand functions for the second duopolist for several values of the first duopolist's price but for only one value for his rate of production, $q_1 = \bar{q}_1$.

If the second duopolist were willing to charge less than the first, his demand would be the same as the whole market or aggregate demand. As soon as he charges more than his opponent, his demand is determined by the method illustrated in Figure 17. (The distance AC in Figure 18 is the q_2 of Figure 17). A typical contingent demand

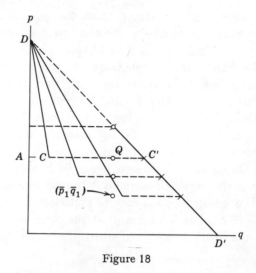

Figure 18

function is given by the curve $DCC'D'$ which has a discontinuity or break in it at the point of equal prices. (This discontinuity comes about only because the products are homogeneous; under other conditions only a bend or "kink" may occur.) AQ is the production of the first duopolist and $AC = QC'$.

In this case the DD' and dd' curves of Chamberlin (or the "species" and "genus" demand curves of K. W. Rothschild) [11] can be represented in Figure 19 (if we assume that at equal price they share the market in some specified manner.)

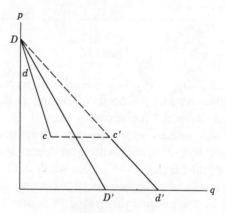

Figure 19

The contingent demand DD' can be expressed mathematically as

$$(1) \qquad q_2 = \Psi(p_2 | p_1 = p_2, \quad q_1 = q_2),$$

which states that q_2 depends upon p_2 but is subject to the condition that p_1 will always equal p_2 and that the production of the second firm will always be matched by the first. (We have changed notation slightly from that used for contingent demand in subsection 2.1; this notation emphasises the role of both players.)

The contingent demand $dcc'd'$ can be expressed as

$$(2) \qquad q_2 = \Psi(p_2 | p_1 = \bar{p}_1, \quad q_1 = \bar{q}_1).$$

q_2 depends upon p_2, and p_1 and q_2 are fixed at given values (see the article by R. C. Coase for observations on this method of treating contingent demand). [12] If we compute every possible value for expression 2 we will have described every demand condition that can arise in this duopolistic market. Figure 18 indicates several of these conditions. Equation 1 selects certain of these values which are relevant to the behavioristic assumption that changes in price by one firm are met immediately by similar price changes by the other.

3. THE ROLE OF INVENTORIES IN STATIC MARKET MODELS

In the Cournot and other quantity-variation models without product differentiation the problem of overproduction and inventory losses did not arise because it was implicitly assumed that the market mechanism disposed of all goods offered at one price. Because the Edgeworth model and indeed almost all discussions of non-co-operative oligopolistic equilibrium models have been presented in a semistatic framework, the role of inventories (as well as financial conditions) has been obscured. We can see from section 2 that unless production rates *as well as* prices are specified we are unable to describe the contingent demand conditions. In terms of game theory this amounts to being unable to describe all *payoffs*. The reason for this is that in a market with price cutting the description of the strategy of a player as the naming of a price is not a complete description. In section 4, since we want to exclude inventory considerations for some models, we will have to make an additional assumption by which we are able to avoid considering inventories but are able to specify a production rate to be associated with every price. A more realistic model of duopoly should include the possibility of inventory accumulation. [13] This entails the setting up of a price-quantity variation model in which a strategy consists of simultaneously naming a price and a production rate. Thus it is possible that some of the goods remain unsold. It is necessary to attach a value to these inventories; this will be a function of carrying costs and the expected demand in future periods. Differences in the value of inventory help to explain the differences between competitive action in markets selling various types of goods. For instance, the value of perishables at the end of a period may be almost nothing, whereas some articles, such as wine, might even appreciate with age.

In order to understand fully the nature of the actions of a maximizing duopolist, given information on the structure of contingent demand, we would like to be able to examine a multiperiod model of price-quantity variation. Mathematical difficulties prevent this from being done at this time; however, a complete formulation of the single-period, price-quantity game is given in section 5 and some of the dynamics are developed in Chapter 10.

4.   PRICE-VARIATION DUOPOLY

4.1. THE MODIFIED EDGEWORTH SOLUTION (Part 1) [14,15]

We are now in a position to explain the fluctuations in a duopolistic market suggested by Edgeworth and to examine how the range of fluctuation depends explicitly upon the nature of the contingent demand. In this model the behavioristic assumption is made that each duopolist acts as if the other's price were going to remain the same as it was in the previous period. This dynamic assumption of double idiocy automatically takes care of the inventory aspects of each individual's strategy. Each firm produces the amount that will maximize its expected revenue obtained from the relevant "misperceived" contingent demand function. All may be caught with inventories; hence their expected payoffs are not their true payoffs. In subsection 4.1 we are interested only in calculating the range of price fluctuation, but we can specify the actual payoffs for the players if we assume, for instance, that all inventories at the end of any period are perishable and must be valued at zero. The indeterminacy and vagueness disappears if we specify an inventory valuation function and include the production rate as a part of a player's strategy. This is done in section 5.

Once more we make use of a specific example, but only to illustrate the nature of the general conditions given in subsection 4.2.

In this example we use the same cost functions as were used in Chapter 4.7. These, together with the method for the calculation of contingent demand which has just been outlined, give us enough information to be able to specify the expected payoffs to the duopolists. Firm 1 has an average cost function of $4 - q_1 + q_1^2$, and firm 2 has an average cost function of $5 - q_2 + q_2^2$.

If each firm maximizes its profit on the assumption that the price of the other firm is held fixed, then each must be able to calculate the revenue it expects to make if it charges a price higher, lower, or equal to that of its opponent.

The expressions for the expected profit to the first firm, if it charges the price p_1 and the second firm has charged p_2, are given here. An explanation follows immediately. (The solution may be understood directly from the explanation of Figure 17.)

(1) $$P_1 = p_1 q_1 - q_1(4 - q_1 + q_1^2), \qquad p_1 < p_2,$$

where $\quad q_1 = 1 + \dfrac{\sqrt{1 + 3(p_1 - 4)}}{3}$, when $q_1 \leqslant \dfrac{10 - p_1}{2}$.

(2) $$P_1 = p_1 q_1 - q_1(4 - q_1 + q^2), \qquad p_1 > p_2,$$

where $\quad q_1 = \dfrac{10 - p_1}{Q_2}$, $\quad Q_2 = 2\dfrac{(q^*)}{q^* - q_2}$, $\quad q^* = \dfrac{10 - p_2}{2}$,

$$\text{and} \quad q_2 = \frac{1 + \sqrt{1 + 3(p_2 - 5)}}{3} .$$

This is subject to the condition

$$\frac{10 - p_1}{Q_2} \lesseqgtr \frac{1 + \sqrt{1 + 3(p_1 - 4)}}{3} .$$

In the first case the first firm charges a price lower than that of the second. Once it has selected its price it maximizes the profits it can obtain at that price by selecting the appropriate production rate. This is done by solving a revenue maximization problem with the market price fixed at p_1. This, however, is subject to the restriction that it will never produce more than the market will buy at that price. (Another way of regarding this is that the firm maximizes profits facing a demand function which is horizontal at the price p_1 up until the point $q_1 = (10 - p_1)/2$, beyond which it ceases to exist.)

In the second case the first firm charges a price higher than that of the second. In order to calculate its profit on the assumption that the other firm's price will remain the same and be lower than its own the firm must calculate the shape of the contingent demand function. In this case it will be one of the upper segments of the contingent demand functions shown in Figure 18 (DC, for instance). Once it has done this it maximizes the profits it can obtain by selecting the appropriate production rate in the same way as before, except that now it is the contingent demand function instead of the aggregate demand function which limits the amount that can be sold at any price.

The numbers q^* and Q_2 are obtained from the geometry of the method of reconstitution shown in Figure 17. $q = (10 - p)/Q_2$ is the equation of the upper part of a contingent demand function.

The formulas in expression 2 state the expected payoff to the first firm for any price it charges which is higher than that of the second. Actually, if the first firm knew the price being charged by the second and wished to maximize profit at a higher price after the contingent demand function had been computed, it would solve for both its price and production rate by calculating the monopolistic maximization of profits, using the contingent demand function to portray the market demand discounted for the influence of its rival.

In general, if a firm charges a higher price than its opponent, it will satisfy the contingent market demand at the price it is charging, i.e., $q_1 = (10 - p_1)/Q_2$ if p_1 is being charged. However, in some cases the firm may not wish to supply all that it can sell at the price it is charging; this is shown in the last condition in expression. The right-hand side of the inequality is the amount that the firm would sell at the price p_1 if there were no limit on what the market would buy.

For the second producer we have

$$(3) \qquad P_2 = p_2 q_2 - q_2(5 - q_2 + q_2^2), \qquad p_2 < p_1,$$

then $\quad q_2 = \dfrac{1 + \sqrt{1 + 3(p_2 - 5)}}{3}$, when $q_2 \leqslant \dfrac{10 - p_2}{2}$.

(4) $$q_2 = \frac{10 - p_2}{Q_1}, \qquad p_2 > p_1,$$

where $\quad Q_1 = 2 \cdot \dfrac{(q^*)}{q^* - q_1}$, $\quad q^* = \dfrac{10 - p_1}{2}$,

and $\quad q_1 = \dfrac{1 + \sqrt{1 + 3(p_1 - 4)}}{3}$

This is subject to the condition

$$\frac{10 - p_2}{Q_1} \leqslant \frac{1 + \sqrt{1 + 3(p_2 - 5)}}{3}.$$

The payoffs or profit conditions which prevail when both pro-ducers charge the same price are not given here and do not influence the determination of the range of fluctuation in the Edgeworth duopoly model or the solution in the price game following. The reason for this is taken up in detail in Appendix C (see the reference given in subsection 4.4.1.)

Given the foregoing information, the firms are able to calculate all payoffs when one is high and the other low in the market. If they keep on undercutting each other, they will reach a price at which neither is interested in carrying out the process any further. This occurs when

$$2(q_1 + q_2) = 10 - p,$$

$$q_1 = \frac{1 + \sqrt{3p - 11}}{3}, \qquad q_2 = \frac{1 + \sqrt{3p - 14}}{3},$$

and gives the "efficient point" at which the prices $p = p_1 = p_2 = = 5.774$ (the formulas for q_1 and q_2 are simplifications of the same formulas given in expressions 1 and 3). At this point any further price cut by one firm merely lowers its own profits. At the efficient point price the optimal production rates of both firms just saturate the market. Above this price they oversaturate the market; hence there may be a motivation to undercut each other. At any price below the efficient point the sum of their optimal production rates does not saturate the market; hence both would be motivated to raise prices. (By optimal production rate we mean the amount a firm will produce at a given price if it can sell all it wants to at that price.)

It is possible that even before the efficient point is reached one of the firms may be motivated to raise its price. This will happen when the profit that a firm can make by monopolistically maximizing against the upper part of the contingent demand function, determined by its opponent's price and production, is greater than the profit it could make by undercutting its opponent. In the example computed here this will happen immediately after

(5) $\quad q_2(10 - Q_1 q_2) - q_2(5 - q_2 + q_2{}^2) = q_2'p_2 - q_2'(5 - q_2' + q_2'{}^2)$,

where

(6) $$q_2 = \frac{1 - Q_1 + \sqrt{(Q - 1)^2 + 15}}{3},$$

and

(7) $$q_2' = \frac{1 + \sqrt{3p_1 - 14}}{3}.$$

The left-hand side of equation 5 is the maximum profit that can be made by charging a higher price than the opponent; the right-hand side is the maximum profit to be made by having a lower price. The q_2 and q_2' are obtained by solving the appropriate maximization problems for the left- and right-hand sides of equation 5.

We find that at $p_1 = p_2 = 6.184$ the high-cost producer is indifferent to undercutting or raising his price to $p_2 = 7.358$. He makes the same profits $P_{2L} = P_{2H} = 1.188$ by doing either. His production at the low price is $q_2' = 1.0443$ and at the high price, $q_2 = 0.4560$. These two prices define the *Edgeworth range of fluctuation*. Both points depend explicitly upon the structure of the contingent demand. We can see immediately from Figure 18 that the upper range point of the fluctuation will in general be at a price *above* the joint monopoly price because the upper branches of the contingent demand functions have a lower elasticity than the aggregate demand. [16]

A graph of the expected payoffs is given in Figure 20. The ordinates represent the profit to the second firm, and the abscissae

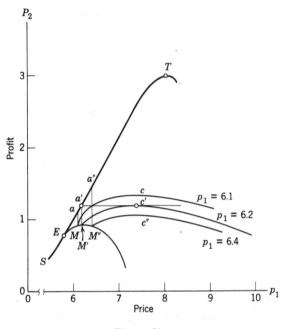

Figure 20

are the prices it charges. The family of curves drawn indicates the profit made by the duopolist, as he varies his price, for various given prices of the first duopolist. As long as the second charges the lower price, his profit increases along his monopoly revenue curve, $Saa'T$, as he raises his price. When his price surpasses that of his opponent his profits first fall steeply (as reflected in the discontinuity in the contingent demand functions shown in Figure 18) and then may rise again until they reach a secondary maximum (which corresponds to the point at which he obtains monopoly profit from the customers still in the market). Given that the first duopolist charges p_1, then, as the price of the second firm varies, its profit follows the course of $SaMc$. We note that each profit curve contains two maxima. One is the maximum at the discontinuity, the other, the secondary maximum at a considerably higher price.

We must stress that the information portrayed in Figure 20 has an *objective* existence and does not really depend upon the dynamics of an Edgeworth model or any other set of behavioristic assumptions. The diagram is of the family of contingent revenue functions for player 2, drawn on the assumption that the price charged by player 1 is fixed and that the quantity player 1 produces at any price is optimal on the assumption that he has the market to himself (or is low man at that price).

The Edgeworth fluctuations are caused by the presence of multiple maxima in the contingent revenue functions (i.e., the revenue obtained by maximizing profits subject to the existence of contingent demand conditions). There has been little work in economic theory to establish the conditions for the existence or nonexistence of multiple maxima. Most discussants of equilibrating processes implicitly assume that there is only one maximum revenue point, write down the marginal conditions which must be satisfied, and assume that by doing this a method for finding and a demonstration of the uniqueness of an equilibrium point has been established (see Chapter 7: 3.1 for further discussion). If there is a sufficiently bad break or kink in the demand function, multiple maxima will usually exist. The actual discontinuity in the contingent demand functions in this example is not important as such. It happens to result in the presence of multiple maxima in the contingent revenue functions. If we had "smoothed out" the discontinuity, replacing the break by a sharp bend, the multiple maxima would still exist. This implies that even with product differentiation or transportation costs present, where the contingent demand and revenue functions are continuous there may still be multiple maxima present. If the maximum revenue associated with the lowest price is not the *maximum maximorum*, then there may be no pure strategy equilibrium point and the Edgeworth fluctuation may exist. In Figure 20 we observe that for the contingent demand curve $Sa'M'c'$ both maxima have the same value. This determines the Edgeworth range. If the second firm is undercut at the price which determines a', it will raise its price rather than undercut its opponent further.

The curve $EMM'M''$ is the profit curve of the second duopolist when he is always just undercut by his opponent. M is the maximum point. If he chooses the price associated with M, then no matter what price his opponent charges he will not make a profit less than this maximum point on the curve of minimum profit. We note that the efficient point lies on this curve. This follows immediately when we consider the actions of the first player who knows that the second player is charging the efficient point price. At that price the first player has no incentive to undercut because at the output determined by marginal costs equaling price he just satisfies the remaining demand at the efficient point. Hence the worst that can happen to the second player is that he will obtain his efficient point profit.

If there is no Edgeworth range of fluctuation, then E is the maximum point on $EMM'M''$ and is an equilibrium point (the Bertrand solution) for the duopolists. This is proved in subsection 4.2.

*4.2. THE MODIFIED EDGEWORTH SOLUTION (Part 2)

Edgeworth [17] claimed that for the case in which the costs of the duopolists follow the law of diminishing returns there will be no determinate equilibrium defined (i.e., no pure strategy equilibrium point). This is not always true. [18] The appropriate conditions for the existence of a pure strategy equilibrium are given in two theorems:

Theorem 1. Given cost curves that are convex from below (U-shaped) and a demand curve that is monotone, decreasing with a second derivative $\geqslant 0$, the condition required for a pure strategy equilibrium to exist at the efficient point in an Edgeworth duopoly is that

$$(q_i p - q_i \gamma_i) > (f^*(q_i)q_i - q_i \gamma_i), \qquad \text{for } i = 1, 2,$$
$$\text{at } E \qquad \text{at } E + \epsilon$$

where $p = f^*(q_i)$ is the contingent demand above E; E stands for the efficient point price, and γ_i is the average cost of player i. This says that the profit obtained by sharing the market at the efficient point is greater than or equal to the profit to be had by charging slightly more than the competitor.

The foregoing condition is necessary; if it were not true, it would pay a player to depart from the efficient point when all others were playing their efficient point strategies; hence the efficient point could not be an equilibrium point.

It is sufficient because above the efficient point $dP_i < 0$ everywhere if the condition holds; hence the efficient point is an equilibrium point. This completes the proof.

We note that the criterion depends explicitly upon the form of the contingent demand. If this is such that there are no interior secondary profit maxima, then there will be no fluctuation and we get a result like that of Bertrand in which the pure strategy equilibrium is also the efficient point. (The following remarks hold true for n persons as well as for the two-person models under discussion.)

Theorem 2. If an Edgeworth duopoly has a pure strategy equilibrium point, then it must be the efficient point.

First, if the market were not satisfied by the production of all players at the equilibrium point, then one player could increase his profits by charging a higher price, leaving his production as before. Therefore, the market must at least be satisfied at the equilibrium point. If, on the other hand, the market is oversaturated at the equilibrium point, there must be a discontinuity in the payoff for a slight decrease in price. (For an infinitesimal price cut dp there is a small but finite addition to the amount sold Δq; as $dp \rightarrow 0$, Δq approaches some finite limit.) We have shown that there is an incentive for one player to undercut, given that he knows the (pure) strategies of the others; hence there is no equilibrium point if the market is oversaturated. Thus, if a pure strategy equilibrium point exists, it must exist at a point at which the market demand is just saturated by the quantities offered by the players at that price, but this defines the efficient point. Hence, if the efficient point exists and the Edgeworth duopoly has a pure strategy equilibrium point, this point must be the efficient point. This proves the proposition. (We observe that an efficient-point solution does not exist for competition among firms with decreasing average costs in the range of demand.)

*4.3. The Price or Bertrand Game

The price game is a two-person, simultaneous-move game in which the strategy of each player consists of picking a price. In order to avoid an inventory problem we adopt the convention that the firms produce only to order. They fix their prices and then supply their demand.

This model is closely linked to the Edgeworth duopoly discussed in subsections 4.1 and 4.2. The conditions stated and proved in 4.2 apply equally well here and serve to show that with the appropriate cost, demand, and contingent demand functions there will exist a class of Bertrand games which have the efficient point as the only equilibrium point.

When the conditions in subsection 4.2 do not hold, then, as we have seen, the Edgeworth duopoly will give rise to a range of fluctuation. What may we say about a price game which has this type of cost-and-demand structure? The existence of a range of fluctuations in the Edgeworth model implies that if the price game has an equilibrium point it is a mixed strategy equilibrium.

As we have noted before (see Chapter 1: 2), a satisfactory economic interpretation of a mixed strategy equilibrium is hard to give. However, here we may interpret it in the following manner: A mixed strategy equilibrium implies that there exists a pair of price expectations such that if each firm maximizes its expected revenue, given information concerning its opponent's expected price policy, neither will be motivated to change his price policy. When there is no pure strategy equilibrium the market is unstable in the usual sense of economic theory. However, if each firm shows that it is willing to vary price in some range, a more general equilibrium may be established. The range of variation and the manner in which a firm may vary its price in the range serve as indices of the inherent instability in the market and as a measure of the violence of the expected price war. [19]

The proof that there exists a unique mixed strategy equilibrium point for a class of Bertrand or price games has been given by Shapley. [20] He has also established the general nature of the probability density functions [21] which must be employed by the players for their strategies to yield an equilibrium.

The problem of finding a mixed strategy equilibrium point devolves into obtaining two functions $f(p_1)$ and $g(p_2)$ such that

(1) $$\int_a^b P_1(p_1, p_2) dg(p_2) = V_1, \qquad a \leqslant p_1 \leqslant b,$$

(2) $$\int_a^b P_2(p_1, p_2) df(p_1) = V_2, \qquad a \leqslant p_2 \leqslant b,$$

where V_1 and V_2 are the values of the game to the first and second players, respectively. By value of the game we mean the greatest amount that a player can obtain if he knows his opponent's strategy. A verbal interpretation of these sets of identities is now given. The function $g(p_2)$ indicates the probability with which the second player will charge any price p_2. $P_1(p_1, p_2)$ is the revenue function for the first player which depends upon the prices of both. The left-hand side of expression 1 represents the expected revenue for the first player, given that he is charging p_1 and that his opponent is using the probability function $g(p_2)$ to determine his price. The numbers a and b indicate the range in which the prices fluctuate. They have to be evaluated mathematically and depend explicitly upon the costs and contingent demand functions.

Expression 1 states that no matter what price the first player selects, if the second player uses $g(p_2)$ as his strategy, then the first player will always obtain exactly the value V_1. Expression 2 makes a similar statement concerning the amount obtained by the second player. Further comment is given in Appendix C.

The example used in subsection 4.1 is such that the simultaneous-move price game with the same cost functions and demand structure does not have a pure strategy equilibrium point. Although we are unable to calculate the density functions $f(p_1)$ and $g(p_2)$ used in the mixed strategy, we can calculate a lower and an upper bound to the value of the game to each player.

We carry out the computation of the bounds for the value of the game to the first player only. The value of the game to a player cannot be lower than the amount he can obtain by using his pure strategy maximin. The worst that can happen to a player using his maximin pure strategy is that he is just undercut. This yields him the profit earned at the point M in Figure 20 (or at an analogous point in the profit diagram for the first player.)

An explicit form la for the curve $MM'M''$ can be obtained. This is the locus of minimal profits when one player is just undercut by the other. Let P_{1U} represent the payoff to player 1 when he is just undercut. Then in terms of price we obtain

$$P_{1U} = (0.700p_1 - 5.183)(0.490p_1^2 - 7.557p_1 + 25.684).$$

This has a maximum at $p_1 = 6.073$ where the profit $P_{1U} = 2.176$.

In this example there will be two payoff diagrams of the form given in Figure 20, one for each player. They each will have a different range of fluctuation, i.e., a different set of prices for which the profit obtained by undercutting is the same as the profit obtained by raising the prices. The higher of the low-price ends of these two ranges serves to obtain an upper bound for the price game. The value of the game to either player cannot be higher than the value obtained by using the pure strategy associated with this point. The proof is given in Appendix C. The highest of the lower ends of the two ranges of fluctuation is at $p = 6.184$ where $P_{1U} = 2.339$. This point corresponds to a' on Figure 20.

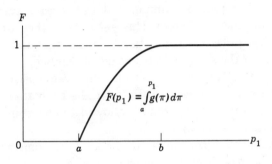

Figure 21

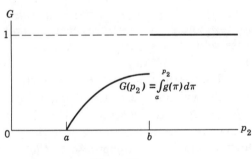

Figure 22

Figures 21 and 22 illustrate the general shape of the cumulative probability distribution functions

$$G(p_2) = \int_a^{p_2} g(\pi)\, d\pi \text{ and } F(p_1) = \int_a^{p_1} f(\pi)\, d\pi,$$

respectively. [22]

In summary we observe that the value of the game to the first player is such that $2.176 < P_1 < 2.339$. The price in the market never falls below 6.073 and the prices can at times be higher than the joint monopoly price.

4.4. The Co-operative Price Game with Side Payments

*4.4.1. Mixed Strategy Solution. Co-operative action under price variation is not necessarily the same as under quantity variation. The joint maximum and the threats available to the firms are in general different. This is so because they are in a position to practice price discrimination against the market and take advantage of the structure of contingent demand.

In order to evaluate the joint maximum we must investigate the general problem of monopolistic price discrimination in a market in which a firm or a combine is allowed to charge more than one price (in this case two.)

A monopolistic firm which can charge its customers two different prices must maximize the following quantity:

$$P = q_1 p_1 + q_2 p_2 - C(q),$$

where $q_2 = \Psi(p_1, p_2, q_1)$, $q_1 \leqslant \phi(p_1)$, $q = q_1 + q_2$, $q_1, q_2 \geqslant 0$, and $p_2 < p_1$. P is the profit, p_1 and p_2 are the prices charged, and q_1 and q_2 are the quantities sold at the different prices. $q = \phi(p)$ is the initial market demand. The condition $q_1 \leqslant \phi(p_1)$ states that at most the monopolist will saturate the market only at the price p_1 (if he does so, then he will not employ multiple-price discrimination). $q_2 = \Psi(p_1, p_2, q_1)$ gives the contingent demand after q_1 has been sold at the price p_1 (see subsection 2.2). $q = q_1 + q_2$ states that total production equals the amount sold. $C(q)$ is the total cost function.

The maximization can be solved explicitly by introducing a Lagrangian [23] parameter to account for the boundary condition that $q = q_1 + q_2$. We maximize

$$F = q_1 p_1 + \Psi(p_1, p_2, q_1) p_2 - C(q) + \lambda(q_1 + q_2 - q).$$

In the two firm examples employed in this chapter this amounts to maximizing

$$p_1 q_1 + \tfrac{1}{2} p_2 \left(\frac{10 - p_2}{10 - p_1} \right) (10 - p_1 - 2q_1) - q_\alpha (4 - q_\alpha + q_\alpha^2) -$$

$$q_\beta (5 - q_\beta + q_\beta^2) + \lambda (q_1 + q_2 - q_\alpha - q_\beta)$$

(The q_α and q_β are the production levels of each plant.) In this example there is no advantage to be gained in charging two prices. We demonstrate this below.

The conditions

$$\frac{\partial F}{\partial q_\alpha} = 0 \ \text{and} \ \frac{\partial F}{\partial q_\beta} = 0 \ \text{imply} \ \frac{\partial C_1}{\partial q_\alpha} = \frac{\partial C_2}{\partial q_\beta} = \lambda.$$

Thus we may interpret the Lagrangian parameter as the marginal cost of production in each plant. The condition $\partial F / \partial p_2 = 0$ yields

$$-\tfrac{1}{2}(10 - 2p_2 - \lambda) \frac{(10 - p_1 - 2q_1)}{(10 - p_1)} = 0.$$

We know that $p_1 < 10$ (at 10 or above there is no demand); there-fore, one or both of the two factors must equal zero. If $10 - p_1 - 2q_1 = 0$, the market is saturated at the price p_1 and nothing can be sold at a higher price. If $10 - 2p_2 - \lambda = 0$, then, for $p_2 > 5$, λ will be negative. This states that the marginal cost of production is negative, which is impossible. Therefore, $p_2 \leqslant 5$, but this implies that the monopolist sells all his goods at prices below the efficient point price (p_1 was assumed to be less than p_2). This will always be false; therefore, this factor is not zero.

The result could have been seen directly from the nature of the random selection of customers in the computation of the contingent demand. In essence, the randomness implies that there is no way in which the colluding firms can sort out customers to obtain extra advantage. Further comment on discrimination is given in Appendix C.

Employing the Nash model, the optimal threat strategies in the quantity-variation game were obtained by solving $\min_{q_2} \max_{q_1}$

$(P_1 - P_2)$ for q_1 and q_2. There were two pure strategy production rates which satisfied this condition. In the price game we must

solve min max $(P_1 - P_2)$ for p_1 and p_2. There are no pure strategy
$ p_2 \quad p_1$
pricing methods which satisfy this. We have to examine the mixed
strategy threats.

In order to evaluate the threat strategies we take a finite approximation of the price game in which each player may pick a price
between 5.7 and 7.7 in units of 0.1. These limits were picked because
it can be shown that any strategy outside this range is *dominated*
by one inside the range. A pure strategy is dominated by another
pure strategy if all resultant payoffs obtained by playing the
second are at least as great and at least one payoff is greater than
that obtained by playing the first. The formulas in subsection 5.4
are used to calculate the payoff matrices. The payoffs when both
players charge the same price are calculated by using the convention that each obtains an amount of the market proportional to
the quantity he would have sold if he had been low man at that
price. (For a detailed discussion see Appendix C.) By subtracting
P_2 from P_1 we obtain the matrix of profit differences given in
Table 6. [24]

The solution of a matrix game of this size (i.e., a game in which
payoff functions can be represented by matrices) requires machine
computation. The mixed strategies employed by the players consist
of the following probabilities (accurate to two decimal places):
$\zeta = (0.51, 0.11, 0.23, 0.03, 0.04, 0.04, 0.03, 0.00, 0.01, 0.00,$
$0.01, 0.00, 0.00, 0.00, 0.00, 0.00, 0.00, 0.00).$
Player 2 uses the strategy
$\eta = (0.43, 0.15, 0.23, 0.00, 0.09, 0.01, 0.04, 0.00, 0.02, 0.00,$
$0.00, 0.00, 0.00, 0.00, 0.03, 0.00, 0.00).$
The value of the minimax is

$$v = 1.0951.$$

Using the foregoing threat strategies to determine the initial
point from which to calculate the division, we find that the side
payment will be of the size 0.5036, which the first firm pays to the
second. The production rates and the final market price are the
same here as in the co-operative quantity-variation example.

4.4.2. PURE STRATEGY OR BERTRAND SOLUTION.   In subsection
4.2 it is shown that a class of non-co-operative price games have

the efficient point as their equilibrium. If we take a game of this class and solve it co-operatively, the firms will maximize $P_1 + P_2$ and will use their optimal threats, determined by the minimax $(P_1 - P_2)$. We can observe immediately that the efficient point is also the *optimal threat point*. This follows because if one player raises his price, given that the other is at the efficient point, he causes loss only to himself; if he lowers his price, the marginal cost of inflicting extra damage is greater than the marginal rate of damage. [25]

4.5. A Comparison of the Results on Price-Variation and Other Duopoly Models

The bar graphs in Figures 23 and 24 make a comparison between the prices charged as well as the profits made by the first duopolist in the price and in the quantity co-operative and non-co-operative games. Although the price game appears to reflect more accurately than the Cournot game the nature of an oligopolistic market, the true threat power of the firms is not shown because the effect of inventory position is not explicitly accounted for. This is discussed in section 5 of this chapter.

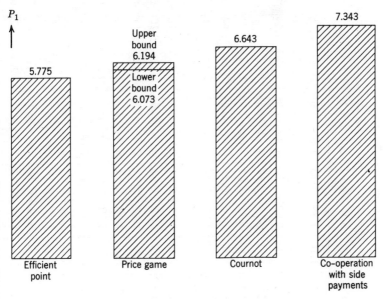

Figure 23

Table 6

p_2 / p_1	6.0	6.1	6.2	6.3	6.4	6.5	6.6	6.7	6.8	6.9	7.0	7.1	7.2	7.3	7.4	7.5	7.6
6.0	1.10	1.19	1.13	1.08	1.04	0.99	0.95	0.92	0.89	0.87	0.85	0.84	0.82	0.82	0.82	0.82	0.83
6.1	1.00	1.10	1.26	1.21	1.17	1.13	1.10	1.07	1.04	1.02	1.01	1.00	0.99	0.98	0.98	0.98	0.99
6.2	1.06	0.92	1.10	1.39	1.36	1.32	1.29	1.26	1.24	1.22	1.21	1.20	1.19	1.19	1.19	1.19	1.20
6.3	1.11	0.97	0.80	1.10	1.56	1.53	1.51	1.48	1.46	1.44	1.43	1.42	1.42	1.41	1.41	1.42	1.42
6.4	1.16	1.01	0.84	0.68	1.08	1.74	1.31	1.66	1.68	1.66	1.65	1.64	1.64	1.64	1.64	1.64	1.65
6.5	1.20	1.05	0.86	0.71	0.49	1.08	1.94	1.92	1.91	1.90	1.89	1.88	1.88	1.87	1.87	1.88	1.88
6.6	1.24	1.08	0.89	0.72	0.51	0.30	1.06	2.16	2.15	2.14	2.13	2.12	2.12	2.12	2.12	2.12	2.12
6.7	1.27	1.10	0.91	0.74	0.53	0.31	0.09	1.04	2.40	2.40	2.39	2.38	2.38	2.38	2.38	2.38	2.38
6.8	1.29	1.11	0.93	0.75	0.54	0.32	0.10	-0.13	1.02	2.65	2.64	2.64	2.63	2.63	2.63	2.63	2.64
6.9	1.30	1.13	0.93	0.76	0.54	0.32	0.10	-0.13	-0.38	1.00	2.92	2.91	2.91	2.90	2.90	2.90	2.91
7.0	1.31	1.13	0.94	0.76	0.53	0.32	0.11	-0.13	-0.38	-0.63	0.98	3.18	3.18	3.18	3.18	3.18	3.18
7.1	1.31	1.13	0.93	0.76	0.53	0.31	0.10	-0.14	-0.39	-0.64	-0.90	0.95	3.46	3.46	3.46	3.46	3.46
7.2	1.31	1.12	0.93	0.75	0.52	0.31	0.09	-0.15	-0.40	-0.65	-0.91	-1.19	0.91	3.70	3.70	3.70	3.70
7.3	1.30	1.11	0.91	0.74	0.51	0.29	0.07	-0.16	-0.41	-0.66	-0.91	-1.20	-1.47	0.79	3.82	3.82	3.82
7.4	1.28	1.10	0.89	0.71	0.50	0.27	0.05	-0.18	-0.42	-0.67	-0.92	-1.20	-1.48	-1.76	0.67	3.91	3.91
7.5	1.25	1.07	0.87	0.69	0.47	0.25	0.03	-0.20	-0.44	-0.68	-0.93	-1.21	-1.48	-1.77	-2.10	0.55	3.99
7.6	1.22	1.04	0.84	0.67	0.44	0.22	0.01	-0.21	-0.47	-0.70	-0.95	-1.22	-1.49	-1.77	-2.10	-2.17	0.41
7.7	1.19	1.01	0.81	0.63	0.41	0.20	-0.02	-0.24	-0.48	-0.72	-0.96	-1.23	-1.50	-1.78	-2.10	-2.17	-2.25

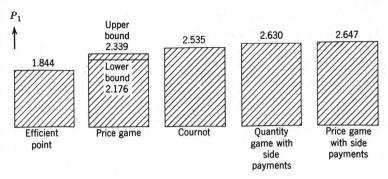

Figure 24

We note that 90 per cent or more of the probability distribution of both players is upon their five lowest prices, with their major concentration on the lowest price. This is to be expected, since the maxima in the contingent revenue functions occur only when a player charges a low price or is undercut considerably. In this particular example the more efficient player (player 1) has a more powerful threat under price competition than he had under quantity competition. The reason for this is not immediately clear.

The expected value in the price game, although higher than the efficient point, is considerably lower than that obtained by the Cournot solution. This is not necessarily always so; it depends upon the specific nature of the contingent demand and costs. [26]

The mixed strategies which may be needed for optimal threats in the co-operative price game serve to indicate the strategic importance of price (and, in the price-quantity model, of inventory) maneuverability in an oligopolistic market. Throughout the first part of this book we have used the concept of mixed strategy, which is hard to rationalize. In Chapter 9 we introduce a closely allied concept, a *behavior strategy*. This appears to be far more natural for economic situations but can best be described in a dynamic setting (the extensive form of a game).

5. PRICE-QUANTITY MODELS

5.1. THE GENERAL EDGEWORTH SOLUTION

We are at last in a position to examine the objective background of the general simple duopoly model i.e., both firms are free to specify their prices and production rates. At the end of the period a firm may find that it has underproduced or that it is left with inventories. To specify such a model completely, both the contingent demand functions and an inventory evaluation function must be given for each player.

The payoff function to player i is

(1) $P_i = p_i \min \left[(q_i, \bar{q}_i) \right] - q_i \gamma_i(q_i) + \delta(q_i, \bar{q}_i) \omega_i(q_i - \bar{q}_i),$

where

$$\delta(q_i, \bar{q}_i) = \begin{cases} 0 & \text{for } q_i \leqslant \bar{q}_i \\ \\ 1 & \text{for } q_i > \bar{q}_i \end{cases}$$

Equation 1 states that the payoff to player i consists of three components. The first is his revenue, which is the product of the price he charges p_i and the amount he sells. The amount he sells may be less than or equal to the amount he has, which is q_i. This depends upon the size of the market demand $\bar{q}_i$, which will be a function of the price charged by player i and the price charged and quantity produced by player j. The second component is the total cost of producing the quantity q_i. The third component is the inventory evaluation. If he sells everything, this is zero, as indicated by the auxiliary function $\delta(q_i, \bar{q}_i)$. If he fails to sell everything, then the inventory evaluation function $\omega_i(q_i - \bar{q}_i)$ assigns a value to the goods which remain.

When we modify Edgeworth's analysis and specify that each duopolist assumes that his opponent's price and output is fixed and that the strategy of each duopolist is to name a price and output we can observe immediately that the range of price fluctuation remains the same as in the price model. This is so because at the bottom of this range the duopolist with the lower price will name a production rate, which is at most the amount that maximizes his profit, on the condition that he is charging the lower price; but this is precisely the same amount as he would produce in the price model. Hence the contingent demand for the other duopolist will be the same for this action in both models and the range of fluctuation, which depends upon the two maxima in the contingent profit function of a player having the same value, will be the same.

The only difference between this model and the previous Edgeworth example is that now it is possible to specify exactly the resultant profits from the play of any two strategies without having to resort to legerdemain to explain the inventory position.

*5.2. THE PRICE-QUANTITY GAME

The price-quantity game is a two-person, simultaneous-move game in which the strategy of each player consists of naming a price at which he will sell his product and selecting a production rate or initial stock position. The solution (equilibrium point) to this game is not known. However, several problems and interesting features may be noted.

The price game described in subsection 4.3 can be regarded as a special case in which both players are always allowed to return excess goods at cost price; thus, loosely speaking, the price game seems to be the most favorable special case of the price-quantity game. One might suspect that the value for the general price-quantity game would be lower than that for the price game because there is a greater risk to each player (the risk of being left with inventories). However, both players face this risk, and it is possible that it might cause them to be more conservative so that the value of the game would be greater to the players.

If the price game has a pure strategy solution (which, as we have seen in subsection 4.2, will be the efficient point), then so has the price-quantity game. The same two theorems which establish the conditions for the pure strategy solution of the price game in subsection 4.2 apply directly to the more complicated model.

We have already obtained bounds on the value of the price game between the value at the pure strategy maxmin and the value at the lower end of the Edgeworth range of fluctuation. Both bounds apply to the price-quantity game. The pure strategy maxmin points are the same because they are computed on the assumption that the player will be just undercut by an opponent maximizing at that price; hence no inventory problem is faced. The Edgeworth range remains the same, as noted in subsection 5.1. However, we may improve on the lower bound for the values of both games by considering the mixed strategy maxmin points. In order to calculate these bounds we treat the payoff matrices of each player separately as though each were playing in a zero-sum game. Because more than one pure strategy will be employed by each player in his mixed maxmin strategy, inventory conditions will have an effect. The maxmin points in the price-quantity game will have a lower value than those in the price game, and we are able to establish a lower bound for the price-quantity game which lies below the lower bound for the price game. Because the ranges between the lower and upper bounds overlap we cannot say which game will have the greatest value.

Although the strategies of a player in the price-quantity game require that he name both a price and a quantity, these decisions are highly correlated. For example, at any price named by a player he will not produce a quantity smaller than he would produce if he knew that he would be just undercut by an opponent producing a maximal amount at that price. He will not produce more than the maximal amount at a given price on the assumption that he will be charging the lower price in the market. An example of how the strategy space for a player is limited by these considerations follows. This was obtained by considering the price-quantity model equivalent to the price model discussed in subsection 4.3. The productions of each player are limited to units of $\frac{1}{10}$ and the prices to units of $\frac{2}{10}$. Although there are 104 possible price-quantity strategies available to the first player, an immediate computation of the limits imposed on the selection of a quantity, given price, cuts the strategies down to seventy.

Figure 25 indicates how the payoff to the first player varies when his opponent is playing a fixed pure strategy ($p_2 = 6.7$, $q_2 = 0.9$). Each line in the figure represents the payoff obtained by the first

p/q	0.2	0.3	0.4	0.5	0.6	0.7	0.8	0.9	1.0	1.1	1.2	1.3	1.4
6.1									×	×	×		
6.3							×	×	×	×	×	×	
6.5						×	×	×	×	×	×	×	
6.7					×	×	×	×	×	×	×	×	
6.9				×	×	×	×	×	×	×	×	×	×
7.1		×	×	×	×	×	×	×	×	×	×	×	×
7.3	×	×	×	×	×	×	×	×	×	×	×	×	×
7.5	×	×	×	×	×	×	×	×	×	×	×		

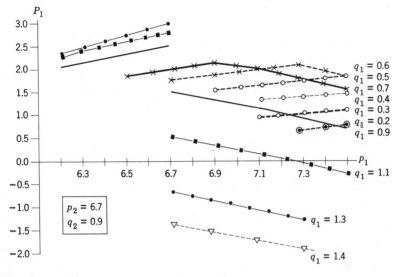

Figure 25

player as he varies his price, keeping his output fixed, given a fixed price and output of his opponent. If, as expected, he selects a large quantity, he will be able to make a high profit if he is not undercut. If he is undercut, then his inventory losses will be considerable and his profit may even be negative. For instance, $q_1 = 1.3$ shows this. There is a discontinuity at $p_1 = p_2 = 6.7$ at which the profits of the first player fall off steeply. If he selects a more conservative stock or production level, he will fail to realize optimum profits if he has the lower price, but he will not be so badly damaged if he is undercut. In fact, he may not be hurt at all in some cases. An example is provided by $q_1 = 0.7$; for this inventory level, given the strategy of the opponent, there is no discontinuity at $p_1 = 6.7$ because the combined productions of both players do not saturate the market. We note that for $q_1 = 0.7$ the optimum profit for the first player occurs when he charges a price $p_1 = 6.9$, even though he is undercut.

It is conjectured that the price-quantity game will in general have a unique equilibrium point if the related price game possesses one and the inventory valuation function is sufficiently regular. Unfortunately, the mathematical analysis required for this game is beyond the scope of this book. [27]

NOTES

[1] J. Bertrand, "Théorie mathématique de la richesse sociale" (review), *Journal des Savants* (Paris: September 1883), pp. 499–508.

[2] F. Y. Edgeworth, *Papers Relating to Political Economy*, **I** (London: Macmillan, 1925), pp. 111–142; also *Mathematical Psychics*.

[3] Edward H. Chamberlin, *The Theory of Monopolistic Competition* (Cambridge: Harvard University-Press, 6th ed., 1950), Chapter IV, p. 60.

[4] Paul M. Sweezy, "Demand under Conditions of Oligopoly," *Journal of Political Economy*, **XLVII** (1939), pp. 568–573.

[5] M. Bronfenbrenner, "Applications of the Discontinuous Oligopoly Demand Curve," *Journal of Political Economy*, **XLVIII** (1940), pp. 420–427.

[6] George J. Stigler, "The Kinky Oligopoly Demand Curve and Rigid Prices," *The Journal of Political Economy*, **LV** (October 1947), pp. 432–449.

[7] R. G. D. Allen, *Mathematical Analysis for Economists* (New York: Macmillan, 1938), p. 110.

[8] O. Morgenstern, "Demand Theory Reconsidered," *Quarterly Journal of Economics*, **LXII** (February 1948), p. 168.

[9] We note that the problem of trading at many prices in small quantities in a homogeneous good is closely related to the following two-country international trade problem. Is it possible for trade to be carried on in such a manner that one participant gains nothing from the trade but is merely moved along the indifference curve on which he started initially? The answer to this problem is yes; it can be shown by considering a limiting process of very many trades, each for a very small quantity of the good and each at a slightly different price.

[10] I am indebted to Kenneth Arrow for pointing out the error in my original formulation of contingent or "reconstituted" demand. This earlier formulation is included here with an interpretation that can be applied to the theory of rationing. Suppose that a government agency wished to satisfy demand for a commodity whose distribution it controls. For political reasons it can charge only one price to the market. It has two sources of supply which charge different prices. The lower-priced source cannot satisfy demand. After the government has bought all of this supply, its demand for the other supply must be worked out. We can compute this "reconstituted demand" as a function of the price charged by the second supplier in the following manner:

The new demand curve is such that

$$q_1 + q = \phi\left\{\frac{q_1 p_1 + q p}{q_1 + q}\right\}.$$

Now

$$\phi^{-1}(q_1 - q) = \frac{q_1 p_1 - q p}{q_1 - q},$$

therefore

$$p = \frac{1}{q}\{(q_1 + q)\phi^{-1}(q_1 + q) - q_1 p_1\}$$

This type of action can be illustrated on an indifference map. Assume that the buying board knows the preference system of a consumer and can charge only one price. In order to satisfy the consumer it buys all the low-priced goods, then commences to buy the high-priced goods until, by charging the consumer the average price for the new amounts, the board is able to satisfy the demand. This is indicated in the tangency condition of the average price line with the indifference map. Ma indicates the quantity restriction of the first supply, and the slope of Ma gives the price; Mb gives the same from the second. Mc indicates the final price and the amount sold.

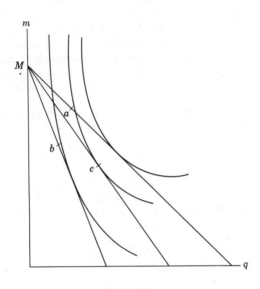

Figure 26

[11] K. W. Rothschild, "The Degree of Monopoly," *Economica* (new series), **IX** (1942), pp. 21–39.

[12] R. H. Coase, "The Problem of Duopoly Reconsidered," *Review of Economic Studies*, **II** (1934–1935), pp. 137–143.

[13] For a general discussion of the role of inventories, see T. M. Whitin, *The Theory of Inventory Management* (Princeton: Princeton University Press, 1953); K. J. Arrow, T. Harris, and J. Marschak, "Optimal Inventory Policy," *Econometrica*, **XIX** (July 1951), pp. 250–272.

[14] See F. Y. Edgeworth, *Papers Relating to Political Economy*, **I** (London: Macmillan, 1925), p. 120.

[15] Some of the material in this section is reproduced from M. Shubik, "A Comparison of Treatments of a Duopoly Situation, Part II," *Econometrica*, **XXIII** (October 1955), pp. 417–431.

[16] As an example of the effect of introducing a "friction" into a duopoly model, we note that if we consider the modified Edgeworth model with player 1 always having to declare his price first and add the condition that the price shift in any one period must not exceed some amount that is considerably smaller than the fluctuation range the solution is changed. This model now has an equilibrium point at the first player's minimax strategy (if mixed strategies are not considered). If we consider the game in which player 2 moves first, his minimax strategy is the equilibrium point. Even a slight change in our basic assumptions may change the the solution. However, before we are in a position to analyze changes, we must fully understand the basic price duopoly problem. For this reason we confine our analysis to very simple models without frictions.

[11] F. Y. Edgeworth, *op. cit.*, p. 118.

[18] A counterexample is given in M. Shubik, *op.cit.*, p. 424.

[19] In most of the work in this book the concept of mixed strategy is not needed. However, even though we may not be easily able to imagine businessmen using dice to make a decision, mixed strategies lay stress upon the possible use of chance as a strategic component in a situation of conflict.

[20] L. S. Shapley, "A Duopoly Model with Price Competition" (abstract), *Econometrica*, **XXV** (April 1957), pp. 354–355.

[21] See S. S. Wilks, *Elementary Statistical Analysis* (Princeton: Princeton University Press, 1951), pp. 106–110.

[22] *Ibid.*, p. 98.

[23] See P. A. Samuelson, *Foundations of Economic Analysis* (Cambridge: Harvard University Press, 1948), pp. 36 and 60.

[24] Only the range of active strategies is shown in Table 6. An extension of the strategy space makes no difference to the solution, since the extra strategies are not used.

[25] In our treatment of price variation we have always assumed that a player is not permitted to produce more than the optimal amount associated with the price he wishes to charge, i.e., the amount he would produce if he could sell all he wished to at a given price. If we do not make this assumption, then the minimax value given here is not defined. We do not need this assumption for the difference game $(P_1 - P_2)$. It is of interest to note that the equilibrium point of the nonzero-sum game defined by the two payoff functions P_1 and P_2 is the same as the saddle-point or minimax of the zero-sum difference game $P_1 - P_2$. This is always the case if the Bertrand game has a pure strategy solution.

[26] This is not always true; it depends upon the shape of the cost and contingent demand functions. See the example cited in M. Shubik, *loc. cit.*

[27] In the above model each entrepreneur has a two-dimensional strategy; hence the payoff space is four-dimensional, i.e., it depends upon p_1, p_2, q_1, and q_2. In order to solve for equilibrium points we must find two probability,

distributions $f(p_1, q_1)$ and $g(p_2, q_2)$ so that

$$\int_\alpha^\beta \int_a^b P_1(q_1, q_2, p_1, p_2)\, dg(p_2, q_2) \equiv \bar{V}_1 \qquad \begin{aligned} a &\leq p_1 \leq b \\ \alpha &\leq q_1 \leq \beta \end{aligned}$$

$$\int_\alpha^\beta \int_a^b P_2(q_1, q_2, p_1, p_2)\, df(p_1, q_1) \equiv \bar{V}_2 \qquad \begin{aligned} a &\leq p_2 \leq b \\ \alpha &\leq q_2 \leq \beta \end{aligned}$$

chapter 6

THE FIRM
IN OLIGOPOLISTIC
COMPETITION:
MANY COMPETITORS

In this best of all possible worlds, the
invisible hand was the most magnificent
of all hands, and pure competition the
best of all possible competitions.

(with apologies to Voltaire)

1. MARKET MODELS WITH MANY FIRMS

1.1. *n*-PERSON NON-CO-OPERATIVE GAMES

The general definition of equilibrium point given in Chapter 4: 2
holds for any number of competitors. Having completed a detailed
examination of duopolistic markets, we would like to confirm our
economic intuition that no matter what type of non-co-operative
behavioristic model we assume, as the numbers of competitors
become large and individual market shares small, the resultant
equilibrium approaches that of pure competition. Cournot indicates
that this would be true for his duopoly model. [1] Again we must
stress that, as before, we do not consider any market imperfections.
If, for instance, there were product differentiation, we would suspect

that different non-co-operative equilibrium points might be reached. These points, however, may be expected to approach the pure competition equilibrium as the cross-elasticities between the products become high.

Four models are examined. The efficient point or price parameter, Cournot or quantity strategy, Bertrand or price strategy, and the price-quantity strategy games are shown to possess the same solution in the limit as the number of firms becomes large. The next four subsections substantiate this statement.

In setting up the models in this chapter several difficulties in economic analysis have to be overcome. The precise meaning of entry into and exit from competition must be given. This is done in section 2, in which the concept of *firm-in-being* is introduced. Using models which include the possibility of entry or exit by firms, we are able to discuss the meaning of overcapacity as well as the role of a dominant firm.

The use of the concept of *industry* has purposely been avoided. Instead, we confine our remarks to groups of competitors. The justification for this is given in section 3.

1.2. The Market with Competitive Price

In a market in which many firms compete in the production of a single good, in which each firm acts under the assumption that it may accept market price as a "given" because it has so little influence, and which has costless and frictionless entry and exit, equilibrium size is determined when no outside firm can enter into production and make a profit. Another way of specifying the equilibrium is to say that the least efficient active firm, the marginal firm, obtains zero profit. [2] Let the nth firm be the marginal one; the average costs of the ith firm are $\gamma_i = \gamma_i(q_i)$ in which q_i is the production of the ith firm. The conditions which must be satisfied by a competitive equilibrium are

(1) $$\frac{d(q_i\gamma_i)}{dq_i} = p, \qquad i = 1, 2, \ldots, n,$$

(2) $$p = \phi(\sum_{i=1}^{n} q_i),$$

(3) $$pq_n - \gamma_n q_n = 0, \qquad q_i \geqslant 0,$$

in which $p = \phi(\sum\limits_{i=1}^{n} q_i)$ is the demand function. The set of equations in expression 1 can be given as

$$(4) \qquad \gamma_i + q_i \frac{d\gamma_i}{dq_i} = p, \qquad i = 1, 2, \ldots, n.$$

If we do not require that equation 3, which sums up the free entry condition, hold, then the equations in expression 4 specify the efficient point solution for a fixed number of firms. We will show in the succeeding subsections that as the number of competitors becomes large the solutions to the other games (i.e., Cournot and price games) approach the efficient point. In section 2 we introduce a method of handling the problem of free entry into competition and show how this added condition causes the solutions which approach the efficient point to approach the competitive market solution.

*1.3. THE n-PERSON COURNOT OR QUANTITY GAME

We assume that there are n firms in competition, each maximizing profits by adjusting output. Then, if a pure strategy equilibrium exists, it may be determined by solving

$$\frac{\partial(pq_i - \gamma_i q_i)}{\partial q_i} = 0, \qquad i = 1, 2, \ldots, n,$$

$$p = \phi(\sum\limits_{i=1}^{n} q_i), \qquad \text{subject to} \quad q_i \geqslant 0.$$

In order to study the behavior of the Cournot equilibrium, as the number of competitors increases, we postulate that the firms are of the same "size," i.e., they have the same average variable costs.

We wish to compare situations in which the market is controlled by a few large non-co-operative firms of the same size with the same market shared between many small firms of the same size. The models constructed for comparative purposes must be such that when there are n competitors each will obtain an nth of the market. There are two ways in which we can formalize this. The most natural would be to leave the aggregate demand function fixed and progressively "shrink" the average cost functions as more firms are considered. An easier way serves our purposes. As we introduce more firms into competition, we "expand" the demand in such a manner that although the individual firms are of the same "size" in every model their size compared with the market becomes smaller and smaller.

Let the demand function in the n-player game be

$$p = \phi_n(\sum_{i=1}^{n} q_i) = \phi_1(\sum_{i=1}^{n} \frac{q_i}{n})$$

$\phi_1(q_1)$ is the demand in the original monopolistic market when there is only one firm producing. The number of units of the product purchased at a given price in the n-person market will be n times the amount bought in the monopolistic market if we use the foregoing demand conditions. We place the following conditions on the demand function: ϕ_1 is continuous, all partial first derivatives $\partial\phi_1/\partial q_i$ exist, and are continuous; $\partial\phi_1/\partial q_i < 0$ and is bounded.

These conditions are equivalent to stating that demand decreases with a rise in price at all levels and that demand is zero for some finite price.

The analytic equations for the existence of a pure strategy equilibrium now become

(1)
$$\frac{\partial(pq_i - q_i\gamma_i)}{\partial q_i} = 0, \qquad i = 1, 2, \ldots, n,$$

where $p = \phi_n(\sum_{i=1}^{n} q_i)$.

These can be expressed as

(2)
$$\gamma_i + q_i \frac{d\gamma_i}{dq_i} = p + q_i \frac{\partial p_i}{\partial q_i},$$

where $i = 1, 2, \ldots, n$, where γ_i [3] is the average total cost function for player i.

We observe that

$$\frac{\partial p}{\partial q_i} = \frac{\partial \phi_n(\sum_{i=1}^{n} q_i)}{\partial q_i} = \frac{\partial \phi_1(\sum_{i=1}^{n} \frac{q_i}{n})}{\partial q_i} = \frac{1}{n} \frac{\partial \phi_1}{\partial q_i}.$$

Therefore, as $n \to \infty$,

$$\frac{\partial p}{\partial q_i} \to 0,$$

as $\dfrac{\partial \phi_1}{\partial q_i}$ is bounded.

Hence the system of equations in expression 2 approaches, in the limit, to

$$\gamma_i + q_i \frac{d\gamma_i}{dq_i} = p, \text{ or } \frac{d(q_i \gamma_i)}{dq_i} = p.$$

These are the equations for the efficient point equilibrium. Furthermore, if the marginal firm makes no profit, then this will be identical with the competitive market. [4]

*1.4. THE n-PERSON PRICE GAME

We demonstrate in this subsection that if firms of equal size are using price strategies, then, as the number of firms becomes large, the market price will approach the efficient point price. [5]

From Chapter 5: 4.3 this is immediately true if the price games have a pure strategy solution, for this solution is the efficient point. We must establish the result for the class of games which does not have a pure strategy equilibrium.

Given a symmetric (i.e., firms with equal costs), two-person price game with a single mixed strategy equilibrium point (see Chapter 5: 4.3), there is associated with this game a class of symmetric n-person price games such that if the aggregate demand function for the two-person game is

$$p = \phi_2(\sum_{i=1}^{2} q_i) = \phi_1(\sum_{i=1}^{2} \frac{q_i}{2}),$$

then the aggregate demand for an n-person game is

$$p = \phi_n(\sum_{i=1}^{n} q_i) = \phi_1(\sum_{i=1}^{n} \frac{q_i}{n}).$$

(It is assumed that the method for computing contingent demand functions is given; see Chapter 5: 2 and Chapter 7.)

Theorem. In the class of games defined, as the number of players n increases, (1) the value of the cumulative density function (see Chapter 5, note 23) of a player's mixed strategy approaches 1 within any arbitrarily small price range whose lower bound is the lowest price active strategy; (2) the lowest price active strategy used by each player in the mixed strategy he employs at the symmetric equilibrium point approaches the efficient point price.

Proof. If a player's price is below the efficient price, the quantity he can sell does not depend on the prices charged by the other players (see Chapter 5: 4.2, Theorem 2). [6] Consider any arrangement of pure strategies by all players except one. If the latter is allowed to pick a pure strategy to maximize against the other strategies, it cannot be below the efficient point, for as his production is independent of the prices of others when he produces below the efficient point price he can always improve his profits by keeping his production fixed and raising his price to that of the efficient point. This same argument applies to any arrangement of mixed strategies. Hence, if there exists a mixed strategy equilibrium, the mix of any player cannot contain an active strategy which is a price less than that of the "efficient point."

It has been proved by Shapley (see Appendix C for the proof) that the efficient point strategy is not among the active strategies employed by the players in this class of games. Hence the value of all these games is above that of the efficient point value, and the lowest price active strategy is above the efficient point price.

Consider that one player is confronted with the mixed strategies of all his opponents. Any pure strategy out of his mix of active pure strategies must give him the value of the game (see Appendix C). In particular, the active strategy associated with the lowest price he names must yield him the same value as that obtained with the highest. The most favorable condition for the utilization of a high price as an active strategy occurs when all the other players have a probability of charging a low price, for then the contingent demand, hence the contingent revenue, will be as favorable as possible. Suppose, in particular, that $n - 1$ players charged their lowest price. There must exist a Δp such that if the $n - 1$ players increased their price by Δp and adjusted their production rates accordingly, the payoff to the nth player, when employing the active pure strategy associated with the highest price he ever charges, is wiped out. As the number of players $n \to \infty$, this distance $\Delta p \to 0$. Hence, in the limit, all the probability distribution must be concentrated on the lowest price strategy used. This proves part 1 of the theorem.

We now show that the lowest active strategy in each player's range for an n-person game must lie between the efficient point price of this n-person game and the efficient point of the analogous $n - 1$ person game, i.e., the game with the demand given by

$$p = \phi_1(\sum_{i=1}^{n-1} \frac{q_i}{n})$$

not

$$p = \phi_1(\sum_{i=1}^{n-1} \frac{q_i}{n-1}).$$

Assume that the lowest price named by all players in the n-person game is at or above that of the $n - 1$ person game efficient point. This implies that $n - 1$ players will have totally saturated the market when they use their lowest price active strategy; hence the nth player will not use his active strategies at the high-price end of his active strategy range because they will have a zero expected payoff. This established the contradiction.

Finally we prove that, in the limit, the efficient point price in the $n - 1$ person game approaches the efficient point price in the n-person game. Let ϵ be any positive number, p the efficient point price in the n-person game, and q the production of each player at this price. Consider q_ϵ to be the production of each player if he is told that he can sell as much as he wishes to produce at the price $p + \epsilon$ (this, of course, is independent of n). If there are only $n - 1$ players in the market, the production of each at the new efficient point will be some $q_{\epsilon'}$. We denote $q_{\epsilon'} - q$ by $\Delta(\epsilon')$. This states that if there is one less player in the market, each of the others will be able to produce some small finite amount more than before, and there will be a slight upward shading of price with the new efficient point price settling at $p + \epsilon'$ where marginal costs once more equal price. We will now show that as the number of players $n \to \infty$ then $\epsilon' \to 0$ and $q_{\epsilon'} \to q$. Suppose that this were not true. There would then be some finite quantity $\Delta \epsilon'$ so that each player in any $n - 1$ person game would produce at least that amount more than he would produce in an n-person game. All in all, the $n - 1$ players produce $(n - 1)$ $\Delta(\epsilon')$ more than $n - 1$ players at the efficient point in the n-person game. At the same price as the n-person efficient point price the $n - 1$ players are able to sell q more units of their product. Now as $n \to \infty$, then $(n - 1)$ $\Delta(\epsilon') > q$ for any finite $\Delta(\epsilon')$; hence $\Delta(\epsilon')$ cannot remain above a fixed positive value but must approach zero (otherwise the market would be oversaturated) and the $n - 1$ person efficient point price approaches the n-person efficient point price.

1.5. The n-Person Price-Quantity Game

The same proof as that given for the price game establishes the result for the price-quantity game with a pure strategy equilibrium. We have already noted in Chapter: 5.2 that if the price game has a pure strategy equilibrium so will any associated price-quantity game, and this equilibrium point will be the efficient point. It is conjectured that if the price-quantity game has a mixed strategy equilibrium the same proof as in subsection 1.4 will establish convergence to the efficient point.

1.6. A Comparison of Four n-Person Market Models

The preceding four subsections have shown that even if we start with four different behavioristic assumptions in static models of oligopolistic competition all solutions tend to the same result as the number of competitors grow, despite the large difference in solutions when numbers are small. The manner in which these solutions approach the same competitive state is indicated in Figure 27. As some of the solutions involve probability consider-ations, the axes of Figure 21 represent price and probability on the abscissa and ordinate, respectively. EE_1 indicates that in all markets in which the firms act as though they had no market control and maintain the same absolute size (regardless of their relative size with respect to the whole market) the price will be the same. There is a probability weighting of 1 on this price which indicates that the efficient point price is determinate in all cases. CC_1, which also has a probability weighting of 1, is the price that

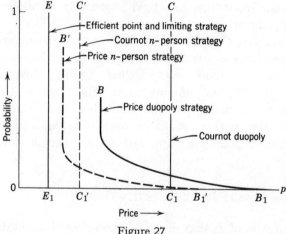

Figure 27

will reign under a Cournot duopoly. $C'C_1'$ indicates that as numbers increase this price moves down towards EE_1. BB_1 describes the probability density function associated with the strategy of the Bertrand duopolist. Price is not determinate but can fluctuate over a range. Even with two competitors there is a tendency to weight the lower prices. $B'B_1'$ shows that when the number of competitors increases it becomes progressively less and less desirable to step out of line with one's price policy. Most of the odds are concentrated on prices lying very close to EE_1, with only a small possibility left for any major price fluctuation. There would be a similar diagram for the price-quantity case which would also involve the inventory position.

2. GAMES WITH ENTRY. THE: FIRM-IN-BEING

2.1. ENTRY INTO COMPETITION

Consideration of entry into and exit from competition brings with it many problems of analysis and observation. Entry may be effected by a new firm investing sufficient funds, finding the necessary talent, and building a new plant; the necessary talent may be obtained by bidding away employees from established firms. Entry can be made by an existing multiproduct firm switching over part of its plant to manufacturing the same product as its competitors. There are borderline cases in which a firm-in-being is allowed to share the corporate cake and is permitted to buy into an existing corporation rather than fight its way in. At this point the old firm becomes a new firm in many ways, although no new entry, in the sense of extra firms coming in, has been made.

Here we must raise a familiar cry. Many of the features determining entry are essentially financial, corporate, and dynamic and are discussed in the chapters on dynamics.

By a *firm-in-being* we mean a potential entrant into competition. Although the precise number of potential entrants cannot be specified empirically, a good estimate of their effect can be obtained by examining the availability of managerial skills, the necessary types of labor, sources of factor supply, and market outlets. Speed of entry, capital structure, credit lines, and financial markets play their roles in the dynamics of entry, but even in a static analysis we can note them as being determinants in the measure of flexibility of action of a firm. Exit conditions play their part in the structure of liquidation values. A potential entrant will think twice before runing the risk of being caught holding a large plant whose liquidation value is determined by the scrap market.

The factors noted combine to portray the major economic features of entry. They will be relevant regardless of the existing legal, institutional, and social conditions. Although licenses, patents, charters, and racial and religious discrimination all serve to shape the conditions for entry into competition, a detailed discussion of these features calls for an empirical study. Mere "conversational economics" on such topics scarcely tends to increase our knowledge of the real world or to improve our abilities for analysis.

Two main types of models are constructed in the following subsections. They are, respectively, markets in which entry is "free and unrestricted" and markets into which entry is closed. The first symbolizes the type of market in which there are no social restrictions, no control over the supply of factors, no important financial or temporal factors which could manifest themselves as frictions, and a plentiful supply of would-be-entrepreneurs. In short, the market portrays the best of all possible classical worlds. The second symbolizes the type of market in which economic factors, noneconomic factors, or a combination of both make entry impossible.

2.2. MARKETS WITH FREE ENTRY OR NO ENTRY

A market with free entry is such that there are always firms-in-being which will come into the market if there is a slight rise in price and will leave it if there is a slight fall. The liquidation value of a firm equals its creation value; hence no loss is suffered by entering and leaving the market.

In the discussion of equilibrium in a market with free entry it has been assumed that the firms-in-being have a higher cost structure than those already in the market. This assumption is directly related to what we mean when we say that one firm is more efficient than another.

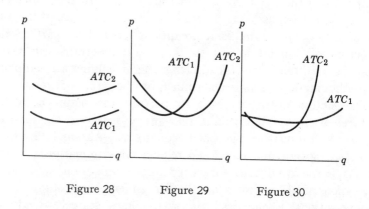

Figure 28   Figure 29   Figure 30

Figures 28 to 30 provide examples of some of the different conditions that may be implied when one firm is said to have higher costs than another. Figure 28 provides the simplest and clearest example. The second firm has costs which are higher than those of the first at every level of production. In Figure 29 the average total cost curves of each firm are of the same shape, but that of the second firm lies to the right of the first firm. The second firm is less efficient for low levels of production but more efficient for high ones. The state portrayed in Figure 30 is one in which the second firm is more efficient than the first in a middle range of production but less efficient for large or small production rates.

In a general theory of economics of the market we may assume that by the "extramarginal firm" we mean a firm with a short-run, average-cost function that is slightly higher (in some relevant production range) than the firm whose average costs at the relevant rate of production are the highest among the actively producing firms.

2.3. A COMPARISON OF A COURNOT MARKET WITH FREE ENTRY AND NO ENTRY

The conditions for a quantity-adjustment or Cournot equilibrium with entry permitted are

$$\frac{d(q_i \gamma_i)}{dq_i} = p + \frac{q_i \partial p}{\partial q_i}, \quad \text{for all } q_i > 0.$$

$P_i = pq_i - \gamma_i q_i \geqslant 0$ for $q_i > 0$ and $P_i = 0$, if $q_i = 0$, $i = 1, 2, .. n$
These conditions state that firms in active production must at least break even or make a profit. Firms which do not produce make zero profit. Firms which do produce charge a price so that marginal cost equals the equilibrium marginal revenue, i.e., the marginal revenue computed on the assumption that the production levels of all others are fixed. It is easy to see that for a fixed number of players the Cournot behavioral conditions will cause each player to restrict production and result in a price higher than would prevail in a competitive market. If there are no entry restrictions, the aggregate output of the active firms may be sufficiently small to enable extra firms to enter and make a profit. The influx of newcomers will stop when no one can enter with profit. The market price may be approximately the same as under pure efficient point pricing competition, the number of active firms, greater, and the production rate per firm, less, as shown in Tables 7 and 8. This is equivalent to the Chamberlinian equilibrium with excess capacity, although this model has production as the independent variable.

The technical method for treating entry into competition in a game theory model is to consider a game which is large enough to have equilibrium points at which not all the players are actively engaged in production. [7] This technique introduces the inactive players explicitly as firms-in-being. The nature of the cost structure of the potential entrants will influence the adjustment path caused by any disturbance.

The general method for calculating equilibrium points when entry is possible is given in Appendix C; an example comparing competitive equilibrium with the Cournot equilibrium with entry follows. We assume that the firms can be arranged in order of increasing costs and, for ease of computation, that the only cost differences between firms are in the level of fixed costs.

Suppose that the market demand were $p = 10 - 0.4 \sum_{i=1}^{n} q_i$, where q_i is the output of the ith firm. Consider a market in which the number of firms and firms-in-being is n (where n is any large number, say bigger than twenty). Let the total cost of production to the ith firm be

$$C_i = q_i(5 - q_i + q_i^2) + 0.9 - \left(\frac{10 - i}{1000}\right).$$

The first term is the total variable costs of production. $0.9 - (10 - i)/1000$ is the fixed cost component for the ith firm. This becomes progressively higher as i increases.

An equilibrium in a market with free entry exists if no active firm is motivated to leave the market or change its production rate and no potential firm is motivated to enter into competition. A simple computation enables us to check the equilibria on the assumptions of competitive and quantity-adjustment behavior by the firms:

Table 7

Efficient Point Solution

k	q	p	P_k
10	1.000	6.000	0.100
11	0.952	5.813	−0.083

The k represents the number of active firms, q, the output of each firm (the outputs will be the same, since they all have the same marginal costs), p is the market price, and P_k is the profit that the kth firm makes. The competitive market can support ten firms. If an eleventh firm came into production it would make a loss. Under the Cournot assumptions the market can support eleven active firms. This amounts to 10 per cent excess plant in comparison

Table 8

Quantity-Adjustment Solution

k	q	p	P_k
10	0.951	6.196	0.382
11	0.906	6.014	0.095
12	0.862	5.864	−0.055

with the competitive solution. The computations were carried out with the equations in Note 8.

*2.4. THE BERTRAND MARKET WITH FREE ENTRY

We know from subsection 1.4 that the competitors in a market using price strategies will either be at the efficient point equilibrium or there will be price instability, with the lowest price charged being above the efficient point price. If the first is the case, then the results under free entry will be precisely the same as those for pure competition.

An explicit example is too difficult to compute here. However, we can discuss the alternatives that can arise if entry is possible when there is no determinate, i.e., pure strategy equilibrium in the market before the entry of new firms. In order to do this we use the following inequality:

$$e_{n+1} \leqslant b_{n+1} < e_n < b_n$$

This was proved in subsection 1.3 and states that the value b_n, for a Bertrand game with n players, is greater than the value of the efficient point solution e_n if the game has a mixed strategy solution. The value of the $n + 1$ person Bertrand game b_{n+1} is lower than the value of the n-person efficient point e_n but higher than or equal to the value of the $n + 1$ person efficient point.

We may interpret the subscripts n and $n + 1$ as referring to the n and $n + 1$ active players, respectively. Three cases of interest are noted:

(1) $b_{n+1} < e_n < 0 < b_n$

(2) $0 \leqslant b_{n+1} < e_n$, and $e_{n+1} < b_{n+1}$

(3) $0 \leqslant b_{n+1} < e_n$, and $e_{n+1} = b_{n+1}$

In case 1 no new firm enters. The last intramarginal firm may have an expected profit of zero or slightly more. By any dynamic interpretation the market is not stable. Prices fluctuate but always stay above the efficient point price. Production is lower than at the efficient point. However, the profit of the last intramarginal firm, if it produced at the efficient point, would be negative, thus indicating the presence of excess capacity in the market. In case 2 a new firm can come in, but the instability remains. In case 3 a new firm can come in; when it does its effect on the contingent demand structure is such that equilibrium is established at the competitive market price.

The same type of argument is conjectured to hold for price-quantity models.

2.5. EXCESS CAPACITY AND MULTIPLE EQUILIBRIA

Up to this point we have avoided discussing the possibility that a multiplicity of pure strategy equilibrium points and mixed strategy equilibria exist in a Cournot game. Actually, the market described in subsection 2.3 is of this type. The equilibrium with the eleven most efficient firms producing is only one of the many equilibria possible. In general, in an n-person symmetric Cournot game, if only k firms can produce at a profit greater than or equal to zero, there will be $n!/[k!(n-k)!]$ pure strategy equilibrium points at which k firms produce and $n-k$ firms are only in being. Even if there are cost differences, there may be equilibria with different and not necessarily the most efficient firms in production. Suppose that in the example given in subsection 2.3 the eleven firms in production were not the eleven most efficient but consisted of the ten most efficient and the twelfth most efficient. This would give an equilibrium position, for if the eleventh most efficient firm (now only a firm-in-being) came into active production there would be twelve firms in the market and all would suffer losses. Hence, given that there are already eleven in active production, it is not motivated to enter. (This holds true for any eleven firms out of the first 106 most efficient; the number 106 is obtained by observing that, as fixed costs are rising by 0.001, if player eleven makes a profit of 0.095 with eleven active players in the market then player number 106 would make a profit of zero.)

This result implies that under oligopolistic competition the equilibrium distribution of resources may depend upon the order of entry of firms as well as upon their relative efficiencies (even without considering asset problems.) A simple example which illustrates this point is the entry of a new gas station into an area which already has several stations. The new plant may be inherently more efficient than several in active production, but the potential entrant may not enter because the profit to all will become negative.. A full treatment requires a dynamic model with ruin possibilities introduced explicitly. These comments also hold for price games.

This equilibrium state with "misallocation of resources" does not take place under the competitive assumptions because the individual entrepreneur uses only the existing market price as his entry criterion, in which case firms may enter, depress the market price, cause losses to many (possibly including themselves), and eventually drive out other firms before establishing equilibrium.

Quantity variation markets may have mixed strategy equilibrium points. Once again we stress that it is hard to give an economic interpretation of such an equilibrium because of the restrictions on the model. The ruling out of costs of entry and exit and asset and other dynamic considerations rids us of much that is important to oligopoly theory. However, in some cases an interpretation in terms of overcapacity can be given.

We may view a mixed strategy equilibrium as a fight carried on by a group of firms which is too large to have all members make a profit simultaneously. In any dynamic model this state will not be stable, for eventually some firms will be driven out of competition. An example of such a game is given here.

Consider two firms with average cost functions $\gamma_i = 10 - 2.5q_i + q_i^2$ and a demand function $p = 10 - 2 \sum q_i$ for $i = 1, 2$. When we solve the equation system $\partial P_i/\partial q_i = 0$ in which P_i is the profit of player i we obtain $q_i(3q_i + 1) = 0$, if we assume that there is a symmetric equilibrium; negative q_i's are inadmissible, and $q_1 = q_2 = 0$ is not an equilibrium point. This indicates that there is no pure strategy symmetric equilibrium point.

There may be a mixed strategy equilibrium. A result obtained by Karlin [9] shows that a mixed strategy in a game of this form involves only two pure strategies. In general, to solve such a game we have

$$H_2(q_2) = a_1 q_2 [\phi(\sum q_i) - \gamma_2(q_2)] + (1 - a_1)q_2 [\phi(\sum q_i) - \gamma_2(q_2)].$$

$H_2(q_2)$ is the expected payoff of the second player and a_1 and $1 - a_1$ represent the probabilities played by the first player we have the conditions

$$H(q_2) = 0, {}^{10} \qquad \frac{\partial H}{\partial q_2} = 0, \qquad q_1 = q_2.$$

In the foregoing example we obtain $a_1 = \frac{1}{8}$. Hence the producer produces $\frac{1}{4}$ with probability $\frac{1}{8}$ or stays out of the market with probability $\frac{7}{8}$. We check this by evaluating the mixed strategy which gives

$$\frac{1}{4} \left[\frac{(1)}{8} \frac{(-7)}{16} + \frac{(7)}{8} \frac{(1)}{16} \right] = 0.$$

The game also has two nonsymmetric pure strategy equilibrium points at $q_1 = \frac{1}{3}$ and $q_2 = 0$ or $q_1 = 0$ and $q_2 = \frac{1}{3}$, respectively (these are obtained by solving the first set of equations without assuming that $q_1 = q_2$ at equilibrium.)

The pure strategy equilibria have only one firm entering the market, whereas the other remains as a firm-in-being. The mixed strategy has both firms active in a market that is "too thin" for two producers of their size.

2.6. MONOPOLISTIC CONTROL BY A DOMINANT FIRM

In subsections 1.3 and 1.4 we showed that for markets with many firms of the same size the Cournot or price-variation behavioristic assumptions led to a solution which approached the efficient-point solution. This is not true if there is any firm in the market which is considerably bigger than the others.[11]

The role of the dominant firm is brought out in a quantity-variation example which also serves to stress the role of corporate structure in competition. We consider a market which has one hundred identical firms in competition, of which fifty are controlled by the same holding company and the rest is run by independent entrepreneurs. We assume that further entry is not possible because of legal restrictions, exhorbitant costs of entry, difficulties in supply markets or in obtaining retail outlets, or to a combination of such factors. Let the average cost functions of all plants be $\gamma_i = 5 -$

$q_i + q_i^2$. Suppose that the demand function were

$$p = 10 - 4\left(\frac{q_1 + 50q_i}{100}\right),$$

$$q_1 = 50q_{j1},$$

in which q_{j1} were the amount produced by each individual plant of the syndicate. The maximizing conditions for the firms which must be satisfied are

(1) $$3q_{j1}^2 + 2q_{j1} - 5 = -2q_i,$$

(2) $$3q_i^2 + 0.04q_i - 5 = -2q_{j1}.$$

We can see that for our purposes the term $0.04q_i$ in the second equation is small enough so that we can ignore it; hence we can write it as

(3) $$3q_i^2 - 5 = -2q_{j1}.$$

This can be interpreted as the replacement of the Cournot action equations for the small firms by the efficient action equations because the two sets of equations differ only by a term which is the partial derivative of price with regard to the particular entrepreneur's production, and in these examples this term is small.

From equations 1 and 3 we get

$$9q_{j1}^4 + 12q_{j1}^3 - 26q_{j1}^2 - 17.3q_{j1} + 18.3 = 0.$$

Solving, we obtain the following results which are placed in Table 9 along with the results for the same industry if all firms acted according to the efficient production model:

Table 9

	q_{i_1}	q_i	$q = (50q_i + q_1)$	p	P_1	P_i
Cournot	0.6893	1.098	89.36	6.425	56.55	1.445
Efficient point	1.0000	1.000	100.00	6.000	50.00	1.000

$q = (50q_i + q_1)$ represents the total production of the industry; P_1, the profit of the syndicate, P_i, the profit of the individual small firm; p, the price in the market. We obtain the interesting result that the small firms gain proportionately more when compared with the efficient point than the large firm. This follows because the large firm cannot effectively "police" the small ones. It is able to take advantage of their limited ability to expand production, but that is all. A fully satisfactory model would examine the full implications of dynamic policing action (Chapter 12: 1.3). Although this static model was given in terms of quantity-variation, a price-variation model would have demonstrated the phenomenon of control more realistically. A firm may be large enough to pursue a "power policy" in the market. This may be profitable, but unless it engages in warfare the active small independents will benefit proportionally, even more than the dominant firm.

If there were instantaneous entry into and exit from an industry and the dominant firm tried to cut back its production, extra-marginal firms could come in immediately, and, as we have seen previously, there would be a Cournot equilibrium with more firms producing than in the efficient model. This merely stresses the inadequacy of a model in which entry conditions, lags, and financial structure are not introduced explicitly.

3.   PARTIAL EQUILIBRIUM ANALYSIS AND AGGREGATION

The process of attempting to define market situations such as monopoly or duopoly calls for a partial equilibrium analysis. For such an analysis to be valid we must examine the nature of the interconnectivity between whatever group we have isolated and the rest of the economy. For instance, attempts to define an industry resolve into a search for subsections of the economy which can be isolated usefully in dealing with a specific set of questions. [12]

An industry may be defined as the set of firms producing the same goods. However, there may be multiple-product firms; hence another definition of industry could be a group of firms in which more than 90 per cent of the output of each by the number of pieces produced or by value is confined to certain types of goods. Both of these definitions may be adequate for some purposes and inadequate for others. For instance, the Census of Manufactures [13] uses establishments rather than firms in its industrial categories. This means that if we wish to use this information to study the aspects of monopolistic power of a multiple-product firm with many unified establishments under its control, but in different "industries;" we will have to unscramble part of the compilation. Most measures of concentration [14] designed to examine different features of monopolistic power, pricing, or distribution require "tailor-made" statistics. Given the specific measure and the appropriate statistics required for the measure, the isolated "partial equilibrium analysis" must justify itself by its results.

We stress that up to this point no attempt has been made in this book to offer a measure of monopoly power. As we have limited ourselves so far to statics, the only interconnectedness there is between our single-plant, entrepreneur-owned firms comes in their joint effect on the market (and factor markets). This could be expressed in terms of cross-elasticities. That this may be done is in itself a reason why we should suspect the usefulness of cross-elasticities as an empirical measure of monopoly power. They give no indication of asset and financial structure which may be more important as determinants of the form of competition than the cross-elasticities.

In general, the problem faced by the use of partial equilibrium analysis can be regarded as follows: Let us represent the whole economy by a set of relations, $\omega_i(a_j, p_k) = 0$; $i = 1, \ldots, n$; $j = 1, \ldots, m$; $k = 1, \ldots, s$. This may be a large complex n-person game, a Leontief system, a Walrasian general equilibrium model, or any other general equilibrium system that one might desire to consider. We may assume that the a_j are variables, such as prices and production rates, and that the p_k are parameters, for instance, government tax rates, the initial distribution of resources in the economy, etc. Given the parameters, we may be able to solve the system and evaluate the variables a_j. A very general problem may require the determination of the quantities of all goods bought and sold, the prices at which they are sold, and the profits made by individual firms, given certain initial conditions and utility functions of all individuals.

If there exists a subsystem of relations in some of the variables $[\gamma_t(a'_u, p_k) = 0, t = 1, \ldots, r$, where $r < n$ (the a_u' form a subset of the a_i; $u = 1, 2, \ldots, b$ and $b < m$)] which can be shown to yield solutions for these variables as close as desired to the solution yielded by the complete set of relations in the relevant ranges of the parameters, we can study the subsystems in the knowledge that the labor of embedding them in the more general system will not be necessary for many purposes of inquiry.

4. SHORT- AND LONG-RUN CHANGES IN DEMAND AND SHIFTS IN COST CURVES

It is evident that our analysis of non-co-operative games is capable of handling short-run shifts in demand by the usual methods of comparative statics, except that here they are dealt with analytically rather than geometrically. A pertinent question to raise is how can we handle long-run changes in demand and the corresponding shifts that they may induce in the cost curves of the firm? This static analysis cannot be suitably generalized to handle long-run cost adjustments without introducing financial and corporate structure explicitly. It is the belief of this writer that the sketching of broad pseudodynamic models of long-run cost adjustments for firms or groups of firms in oligopolistic competition is a waste of time, unless accompanied by specific information as to the type of firm being considered. The problem is complex, and there is no reason to suspect that facile curve drawing is going to yield a general solution. The mere changing of the cost components of the payoff functions in the non-co-operative game models is technically feasible but empirically next to meaningless as a method for studying long-run cost adjustment.

NOTES

[1] Augustin Cournot, *Researches into the Mathematical Principles of the Theory of Wealth* (New York: Macmillan, 1897), p. 84.

[2] Strictly speaking this condition always obtains only if there is an infinite number of firms, each with costs just lower than its successor; otherwise it may be possible for the "marginal firm" to make a small profit.

[3] We assume that $\dfrac{d\gamma_i}{dq_i}$, $\dfrac{d^2\gamma_i}{dq_i}$ exist and are continuous.

$$\frac{d\gamma_i}{dq_i} \to -\infty \text{ as } q_i \to 0 \text{ from above,}$$

$$\frac{d\gamma_i}{dq_i} \to +\infty \quad \text{as} \quad q_i \to q^*,$$

$$\frac{d^2\gamma_i}{dq^2_i} > 0 \qquad \text{for all } q_i \text{ and } q_i \geq 0.$$

These are merely the conditions for "U-shaped" cost curves, taking into account that in the short run under consideration here there is an upper limit q_i^* to the production of every firm.

[4] In this model we did not allow for entry; we merely compared markets with fixed but different numbers of competitors in order to establish that the Cournot equations approach the efficiency equations. Consideration of entry will yield the extra condition on the number of active firms as shown in section 2.

[5] The mixed strategies employed at the non-co-operative equilibrium point in any finite game converge in the probability sense to the distribution with a probability of 1 at the efficient point. This is illustrated by Figure 25 and the explanation following.

[6] The strategic independence of the production rate for prices below the efficient point is based upon the assumption that players never produce more than their optimal production at the price they charge. In industrial wars this may not be true.

[7] A technical point arises in defining the strategy space for the players. Strictly speaking, the strategy space is one and a "half" dimensional. It consists of a range of production rates and the strategy to enter. In a dynamic model this difference becomes important when entry and exit have costs and when we wish to distinguish between being in competition but producing nothing, yet paying overhead and not being in competition. It is also desirable to make the realistic assumption that there is a lower bound to the possible production rate of a firm which is greater than zero. In this manner the average cost functions are bounded to the left, and we treat zero production rate as a singularity. In the models here it is assumed that no overhead is incurred at zero output; hence there is no distinction between a firm in actual existence producing zero and a firm-in-being.

$$q = \frac{-\left(1 + \frac{2k}{n}\right) + \sqrt{\left(1 + \frac{2k}{n}\right)^2 + 15}}{3}$$

for the efficient solution,

$$\text{and } q = \frac{-\left(1 + \frac{2(1+k)}{n}\right) + \sqrt{\left(1 + \frac{2(1+k)}{n}\right)^2 + 15}}{3}$$

for the Cournot game.

[9] Specifically, the property is that both payoffs have third derivatives which do not change signs. Hence, according to Karlin, the optimal strategies

cannot contain more than 1½ points when the end points of the range count as half a point. The applicability of this result was pointed out by L. S. Shapley. Samuel Karlin, "On a Class of Games," in H. W. Kuhn and A. Tucker, eds., *Contributions to the Theory of Games*, **II** (Princeton: Princeton University Press, 1953), pp. 159–172.

[10] This equation holds because at an equilibrium point all pure strategies employed by a player must yield him the value of the game. One of the strategies employed is to produce nothing, and this has the payoff of zero.

[11] Consider any model in which, as $n \to \infty$, the relative size of the dominant firm as compared to the whole market approaches some finite number greater than zero.

[12] See M. R. Conklin, and H. T. Goldstein, "Census Principles of Industry and Product Classification, Manufacturing Industries," in *Business Concentration and Price Policy*, report of National Bureau of Economic Research (Princeton: Princeton University Press, 1955), pp. 15–56.

[13] — —, *op. cit.*, pp. 18–19.

[14] See A. G. Papandreou, "Market Structure and Monopoly Power," *American Economic Review;* **XXXIX** (September 1949), pp. 883–897; K. W. Rothschild, "The Degree of Monopoly," *Economica*, **IX** (February 1942), pp. 214–239; T. Scitovsky, "Economic Theory and the Measurement of Concentration" in *Business Concentration and Price Policy* (Princeton: Princeton University Press, 1955), pp. 101–118.

chapter 7

THE ROLE OF PRODUCT DIFFERENTIATION AND OTHER VARIABLES IN OLIGOPOLISTIC COMPETITION

There are nine and sixty ways
of constructing tribal lays,
And every single one of them is right.
In the Neolithic Age.   Rudyard Kipling

1. INTRODUCTION

The analysis of non-co-operative static market models has been carried out in terms of firms selling undifferentiated products with no consideration of transportation costs, advertising, or other possible factors which affect even a static market.

Many important variables—such as product differentiation, transportation costs, and advertising—must eventually be introduced in the construction of a realistic dynamic theory of oligopoly. As a first approximation, if we do not change our assumptions concerning behavior, these added variables play much the same role in the non-co-operative market theory as friction does in the general thèory of motion. They modify the solutions obtained from models which leave them out of consideration. The specific effects they have are manifested in (1) changing (usually enlarging) the strategy space for each player; (2) changing the set of attainable prospects; and (3) changing the payoff functions. If we use the *same behavioristic assumptions* as before, we will get the same sort of solutions with these added features accounted for.

It may be argued that when we consider advertising, for instance, we must not only add variables or modify parameters of our models but must change the behavioristic assumptions as well.

For the most part the new variables introduced here transform the payoff functions and strategy spaces of the players in such a manner that if we wish to restrict ourselves to static theories (such as those of Cournot, Edgeworth, Nash, and the Chamberlin large-group theory) we merely obtain solutions which are quantitatively different but conceptually the same. The behavioristic assumptions in the theories noted are the same. The economic content, i.e., the number and nature of the variables used, varies in the different non-co-operative models, and it is for the reason of economic relevance that we may claim that Chamberlin's analysis is less unrealistic than that of Cournot.

In this chapter we have two goals. They are the study of the changes in the payoffs and available strategies in a single period caused by the new variables considered and a reconsideration of previous theory in light of this study. When these goals have been met we will be able to consider oligopoly in a dynamic structure, introduce new variables, and examine different theories of behavior.

Economic theories of market form and behavior have tended to stress equilibrium analysis. This static approach has been evident in the first part of this book. The effect of added variables with many transient states in dynamic models may be to produce nonequilibrating systems. The addition of new factors may bring a qualitative change as well as a quantitative change to a theory. This certainly appears to be true when we examine a dynamic theory of oligopoly and observe the limitations placed upon the plausibility of our behavioristic assumptions by the nature of information, corporate structure, and financial conditions. We postpone discussion of dynamics until Part Two.

2. DEMAND IN A GENERAL OLIGOPOLISTIC MARKET

Demand in an oligopolistic market depends upon a complex interaction of factors brought about by product differentiation, transportation costs, capacity limitations, and advertising.

In our study of price-variation duopoly in Chapter 5 great difficulty was encountered in formulating the demand conditions in the market. Using the theory of consumer's choice, a method was developed for calculating an individual's demand for a good, given that he was able to purchase an insufficient amount at a lower price. In order to calculate the residual market demand when one firm offered its product at a lower price than the other we had to specify a manner in which customers were served. By taking the foregoing steps we were finally able to construct the *contingent demand functions* for the duopolists. As we happened to study a market dealing in a homogeneous product and assumed that there were no frictions which prevented customer movement with changes in price, we obtained a family of contingent demand functions which had a discontinuity whenever the price of one duopolist changed from lower than to higher than that of his opponent. In this section we will generalize the problem and investigate the nature of contingent demand functions in an oligopolistic market with n firms, each with capacity limitations, product differentiation, and transportation costs. Advertising effects are dealt with later. It is evident from the complexities already encountered in deriving contingent demand in a duopolistic market that we cannot hope to obtain the complete contingent demand family in an oligopolistic market. For practical purposes this may not always matter. We are usually interested only in a very narrow pattern of the movement of demand in a dynamic oligopolistic setting. In many cases the kinked demand function may possibly serve as an adequate tool for the oligopolist or the economic theorist, if he specifies the manner in which he is able to construct such a curve. Before we discuss the dynamic kinked demand curves we can examine the implications of the theory of consumer choice for a static situation.

Suppose that there were n firms in a market, each selling a differentiated product. The differentiation may be caused by different services, transportation costs, or technically different products. If we wish to examine this market during one period, leaving out advertising and assuming that each firm traded in only one product, we must consider $2n$ variables, the n prices and n production rates of the competitors. We can write the demand function of a single competitor in two different ways, depending upon whether we wish to regard his output or his price as the independent variable. Regarding price as the independent variable we can write

$$(1) \qquad q_i = \phi_i(p_i; \; \tilde{\boldsymbol{q}}_i, \tilde{\boldsymbol{p}}_i),$$

in which $\tilde{\boldsymbol{q}}_i$ stands for q_i, q_2, q_3, $\ldots$, q_{i-1}, q_{i+1}, $q_{i+2} \ldots q_n$, and, similarly, $\tilde{\boldsymbol{p}}_i$ stands for an array of $r - 1$ prices p_j, with only the price p_i omitted. Regarding quantity as the independent variable we write

$$(2) \qquad p_i = \zeta_i(q_i; \; \tilde{\boldsymbol{q}}_i, \tilde{\boldsymbol{p}}_i).$$

For every fixed set of $2(n - 1)$ numbers, the prices and production rates of all other competitors, there will be a *contingent demand function* for player i. In other words, in order to describe completely the demand conditions faced by every single player we must consider a $2n$ dimensional diagram in which we hold $2(n - 1)$ numbers fixed for every possible combination of values they can take and then draw the two dimensional demand relation between the remaining price and quantity. Symbolically, a single contingent demand function with price as the independent variable can be expressed as

$$(3) \qquad q_i = \phi_i(p_i | \tilde{\boldsymbol{q}}_i = \tilde{\tilde{\boldsymbol{q}}}, \quad \tilde{\boldsymbol{p}}_i = \tilde{\tilde{\boldsymbol{p}}}_i),$$

where $\tilde{\tilde{\boldsymbol{q}}}_i$ and $\tilde{\tilde{\boldsymbol{p}}}_i$ are fixed values for $\tilde{\boldsymbol{q}}_i$ and $\tilde{\boldsymbol{p}}_i$. Similarly, if we take quantity as the independent variable, we may write

$$(4) \qquad p_i = \zeta_i(q_i | \tilde{\boldsymbol{q}}_i = \tilde{\boldsymbol{q}}_i, \; \tilde{\boldsymbol{p}}_i = \tilde{\tilde{\boldsymbol{p}}}_i).$$

We examine three major categories of contingent demand functions and several subcategories.

(1) Suppose that a group of firms is selling a homogeneous product and that each firm is capable of supplying the market by itself. Then, if a firm has a price lower than all the others, it faces the complete market demand; for a price higher than any other

firm it has no demand. The contingent demand curves resemble
the curve shown in Figure 31.

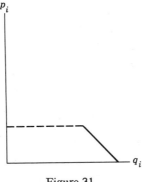

Figure 31

We consider that the firms are selling a homogeneous product
but that their capacities are limited (they may be unable or unwilling to supply more than a certain amount at the price they charge).
The contingent demand (with price as the independent variable)
may take on the form shown in Figure 32. Each discontinuity
occurs at a price charged by an opponent whose production does
not saturate the market remaining at that time. In order to be
able to specify the actual contingent demand we would need to

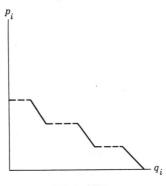

Figure 32

know the convention under which customers made their purchases
from the sellers. We have already noted this problem in Chapter 5:
2. It still exists here.

(2) Suppose that the product of each firm were absolutely unrelated to those of the other firms. In this case each firm could be regarded as an isolated monopolist. Whether a competitor has capacity limitations or not has no bearing upon the demand faced by the individual. He faces a normal two-dimensional demand function regardless of the prices or production rates of his opponents. This is shown in Figure 33. No monopolist's actions affect those of the others.

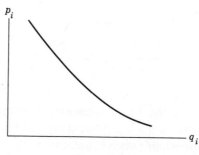

Figure 33

(3) If the goods are not perfect substitutes but there is some relationship between them and no firm has any capacity limitations, then a wide class of contingent demand functions may be obtained, the relevant shapes in any case depending upon the exact nature of the complementarity and substitutability relations between the products. If there are no discontinuities in the complementarity and substitutability relations, then we do not expect discontinuities to occur in the contingent demand. For example, Figure 34 illustrates a special case for a duopolist whose demand is given by $q_1 = 10 - \frac{3}{2}p_1 + (p_1^2 - p_1^3)/p_2$. There are no capacity limitations, and we assume that each duopolist has small costs and large inventories (i.e., he will always be motivated and able to fulfill any available demand). There is an inflection in the contingent demand functions at $p_1 = \frac{1}{3}$.[1] The demand relationship has the property that an increase in price causes a fall in demand.[2] Generally, if there are many firms in the market, we may expect any number of inflections and many shapes for the contingent demand functions.

If there are substitutability relations between the products and

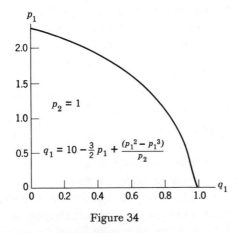

Figure 34

the firms have capacity limitations, we may expect kinks to occur in the contingent demand functions. Figure 35 illustrates an example computed by Roy Radner. This arises in a duopolistic market in which the competitors sell a homogeneous product but are spacially separated and add transportation costs to the prices they charge. Each producer is assumed to have a U-shaped average cost function. Details of this example, supplied by Radner, are given in Appendix C.

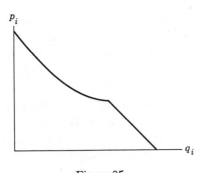

Figure 35

This brief discussion of contingent demand is given for two purposes. First, it bears directly on the results of the Edgeworth, Bertrand, and Chamberlinian theories of non-co-operative price-variation oligopoly; and, second, it helps us to understand certain aspects of the Chamberlinian small group theory and the other semidynamic theories involving kinky oligopoly demand curves. Once we have investigated these refinements to the static theories we will be in a position to start to construct a theory which includes asset and financial structure and the pattern of industrial control.

Our examination of the Edgeworth duopoly model in Chapter 5: 4 showed that the existence or nonexistence of a stable equilibrium point depends upon the presence of multiple maxima in the contingent revenue functions (see Figure 17). If there are maxima in the contingent revenue functions which yield as high or a higher profit than the maximum which occurs at the lowest price (see a' and c' in Figure 20), then the equilibrium is destroyed. Because of the great arbitrariness of the possible shapes for the contingent demand functions we have no way of knowing, in general, whether a unique equilibrium exists, multiple equilibria exist, or no equilibria exist. Even the condition that entry into competition is possible (by this Chamberlin means that a new firm may start to produce a close substitute [3]) does not necessarily improve the state of affairs, as may be inferred from Chapter 6: 2.3 and 2.4. We discuss this at greater length in subsection 3.2.

2.1. Static and Dynamic "Kinks" in Demand

Much of the confusion in economic theory and in legal attempts to dabble in economic theory has been caused by a refusal or inability to separate the physically measurable factors of a problem from the behavioristic factors. The kinky oligopoly curves used by Sweezy, Stigler, and others obviously contain components which are determined by the technological features of the firms, the nature of consumer demand, and the behavior of the firms in competition. We have noted in section 2 that to every $2n - 2$ fixed prices and production rates there will be an *objectively defined* contingent demand function relating the demand for the product of the remaining firm to the price charged by the remaining firm. We emphasise that this is objectively defined. We do not assume that the other firms are producing maximal rates or are in any sort of equilibrium; they may be overloaded with inventories, or they may have produced too little at the price they have chosen. However, they have made their choice and this is taken as given.

If we work out every possible contingent demand function to every player for every possible array of prices and outputs of his competitors, we will have described every possible *objective outcome* to any set of actions by all players. Furthermore, if we know the inventory loss functions and the cost functions of all players, then by combining this with the knowledge of contingent demand we will be able to describe objectively the payoffs which will be received by every player as the result of any set of actions taken by all players.

The kinky oligopoly demand curve describes a time path through the contingent demand space; in other words, it describes the demand conditions which will prevail, provided a behavioristic conjecture concerning the actions of the other players holds true. We express a Sweezy-type dynamic demand curve symbolically by

$$q_i(t) = \phi_i(p_i(t)|\tilde{\boldsymbol{p}}_i(t)),$$

which says, in words, that the demand faced by the ith individual at time t is determined by the physical conditions (i.e., the contingent demand space) and the strategies of all the other firms. Thus the "demand" function describes the state of the demand having taken into account the reactions of the others. This, of course, simplifies the study of oligopoly because it cuts down a complex demand problem through time into one simple curve.

Two problems must to be handled. First, are the behavioristic assumptions used to enable us to draw the kinked dynamic demand curve (with built in competitor reactions) valid? Second, given that we have made some behavioristic assumption and obtained a kinked demand curve, what does the firm maximize when faced with such an expected demand? Neither of these problems can be handled adequately without investigating the asset structure of the firms and their corporate and control structure. Sweezy and Stigler do not specify enough about the actual structure of the markets to which they wish to apply the kinky demand analysis. If they did, they would be able to justify their assumptions by demonstrating that the behavior of the particular firms being examined was constrained by technological, financial, and corporate facts within very narrow bounds. For instance, in competition between firms with high capitalization, high overhead, high substitutability of product, large funded debt, small owner equity, and majority stockholder control, a price cut by an opponent has to be met promptly if imminent bankruptcy is to be avoided.

In industries which lack this structure it is not easy to make a meaningful behavioristic assumption. In one case the behavior may be uniquely determined by the physical environment; in other cases, such as the outcome of a minor haggle between two unskilled and equally wealthy and disinterested bargainers, a psychological knowledge of the individuals may be required.

In the small group case Chamberlin's DD' curve is really a special type of kinked oligopoly demand curve for which the behavioristic assumption held by the few oligopolists is that if one cuts price all others will cut immediately.

The kinks, inflections, breaks, or discontinuities in these curves are caused by the capacity limitations of firms, in other words, the *supply conditions*, combined with the properties of substitutability and complementarity of goods as well as the effects of transportation costs. All these pathological conditions show up in the objectively defined contingent demand functions and are reflected in the kinked demand curves.

2.2. Transportation Costs, Product Variation, and Contingent Demand

In the remainder of this chapter we restrict ourselves to the static one-period analysis. The presence of transportation costs increases product differentiation and helps to delineate market areas. Formally, it causes a transformation of the contingent demand conditions. Practically, it also introduces several technical difficulties into the theory and measurement of market demand. These, together with a problem, are given in Note 4 at the end of this chapter.

It is evident that the effect of product variation upon a static market model can be formally accounted for by enlarging the strategy space of each player and enlarging and changing the payoff functions accordingly. The measure of the effect of product variation varies heavily from market to market. Commodity breakdowns into consumer durables, style goods, heavy industrial equipment, light industrial equipment, etc., have to be made before the appropriate modifications can be made to the strategy spaces and payoff functions.

In a static theory the importance of product variation, and its close relation, innovation, must remain hidden. The reason for and the nature of the vast expenditures by corporations on product variation and innovation is closely related to the nature of the financial, corporate, and legal structure of competition. This is discussed in Chapter 10.

3. ADVERTISING

Advertising has been treated in oligopoly theory as a cost and as a method for changing demand. Formally, if we discuss only the theory of firms in non-co-operative competition, we can incorporate advertising into the game model by enlarging the strategy space of each player and defining the new market demand functions as $q_i = \phi_i(p_i; \tilde{q}_i, \tilde{p}_i, a)$ where a stands for the array of advertising outlays $a_1, a_2, \ldots, a_n$. This tells us very little. The real problems raised by advertising lie in the investigation of demand under uncertainty and ignorance and also in the reasons why corporations are willing to compete via advertising rather than price.

We present a brief discussion of the demand problems caused by advertising. The reason for corporate competition via advertising and product differentiation rather than price is taken up in Chapter 10.

Chamberlin, in his discussion of selling costs, draws a distinction between two types of advertising — those which he classifies as manipulative in contradistinction to those which are informative. He maintains that the "distinction ... is perfectly clear analytically." [5] This is not at all so. The distinction may be clear in terms of most of our social backgrounds and moral opinions. On the other hand, we have been unable to formulate an operational distinction between the two because we do not know what we mean by rational or economic action in situations involving incomplete information. What is manipulative and what is informative is open to question. Chamberlin's distinction may suffice for some practical problems of economic policy, but it is not analytically precise.

In a subjective theory of value the demand for a product depends upon what buyers *think* it is worth to them. The buyer's desire for a particular good can be characterized as depending heavily upon his information state. Apropos of this observation, we comment upon the many attitudes toward advertising. Its proponents have called it "educational" and a useful medium for spreading information of value to the buyers, whereas its opponents have claimed that it is wasteful and misleading and not needed at all in a highly educated and "rational" community. The theory of consumer choice as presented by, say, Pareto, [6] Slutsky, [7] Hicks, [8] and Samuelson [9] has been essentially a theory of choice among a well-defined set of known alternatives. Under these conditions it is possible to attach meaning to a concept such as "rational action," and it is possible to define and discuss the acts of an "economic" man. As soon as a man is forced to choose between incompletely defined sets of alternatives, we must re-examine what is meant by rational action. If his choice sets include probability distributions, we are forced to consider an enlargement of the individual's choice scale to evaluate his reaction to risk. If an individual can pay to obtain more information about his choice sets, rational action must be enlarged to include methods of statistical decision and testing. [10] If choice sets contain blanks in the information, we must postulate some method to fill them in or approximate them (see Chapter 8), and the theory of rational or economic action, as discussed in most presentations of the theory of consumer choice, must incorporate a theory of learning.

Those opponents of advertising who feel that advertising would be unnecessary if men were rational or economic are referring implicitly to a world of complete information.

Given a world of incomplete information, it may very often pay entrepreneurs to misrepresent, distort, and confuse the facts by means of their information agencies, among which advertising is usually dominant. Thus, we have the housewife being told that "So-and-so's macaroni has more vitamin X in it per pound than an eight-ounce glass of orange juice," or that "Such-and-such is not another cleaner but a real soap." The aid to the consumer given by either of these statements is rather dubious, yet it is interesting to note that the value of supplying additional irrelevant, though correct, information is recognized in advertising.

The informational aspects of many economic situations are such that entrepreneurs may wish to make similar goods appear different, as in the case of soap advertising. The reverse procedure may also prove profitable. Attempts to make different goods appear the same are not unknown. In periods of rising food prices restaurants may adulterate their food yet advertise products of former quality. Many of the Federal Trade Commission cases concern misrepresentation. [11]

It is natural to expect a great difference between advertising methods and information flows put out by firms supplying consumer goods and those supplying factors of production. In the case of consumer goods the choice sets facing the purchasers are very broad and rather poorly known. The number of consumer goods has greatly increased, especially in the last thirty years or so, and comment that is often overheard is that the modern shopper knows very little about quality, whereas a generation or two ago the housewife was an expert on quality of many products. This may well be an old wives' tale. However, it is possible that the number of products faced by the modern consumer has grown to such an extent that an expert knowledge of only a very limited number can be expected.

Firms producing factors of production have to take into account the fact that most producers are technically competent and have a relatively well-defined choice set which is more or less determined by technical considerations. This means that it is more difficult for two firms producing heavy-duty electrical breakers to use advertising distortions with any financial success against their consumers than it is for two producers of cosmetics. The difference between advertising methods in trade journals and magazines of a popular nature may be cited in illustration. We can reformulate the distinction between the advertising problem for consumer goods and that for productive factors. For the most part, when selling factors of production the entrepreneur has to take his customers into account as actual participants in a relatively well-defined game in which there is quite a large amount of information present. If a producer were to make a gross exaggeration concerning one of his products, the consumers receiving this information would have enough background to be able to decide whether to reject it, accept it, or spend time and money investigating it. In a great many factor markets the complete oligopolistic structure of the buyers and sellers must be considered.

When selling consumer goods a firm may regard its customers as a mechanism, the behavior of which it hopes to predict through methods such as market research. The customers are not thought of as individual, economic maximizers, but rather as an aggregate which may be defined in sociological terms such as "the lower middle-class Italian housewife." This type of prediction model may be successful as long as the consumers do not think about communicating and organizing or that the costs of doing so are too high. The meaning of costs which are "thought" to be too high can be demonstrated in terms of a situation as seen by the participants and by an "umpire." The umpire, who is omniscient, understands that if the buyers spent 1000 dollars in organizing they could save themselves 1500 dollars. However, since each buyer has only his own information set from which he can infer, he may not know this. He may have no method of finding out, unless he is willing and able to buy extra information and has reasons to believe that it would be worth his while to do so.

4.   REBATES AND DISCOUNTS

There is a host of market phenomena which cannot be handled analytically by the static theory of non-co-operative games. Some of them may imply the existence of a certain amount of collusion between groups of sellers or buyers or both, whereas others may just amount to an enlargement of an individual's strategy space in a non-co-operative situation, although it is by no means clear that this is the case. The policies followed by dealers for automobile trade-in allowances may have elements of collusive practice. Yet trade-in allowances represent an enlargement in the type of strategies available and can be used in a highly competitive manner. A railroad's differential rates or rebate system (which is now illegal), base point pricing, such as "Pittsburgh plus," [12] zone pricing, and other transportation formulas are usually collusive, although in other cases, the act of a group of small firms agreeing to combine shipments in order to take advantage of quantity discounts or carload lot savings can hardly be called collusive. In fact, this type of external economy can be fitted into the non-co-operative game analysis.

In our brief discussion of additional market features we noted that some extra variables merely complicated the strategy and payoff spaces. Others, such as advertising and product variation, did this but also introduced extra problems concerning demand and brought up problems of corporate behavior which cannot be explained adequately within a static model.

As a final step in our analysis of static models, we will introduce the extra variables, already discussed, into the non-co-operative oligopoly models which have been presented in the previous chapters and examine the results we obtain.

5.   PRICE-VARIATION OLIGOPOLY WITH PRODUCT DIFFERENTIATION

5.1. PRICE DUOPOLY WITH PRODUCT DIFFERENTIATION

If the contingent demand functions faced by each firm in a price-variation duopoly happen to be continuous and without kinks, then it may be possible to solve for a non-co-operative Edgeworth, Chamberlinian, Nash equilibrium point (if it exists) by setting up two equations analogous to those used in Chapter 4.3.1 for the Cournot duopoly. Here, however, they must be set up in terms of price. Let $q_1 = \psi_1(p_1, p_2)$ and $q_2 = \psi_2(p_1, p_2)$ [13] be the demands for the first and second products expressed in terms of the prices of both. Then we can express the payoff function P_i of player i by

$$(5) \qquad P_i = p_i \psi_i(p_1, p_2) - C_i[\psi_i(p_1, p_2)],$$

where C_i is the total cost of production for player i. Setting $\partial P_i/\partial p_i = 0$, we obtain

$$\psi_i + p_i \frac{\partial \psi_i}{\partial p_i} = \frac{\partial C_i}{\partial \psi_i} \frac{\partial \psi_i}{\partial p_i},$$

or

$$\psi_i \left/ \frac{\partial \psi_i}{\partial p_i} \right. + p_i = \frac{\partial C_i}{\partial \psi_i},$$

which can be written as

$$(6) \qquad p_i(1 + e_{ii}) = \frac{\partial C_i}{\partial \psi_i},$$

where e_{ii} is the contingent elasticity of demand for the ith player's product as he varies price.

There are many difficulties concerning the formulation of these duopoly equations. Stigler, for instance, has used approximately the same equations as those given here. [14] However, he failed to note that they are not completely defined (see Note 13); that even if they were defined they are not usually differentiable; that if by luck they are differentiable the revenue functions may have multiple maxima caused by the shape of the contingent demand functions, which in turn may mean that no pure strategy equilibrium exists. These comments as well as the Cournot or quantity model with product differentiation are discussed in detail in Appendix C. [15]

5.2. PRICE-VARIATION OLIGOPOLY WITH PRODUCT DIFFERENTIATION AND ENTRY: THE CHAMBERLIN MODEL

We now consider the effect of entry upon the price model with product differentiation. Reference to Chapter 6: 2.3 and 2.4 will show that there is no real difference between the problem presented there and here. As before, we will get many equilibrium points, in general, if we get any. Chamberlin stresses [16] that new entrants will sell differentiated products; i.e., the products will not be absolutely identical with those of firms already producing. When we assume different cost structures for the various firms, as well as product differentiation, we can expect that there will be many possible final equilibrium positions with different groups of firms active or "in-being," depending upon the time path of entry. (This is not brought out in Chamberlin's work.)

We summarize our observations on Chamberlin's large-group adjustment theory:

(1) It is a behavioristic theory of the classical static type given by Cournot, Bertrand, and Edgeworth. All can be described as Nash non-co-operative games.

(2) It adds realism to the older analyses by stressing the importance of product variation, selling costs, and entry conditions. However, most of the importance of these variables lies in dynamics, and no real dynamic analysis is given. Entry conditions are not

discussed explicitly, financial conditions are not mentioned, and no one is told what the firms are meant to be maximizing.

(3) Chamberlin's use of his diagrams, especially his DD' and dd' curves, is inadequate. At the very least, they ignore all aspects of the supply side of oligopolistic demand (see section 2 of this chapter).

(4) It may be claimed that the Chamberlinian analysis is meant to be dynamic. A theory which does not mention inventory conditions, does not make explicit use of an interest rate structure, and does not investigate any explicit patterns of discounted income streams can hardly be interpreted as dynamic.

(5) The important result that at equilibrium excess capacity will exist is obtained by Chamberlin's extension of the classical theories of oligopolistic competition. However, other than that, it provides no theory of the distribution of resources, since the equilibrium it obtains will rarely be unique. The type of symmetry assumptions we usually load on a competitive market model to make everything unique and "nice" are precisely the assumptions that are, in general, nonsense in an oligopolistic market.

(6) Chamberlin appropriately calls his book monopolistic competition, thereby indicating that he is limiting himself to a very minor part of the problem of oligopoly. He leaves out an explicit analysis of collusion or co-operation, although it comes in implicitly and incompletely in his discussion of small-group equilibrium. This topic is dealt with in Chapter 10.

6. NON-CO-OPERATIVE STATIC THEORIES OF OLIGOPOLY

In Part One of this book, in the course of studying the nature of the strategy and payoff spaces in a single-period market in which different strategic variables are manipulated by the players, we have examined several basic models of oligopolistic competition. These theories all help to illustrate important strategic properties of different variables. But by themselves they are not sufficient to yield a very satisfactory explanation of oligopolistic competition. The underlying stress in these theories has been a concern with the "real" features of the economy. Production, allocation of factors, and sales in the market are discussed in detail. Inventories, production scheduling, distribution systems, assets, financing, and control of decision making are scarcely considered.

An understanding of economic market forms requires an understanding of economic power. In order to begin to understand the nature of economic power we must combine a study of the nerve system of control with the flow of finance and the apparently more physical movements of production and the markets.

NOTES

[1] This can be seen from the second derivative of the demand function with respect to p_1.

[2] It is sufficient to assume that the prices p_1 and p_2 are only defined above a minimum, say $\frac{1}{4}$.

[3] Edward H. Chamberlin, *The Theory of Monopolistic Competition*, (Cambridge: Harvard University Press, 6th ed., 1950) Chapter IV, p. 197.

[4] Population density estimates and the explicit nature of transportation charges must be added to our swelling list of relevant variables.

A number of interesting, but unsolved, problems connected with non-co-operative oligopoly models occur when transportation charges are considered. For example, assume several oligopolists are selling a homogeneous product to a market area in which transportation costs are an important factor. Each is free to choose the price he will charge and has the option of absorbing freight costs in whole or part. In each acts non-co-operatively, under what conditions will it pay to absorb all or part of the freight charges?

[5] Edward H. Chamberlin, *op. cit.*, pp. 121, 131.

[6] V. Pareto, *Manuel d'économie politique* (Paris: Girard 2nd. ed., 1957), Appendix.

[7] E. Slutsky, "Sulla Teoria del Bilancio del Consumatore," *Giornale degli Economisti*, LI (1915), 1–26 (translated by Olga Ragusa), reprinted in *Readings in Price Theory* (Chicago: R. D. Irwin, 1952), pp. 27–56.

[8] J. R. Hicks, *Value and Capital* (London: Oxford University Press, 1939), Part I.

[9] P. A. Samuelson, *Foundations of Economic Analysis* (Cambridge: Harvard University Press, 1948), Chapter V.

[10] See A. Wald, *Statistical Decision Functions* (New York: Wiley 1950); also, D. Blackwell, and M. A. Girshick, *Theory of Games and Statistical Decisions* (New York: Wiley, 1954).

[11] See the Federal Trade Commission's news summaries or press releases from its Office of Information.

[12] A. R. Burns, *The Decline of Competition* (New York: McGraw-Hill, (1936), pp. 280–328.

[13] Strictly speaking, these functions are not completely defined until the

capacity conditions of the firms are stated. This technical point is taken up in Appendix C.

14 G. J. Stigler, "Notes on a Theory of Duopoly," *Journal of Political Economy*, **XLVIII** (1940), 521–541, especially p. 535.

15 We will see that all the difficulties faced in formalizing the price duopoly models arise when we introduce product differentiation into the Cournot duopoly model.

16 E. H. Chamberlin, *op. cit.*, pp. 196–197.

PART TWO

The Dynamics of Oligopoly:
Mathematical Institutional Economics

chapter 8

THE ROLE OF INFORMATION IN THEORIES OF COMPETITION AND OLIGOPOLY

The worst use of theory
is to make men insensible to fact
Lord Acton

1. INTRODUCTION: MATHEMATICAL INSTITUTIONAL ECONOMICS

The subtitle of Part Two, "Mathematical Institutional Economics," has been chosen in order to emphasize the viewpoint of this writer that there is a general theory of oligopolistic market forms which is mathematical but that the specific application of this theory to the market form and the nature of competition between any group of firms requires considerable empirical investigation *before* it is worthwhile specifying the behavioristic assumptions to be made about "leader-follower" relations, time lags, adjustments, and other conjectural hypotheses. The theory of pure competition has so many simplifying assumptions that if they were to hold true the hypothesis made concerning the behavior of an individual in a purely competitive market would appear to be reasonable. Once we are given these we are in a position to discuss the growth and decay of competitive industries in the short run and in the long run without having to worry too much about factual detail. Broadly speaking, if competitors are many and small, entry is free, products barely differentiated, and costs rising, behavioristically one competitive market will be the same as another, and economics is then reduced to the problem of mapping out a general adjustment process. Once we abandon the simplifying assumptions of pure competition we observe that the reasonability of a hypothesis concerning the behavior of individuals in different markets depends very heavily upon the objective background of the market. We expect that the price-cutting policies of two street vendors of fruit on a hot day will be somewhat different from those exhibited by two corporations selling heavy machinery and each having many millions of dollars tied up in a fixed plant.

There is every need for the construction of a general theoretical framework which provides us with the apparatus to study the nature of any action and the meaning of any contingency that may arise in any market. There appears to be little need to add to the list of reaction functions without specifying the group of firms that is meant to act in the manner suggested and without substantiating the claim.

Before we attempt to erect the apparatus necessary for the examination of market forms in a dynamic setting we must take several preliminary steps. In the remainder of this chapter we discuss the role of information conditions in theories of market behavior. This is necessary because so much theory has been implicitly based on the assumptions of rational choice under complete information, or, when this is not the case, the information conditions assumed have been implicit rather than explicit. In some cases, of course, information conditions do not really matter. If the Cournot duopolists choose to act as perfect idiots, their behavior is independent of their information state. However, the state of information may be a determining factor of primary importance in some markets. The logical problems posed in attempting to define rational action under limited information are many and vexatious. We may be able to solve few of them in any general way. At least we can try to specify them and avoid the type of barren and unnecessary paradoxes such as those posed in the economic writings on perfect foresight.

2. LACK OF INFORMATION

New methods of processing information, new automatic machines, tabulating methods, and new information agencies are coming into existence at an ever-increasing pace. Special information is often the key to new markets or the factor which enables a firm to keep a "jump ahead of the crowd." Information concerning new designs, production, costing, or inventory methods are among the most closely guarded secrets of industry. The corporation or firm operates in a welter of uncertainty and halfknowledge under conditions that sometimes make special information its most valuable asset.

In a letter to Malthus Ricardo [1] wrote:

It would be no answer to me to say that men were ignorant of the best and cheapest mode of conducting their business and paying their debts, because that is a question of fact, not of science, and might be urged against almost every proposition in Political Economy.

It would be maligning the name of this great general theorist and practical man to imply from this that Ricardo, a stockbroker, was not aware of the role of information. However, it is the opinion of this writer that, at least in the study of "propositions of Political Economy" concerned with market forms, not only can the question of the state of information and ignorance be urged against the propositions, it should be.

The theories of individual demand and action of the individual firm as they are presented today are, for the most part, more or less theories of "rational action under complete information." It is assumed that the individual always knows fairly well what he wants and also is subjectively certain of the consequences for him of all the alternative paths of action open to him. This feature is brought to the surface when we compare verbal and mathematical presentations of the same theory. The mathematically stated theories often assume that the individual is completely informed about every choice alternative faced (i.e., his indifference maps are completely known), and the firm is at least completely informed about the nature of its average cost function. The verbal theories make these assumptions implicitly. The little empirical work that has been done in economics seems to indicate that both of these assumptions are false. For example, the usefulness of the new linear programming methods that have come into economics recently is not due to the fact that the industrial processes of any form are of a linear nature but that a linear approximation is probably the only one that is economic to take. In other words, it may cost more than it is worth to find out more precisely what a firm's production function actually looks like.

These comments do not necessarily invalidate the use of the current theories of individual choice and action of the individual firm. They just have to be looked at in a different light. We may regard them as sets of logical propositions based upon assumptions which appear on an a priori basis to be worthwhile studying but which offer little encouragement to those who would like to find a close correspondence between actions observed in some parts of the economic world and actions predicted by such theories.

In order to construct a theory of economic action which might merit testing we may be able to use the theories mentioned as a point of reference and examine the changes or modifications which appear to be called for.

We have suggested that the theories of consumer behavior and of production for the firm are theories of "rational action of the individual under complete information." The game treatment of competition and collusion presented in Part One rests, for the most part, on the assumption of complete information [2] and may be described as a theory of "rational action of competing individuals under conditions of complete information," i.e., under the assumption of complete information about the individual payoffs (which amounts to knowledge of all cost functions and the contingent demand schedules). Why and how should a modification of the information conditions take place? Could it not be that the multiplicity of actions available to an individual under complete information would be lessened if his information were lessened? Action in the market involves information flows, confer-

ences, telephone calls, investigations, paper work, research, inter-
views, and bargaining. All these cost time and money and as such
must enter directly into cost and revenue computations. We must
investigate whether or not the cost of making choices is sufficiently
large to have an effect on the individual's actions. We turn
now to the discussion of information and communication expenses.

3. COSTS OF INFORMATION

When costs are introduced and attached to communications
and information they quickly put bounds at least upon short-run
coalition possibilities. Consider a firm [3] as an organization designed
to obtain, process, store, and act on information. With this as
our starting point, let us examine the simple sort of economic
n-person game, outlined in Part One, in which we assumed that
all talk, knowledge, and communication were free; hence we did
not even bother to look at the amounts involved. We can work out
the bounds for complete information and communication in order
to see how they grow with n. The problem of taking aggregates
and operating with less information is discussed later.

Information storage is examined first. We assume that any
firm has a given finite upper bound to its capacity for storing
information. This storage can be regarded as an ability to keep a
certain amount of numbers. Let this amount for a particular firm
be I_i. Let the ith player have σ_i strategies open to him. (These
can be regarded as decisions to produce 10, 11, 12, ..., goods to
bring to the market.) Then the total amount of numbers needed
for complete knowledge of the number of possibly different payoffs
in an n-person normalized game is

$$n \prod_{i=1}^{n} \sigma_i.$$

If we considered, just for purposes of illustration, that each player
had the same number of strategies k, then this becomes nk^n.
As the number of people in the game increases, the ratio of information that a firm can store in comparison to the amount that it

needs for complete knowledge is

$$\frac{I_i}{n \prod\limits_{i=1}^{n} \sigma_i}, \text{ or in the simpler case } \frac{I_i}{nk^n}.$$

This ratio goes to zero asymptotically at a very rapid rate. If there were two players in the game and each had ten strategies, then two hundred numbers would have to be stored. Increase the number of players to ten, and 100,000,000,000 numbers are required for complete information.

The firm will have an upper limit on the amount of information it can obtain. Let one number represent an observation or computation. If we assume that there is no trouble involved in gathering information, other than making a telephone call to the bureau of statistics, noting down the information, and handing it to the information storage section, we have a problem of the same order of magnitude as that in the storage section. Actually, it will be much worse because the obtaining of information is rarely as simple as the method outlined. [4] If the upper bound to the firm's ability to obtain information is P_i, the proportion that it can handle to the amount that it needs is

$$\frac{P_i}{n \prod\limits_{i=1}^{n} \sigma_i}, \text{ or in the simpler case } \frac{P_i}{nk^n}.$$

Once the firm has obtained and stored all the numbers it needs it must process them. For instance, if the firm is to take advantage of the fine structure of coalition possibilities that exists in the von Neumann and Morgenstern solution, it must evaluate the power of every possible coalition that can be formed. If there are n players, each firm must evaluate all possible combinations which give

$$\sum_{r=1}^{n} {}_nC_r - 1, \text{ or } 2^n - 1$$

(not counting the empty coalition), numbers that must be processed and evaluated from the data on hand.

We can see quickly even without this method of *reductio ad absurdum* that certain theories based upon complete information or which try to correct for the lack of complete information by behavioristic assumptions not generally true (or never true) are of little use to the applied problem of investigating market forms unless the appropriate corrections and modifications are made. As an example we cite the von Neumann and Morgenstern theory of solution to a general n-person game. It appears to be of use in the investigation of certain general problems in pure economic theory, as suggested elsewhere. [5] It is also of use in some specialized problems, but, in the estimation of this writer, it may not be directly useful in a theory which is concerned with the explicit form of markets and oligopolistic behavior. [6]

Three conditions on information and communication have been examined; namely, gathering, storing, and processing information as well as communicating. [7] They all appear to involve an increase of numbers with the nth power, where n is the number of players. It is evident that a theorist must demonstrate why the conditions do not matter for his theory, how he approximates for their effect, or where the applied economist can correct the theory to fit the facts and still have a nonvacuous use for it.

Practical consideration of these effects calls for an investigation of the roles of trade journals, trade associations, market research boards, and business forecast agencies. We pursue this investigation further in Chapter 11.

4.   INFORMATION AND THE CONDITIONS FOR PURE COMPETITION: PERFECT KNOWLEDGE

This section is included in order to indicate the difficulties that can be encountered and the confusion generated by an incomplete specification of information conditions.

The distinction has often been drawn between pure and perfect competition. [9] The following phrases are used as their authors use them.

Knight suggests that, "Chief among the simplifications of reality prerequisite to the achievement of perfect competition is, as has been emphasized all along, the assumption of *practical omniscience* on the part of every member of the competitive system." [10] Morgenstern [11] has pointed out many of the logical difficulties involved in an assumption of this nature, yet very little formal analysis of the information aspects of pure competition has been made.

That such statements as Enke's comment, "The orthodox theory of the firm granted *perfect knowledge of present and future* comprises a set of logical propositions which are in themselves irrefutable," are still made in the literature is certainly an indication of the lack of precision extant even now. [12] The joker in the above sentence is what is meant by perfect knowledge of present and future.

Chamberlin differentiates between pure and perfect competition. He maintains that the word "perfect" implies such things as "an absence of friction in the sense of an ideal fluidity or mobility of factors such that adjustments to changing conditions which actually involve time are accomplished instantaneously in theory. It *may imply perfect knowledge of the future* and the consequent absence of uncertainty." [13]

Stigler [14] offers as his conditions for perfect competition the following statement:

The basic requirements for perfect competition, it will be recalled, are three: (1) All economic units (i.e., households, firms, owners of resources) are so small as to exert no perceptible influence on prices; (2) there are no social restrictions on the mobility of resources or on prices; and (3) *all individuals possess complete knowledge*.

What is this *perfect knowledge* that is mentioned in the quotations above? Can we define it in such a manner that it is consistent with our intuitive idea of what we mean by pure competition?

(1) In its strongest meaning we have all competitors not only knowing all prices, cost functions, and other facts in the economy but also what everyone else is going to do. Suppose that *ab initio* everyone decided randomly to charge a monopoly price; then this price would be stable unless people were allowed to change their minds once they knew what the others were doing, in which case the others would not have complete information of the type assumed. Hence either everyone knows what everyone else is going to do, in which case the monopoly price is stable, or we must break our assumption concerning the meaning of *perfect knowledge*. J. M. Clark has pointed this out. [15]

(2) *Perfect knowledge* may mean that every individual knows

all the price functions and cost functions in the economy. He knows the value of every situation to everyone, but, apart from knowing that all are trying to maximize for themselves, no man knows what action the other is going to take. This is a game situation with complete information concerning payoffs given. We have discussed in the first parts of this chapter the improbability that firms will have this amount of information in a market in which there are many competitors. It is too expensive and it requires far too much detail to be handled by the individual firm. Let us suppose, however, that the firms had this information. Then it is highly likely that no matter how many firms were involved, unless the costs of combining were prohibitive, combinations would be formed. The *more information there is in a market, the more likely it is that combinations will result.* We stress that, given complete information of the type postulated here, combinations may be formed, unless coalition costs are high, no matter how many individuals there are in the market. [16]

(3) *Perfect knowledge* may mean only the knowledge by the entrepreneur of his own cost function and a knowledge of the last or current market price. Although this is hardly what one would expect to come under the title of perfect knowledge, it is far more reasonable than the previous assumptions. (Attempts by this writer to discover an empirically given cost function for an industrial activity indicate that firms probably do not know very much about even their own cost functions, except around their usual operating level.)

Three different meanings have been given to perfect knowledge. The first is meaningless [17] or, if modified to be meaningful, is certainly not necessary to the existence of pure competition. In fact, it is compatible with joint monopolistic pricing. The second is not necessary to the existence of pure competition and is implausible in the absence of explicit conditions indicating why collusion should not take place between completely informed entrepreneurs. The third is satisfactory from the point of view of motivation (i.e., lack of information and costs of obtaining it stand in the way of collusion) but hardly appears to conform with the spirit of the quotations on perfect knowledge. [18]

5. GAMES AGAINST "NATURE"

Fortune brings in some boats that are not steer'd.

Cymbeline, Scene 3, Line 46.

5.1. ACTION UNDER CONDITIONS OF LOW INFORMATION

It appears more natural to regard action in a market which is almost purely competitive as being action under low rather than high information conditions. We can formalize a market model of this as an *n*-person non-co-operative game in which players are not completely informed about the rules. If each player knows only his own costs and some of the previous prices ruling in the market, then neither non-co-operative game theory nor the theory of competition give conditions which are satisfactory in general to describe the attainment of an equilibrium.

Knight has made the distinction between risk and uncertainty [19]. His concept of uncertainty is related to uninsurability. We break down the Knightian uncertainty into two categories. The term *behavioristic uncertainty* refers to a state in which a player may be completely informed about the rules of the game, i.e., his own environment, but he does not know what type of behavior he can expect from his opponents. Even Lloyds might have been unwilling to insure Androcles against the lion at a reasonable premium, although the rules of the game were completely known. The other Knightian uncertainty can best be described as *ignorance*. This occurs when a player does not know all the rules of the game. He does not know some of his payoff values. We illustrate the differences in information conditions by examples.

1. *Perfect Information.* Chess or checkers are games with complete information concerning the rules and with no secret moves by either player, i.e., no moves of which the other player is not immediately informed. They have (at least in theory) pure strategy solutions. There is no risk or uncertainty of any type involved in playing (this, of course, is only theoretically true because no human being can possibly perform the calculations to make chess or checkers a "sure thing").

2. *Complete Information.* Roulette is a game with complete

information, but, since there is a chance move in the play (whose probabilities are known), it also involves *risk*.

3. *Complete Information in a General n-Person Game.* In Part One we describe oligopolistic markets by means of general n-person, single-period games with complete information. [20] We assume that all players are informed about all technological features of the market. We define an equilibrium point and then proceed to investigate the equilibria in various models. Each player has complete information concerning the rules of the game, and risk is present in the sense that players can use mixed strategies. However, the Knightian concept of uncertainty appears, not in the description of the game, but in the description of its solution. In order to talk about equilibrium points we have had to make behavioristic assumptions concerning the actions of individuals in the market. By doing this we assume away *behavioristic uncertainty*.

4. *Ignorance.* Consider a game in which a player is told that he must choose the number 1 or 2. In the next room another player or a machine will choose the number 1 or 2. When a pair of numbers has been chosen a payoff will be awarded to the player. The payoff matrix for the player is

	1	2
1	10	-15
2	-13	?

He knows three of his four possible payoffs. He does not know the payoffs of his opponent. In fact, he does not even know if his opponent is another human, being an animal, or a machine. This game involves both behavioristic uncertainty and ignorance.

Almost all markets contain elements of these uncertainties. A purely competitive market, as suggested in the foregoing, is such that the players do not know everything about each other's payoff. There is a considerable degree of *ignorance* present. The players do not know the behavior patterns of their opponents. However, economists make the assumption that each individual *behaves* as though he has no influence on price. Whether this assumption is correct and truly removes the behavioristic uncertainty can be answered only by observation. It appears to be a reasonable assumption, although in some cases, as the literature on the "cobweb theorem'' [20] and the hog cycle indicates, it implies that individual actions add up to aggregate idiocy and dynamic instability.

There has been considerable recent mathematical and statistical investigation of behavior under conditions of partial or complete ignorance. A literature has sprung up on the subjects of *games against nature* (or games against an unknown adversary) and *statistical decision making*. The mathematical models discussed in games against nature are very simple. They have the advantage that they illustrate the difficulties in more complex problems, and they enable us to see the merit or the weakness of certain behavioristic assumptions used to resolve the indeterminacy present.

5.2. GAMES AGAINST NATURE

A game against nature can be described as follows: A player must choose a strategy in a game played against an unknown opponent whose payoff matrix is also unknown. The terminology of L. J. Savage [21] is more natural to this type of problem than the usual game-theory terms. An individual must choose an act which will yield him a payoff according to the true state of nature at the time he selects his act. He is not aware of the true state of nature. The game of picnic illustrates the formal scheme. Abstracting from the ants, we build a simplified model of the picnic decision problem:

	State of Nature	
Acts	Rain	Shine
Picnic	-10	10
Stay home	0	-5

There are two acts, two possible states of nature, and four outcomes. Each outcome is associated with a utility value to the decision maker. The four entries in the matrix are his evaluations for the four outcomes.

Many ways to solve the problem of action under ignorance have been suggested. Among them are the *maximin principle*, the *minimization of regret*, the *Bayesian principle*, and the *principle* of *insufficient reason*. Hurwicz has suggested a principle that combines the consideration of the best and worst possible outcomes, [22] and Shackle has presented an original theory based upon *potential surprise*. [23] The meaning and examples of the first three conventions are given here. For the remainder the reader is referred to Arrow, [24] Milnor, [25] and especially Luce and Raiffa, [26] who present a detailed discussion of games against nature.

We may regard a purely competitive market as a game against nature by letting the *act* of a player be the selection of an output and the *states of nature* the prices which can rule in the market after the player (and all the other classical wheat farmers or hog raisers) has chosen his production rate. We consider a specific example in which there are three states of nature (low, middling, and high price for wheat) and three acts among which the farmer must choose (different rates of production). The payoff matrix is given in Table 10.

Table 10

State of Nature

Acts	Low Price	Medium Price	High Price	Row Minima
Low production	6	8	10	6
Medium production	8	12	16	8
High production	6	12	18	6
Column maxima	8	12	18	

The maximin principle is very conservative. It works on the assumption that nature is always malevolent. Nature will always try to provide rain if the statistician tries to go on a picnic. In the example given the farmers expect a low price and hedge accordingly. We observe that the matrix has a saddle-point given by two pure strategies (see Chapter 1: 2). No cobweb effects would be produced by these pessimistic farmers.

The minimization of regret principle is also conservative but of a different type. Savage has suggested that businessmen may wish to minimize their disappointment. They may wish to minimize the difference between the amount they actually obtained and the amount they would have obtained if they had known in advance what nature would do, and had adopted the appropriate strategy. The regret matrix is obtained by replacing each entry in the original payoff matrix by a number which is the maximum column element minus the entry. For column J the entries become $\max(a_{i,J}) - a_{i,J}$, where $a_{i,J}$ stands for the payoff from the ith act and Jth state of nature. The regret matrix for the example in Table 10 is given in Table 11. For the sake of abbreviation we identify the acts and states of nature by numbers.

Table 11

	1	2	3	Row maxima
1	2	4	8	8
2	0	0	2	2
3	2	0	0	2
Column minima	0	0	0	

We observe that there is no saddle-point defined by two pure strategies in this example. We have noted the row maxima and column minima because the roles of the players are reversed in comparison with our previous examples. The player wishes to *minimize* regret. In order to solve for the mixed strategies used by the player and nature we use the procedure outlined in Chapter 1:2 for games in which both sides have only two strategies. We can do this because by looking at this matrix we are able to reject one strategy from the set of each player, knowing that it will never be played. The player, farmer, or statistician will never use his first strategy, regardless of the outcome, because he will always do as well or better by using his second and third acts. Nature will reject her second strategy, regardless of what the player does, because she can be equally or more malevolent by using her third strategy instead of her second. Solving the remaining 2×2 game we obtain the mixed strategies of $(0, \frac{1}{4}, \frac{3}{4})$ for the player and $(\frac{3}{4}, 0, \frac{1}{4})$ for nature. The player obtains a "regret value" of $\frac{3}{2}$. Sometimes he hedges too closely and is caught with medium production in a high market; at other times he risks a high production rate. In actual profits the player makes between $\frac{1}{4}(8) + \frac{3}{4}(6) = 6\frac{1}{2}$ or $\frac{1}{4}(16) + \frac{3}{4}(18) = 17\frac{1}{2}$. Compared with 8 in the first example, his expected profit is $(6\frac{1}{2})(\frac{3}{4}) + (17\frac{1}{2})(\frac{1}{4}) = 9\frac{1}{4}$.

Utilizing the third principle, the Bayesian principle, the player assigns an *a priori* distribution to what he expects nature to do. He maximizes his expected income on this assumption. If the player expects the market price to remain the same as it was in the last period, we may obtain the familiar economic model of the wheat farmers chasing prices through periods of overproduction and underproduction.

In most economic situations each entrepreneur usually has some hypothesis about his market based upon his previous experience and information. The first two principles assume nothing except that nature is out to ruin the player. The third principle does not suffer from this drawback. However, it involves us in a discussion of the meaning of subjective probability (see Savage [27]).

5.3. A PROBLEM IN INVESTMENT IN INNOVATION

A very important problem which amounts to a game against nature is found when we consider a firm faced with eventual bankruptcy if its affairs continue in the manner in which they have been going; but it is in a position to take a risk by putting into production an innovation. [28] If the innovation sells, it will yield a high return, and, if it does not, the firm will be damaged more heavily than otherwise. We consider a simple situation in which, if the firm continues in its present line, it will be ruined in two periods, no matter what happens; if it innovates and is successful, it will make a profit; if it is unsuccessful, it will be ruined in one period. For any one period we may have this payoff matrix:

	Poor Market for Innovation	Good Market for Innovation
Innovate	-1	1
Do nothing	$-\frac{1}{2}$	$-\frac{1}{2}$

Suppose that the entrepreneur were ruined if he lost one or more by the end of the second period. If we ignore the effect of the rate of interest on the discounted value of next year's revenue, we can replace this two-period sequential game against nature by the single matrix game in which nature has four strategies and the entrepreneur has three. If the entrepreneur innovates in the first period, then we assume that he has committed himself for the second period as well. Denote "innovate" by I and "do nothing" by N. His strategies then are II, NI, and NN. Denote a poor market by F and a good one by S. Then nature's strategies are FF, FS, SF, and SS. This gives us this matrix:

	FF	FS	SF	SS
II	-2	0	0	2
NI	$-1\frac{1}{2}$	$\frac{1}{2}$	$-1\frac{1}{2}$	$\frac{1}{2}$
NN	-1	-1	-1	-1

The maximin strategy against this action is for the entrepreneur never to risk. The value of the game to him is -1, and he is ruined in two periods. If we form the regret matrix, we have

	FF	FS	SF	SS
II	1	$\frac{1}{2}$	0	0
NI	$\frac{1}{2}$	0	$1\frac{1}{2}$	$1\frac{1}{2}$
NN	0	$1\frac{1}{2}$	1	3

A strategy for the entrepreneur is mixed and is $(\frac{1}{2}, 0, \frac{1}{2})$; his expected "regret" is $\frac{3}{4}$. Nature plays $(\frac{3}{4}, 0, 0, \frac{1}{4})$.

If we used a Bayes principle postulating that the four strategies of nature were equiprobable, then the entrepreneur would invest immediately and have an expected profit of 0.

We see that the three conventions give us three different answers to this simple problem. There are several features that have not been accounted for in the foregoing models which might help to clarify the problem. We have restricted the strategies of the entrepreneur quite heavily. A realistic enlargement here would be to include a cost and a possibility of doing market research. This would enlarge his strategy space to twelve instead of three strategies if he had a choice of research or no research at every period. A careful specification of the financial restraints on the firm might also help. For instance, if the creditors were closing in, the firm might not be permitted to risk losing more than one.

None of the conventions is infallible. The major test for their use is this question: Do they provide "reasonable" resolutions to our problems (also are there criteria to judge the "reasonability" of a result)?

6. CONCLUSIONS

Pure theory can aid us in clearing up some of the conceptual difficulties met in trying to understand the nature of action under ignorance. Several criteria for action have been suggested. None is useful for general application. The best that an economist can hope to do at this time is to try to specify the information conditions in the market he wishes to study and then use the criteria which appear to apply.

An interesting problem is posed by information conditions in cases of trade restriction. A market may exhibit certain features of collusive action, such as high price and restricted production. Yet upon examination the officers of the corporations will claim that although the *ex post* observations are correct, the *ex ante* picture is fraught with uncertainty, that the firms did not collude but merely were conservative in their policies. We cannot sort out the two explanations of motivation which are possible here. However, if observation indicates that the firms had a fairly steady demand for many years, then it may be argued that collusion becomes a more plausible explanation than conservatism.

NOTES

[1] James Bonar, ed., *Letters of Davido Ricard to Thomas Robert Malthus, 1810–1823* (Oxford: Clarendon Press, 1887), p. 18.

[2] J. von Neuman, and O. Morgenstern, *Theory of Games and Economic Behavior* (Princeton: Princeton University Press, 3nd ed., 1953), p. 30.

[3] M. Shubik, "Information, Theories of Competition, and the Theory of Games," *The Journal of Political Economy*, **LX** (April 1952), pp. 145–150.

[4] "Of course competitive data are not easy to obtain. Competitors are notoriously cagey about publishing their sales figures in convenient form for other's analysis." J. W. Redfield, "Elements of Forecasting," *Harvard Business Review*, **XXVIII**, No. 6 (November 1950).

"When a corporation operates in a number of states, the expense and trouble of rendering the required information may be considerable. Businessmen frequently prefer secrecy, feeling that the information divulged may be of advantage to competitors or have an undesirable effect upon their relations with the public." H. G. Guthmann, and H. E. Dougall, *Corporate Financial Policy* (New York: Prentice-Hall, 2nd ed., 1948), p. 21.

[5] M. Shubik, Edgeworth Market Games in R. D. Luce and A. W. Tucker, eds., *Contributions to the Theory of Games* (Princeton: Princeton University Press 1959) **IV**.

[6] This criticism may not hold for markets with only four or five firms in which coalition possibilities are relatively few and information conditions high.

[7] Dr. R. Richter has also suggested that the costs of preparing alternative strategies may be considerable.

[8] The difference appears to be that *pure competition* is the best of all logically possible worlds, whereas *perfect competition* is the best of all logically impossible worlds (it involves an infinite regression). This point has been noted by Marschak in his classification of miracles. He distinguishes between those which are mere physical impossibilities and those which are logically impossible.

[9] Italics mine. F. H. Knight, *Risk, Uncertainty and Profit* (London: London School Reprints of Scarce Works, No. 16, 1933), p. 197.

[10] Italics mine. O. Morgenstern, "Perfect Foresight and Economic Equilibrium" (translation), *Zeitschrift für National Ökonomie*, **VI**, Part 3 (1935).

[11] Stephen Enke, "On Maximizing Profits," *American Economic Review*, **XLI**, No. 4 (September 1951), p. 578.

[12] Italics mine. Edward H. Chamberlin, *The Theory of Monopolistic Competition* (Cambridge: Harvard University Press, 6th ed., 1950), p. 6.

[13] Italics mine. G. J. Stigler, *The Theory of Price*, p. 197.

[14] J. M. Clark, *Studies in the Economics of Overhead Cost* (Chicago: University of Chicago Press, 1923), p. 417.

[15] In order to establish this point we have to specify entry and policing conditions and then show that in some markets it may not pay any individual to double-cross the others. Trade unions provide examples of such market situations.

[16] The first criterion can be made meaningful if we assume that all players are informed about each other's strategies after they have been picked and no one is allowed to change. This amounts to a model which has threats of the type suggested by Nash. Otherwise, the condition must be interpreted as leading to an infinite regression.

[17] For further discussion on information and uncertainty see M. Shubik, "Information, Risk, Ignorance, and Indeterminacy," *Quarterly Journal of Economics*, **LXVIII** (November 1954), pp. 629–640.

[18] F. H. Knight, *op. cit., passion*.

[19] Actually, if we wish to interpret the non-co-operative theories to be those which explicitly assume the unrealistic classical behavioristic assumptions, we can relax the complete information condition.

[20] Louis H. Bean, "The Farmers' Response to Price," *Journal of Farm*

Economics, **XI** (July 1929), pp. 368–385. See also Mordecai Ezekiel, "The Cobweb Theorem," *The Quarterly Journal of Economics* (February 1938), pp. 255–280.

[21] L. J. Savage, *The Foundations of Statistics* (New York: Wiley, 1954), Chapter II.

[22] L. Hurwicz, "Some Specification Problems and Applications to Econometric Models" (abstract) *Econometrica*, **XIX** (July 1951), pp. 343–344.

[23] G. L. S. Shackle, *Expectations in Economics* (Cambridge: Cambridge University Press, 1949), p. 3.

[24] K. J. Arrow, "Alternative Approaches to the Theory of Choice in Risk-Taking Situations," *Econometrica*, **XIX** (October 1951), 404–437.

[25] J. W. Milnor, "Games Against Nature," in R. M. Thrall, C. H. Coombs, and R. L. Davis, eds., *Decision Processes* (New York: Wiley, 1954), pp. 49–59.

[26] R. D. Luce, and H. Raiffa, *Games and Decisions* (New York: Wiley, 1957) Chapter XII.

[27] L. J. Savage, *op. cit.*, p. 30.

[28] I am indebted to John Chipman who suggested the treatment of this problem as a game against nature.

chapter 9

THE EXTENSIVE FORM OF A GAME: A PRELIMINARY TO DYNAMICS

1. THE ECONOMIC MEANING OF THE EXTENSIVE FORM OF A GAME

Part One deals with static models of highly simplified markets. It offers at best a limited study of the basic anatomy of the market. Chapter 7 adds a certain amount of flesh to the skeleton. The objective background of a single period game is, at least in theory, totally described. In other words, given the strategies of all players, we have been able to specify the payoff associated with any set of strategies. This payoff depends upon the number of players, costs, product differentiation, transportation, and a host of other directly observable market features.

On occasion we have discussed some of the models in Part One as though we were describing a dynamic path to an equilibrium. In reality, the dynamic aspects of the theory in Part One are only "conversational." It is foolish to entertain the delusion that the Cournot, Edgeworth, Chamberlinian, or other "reaction-curve" assumptions are good approximations of non-co-operative behavior in the market *and* that we can leave all aspects of asset and corporate structure safely assumed away in a *ceteris paribus* condition and still come out with a useful theory of oligopoly.

Before we are in a position to examine the detailed meaning and effect of any type of behavioristic assumption or reaction curve we must be able to describe with reasonable verisimilitude the salient observable features of a market in a dynamic setting. In Chapter 8 we have already noted the many problems that are posed by limited information. Before we can take account of all of them we set ourselves the easier task of describing the setting or objective background of a market in which trading takes place through many periods and in which at least we, if not the competitors, have all the information concerning costs, demand, interest rates, time lags, product differentiation and other non-behavioristic features of the market. In order to do this we must divide our problem into three stages. In the first stage we are able to describe in detail a game which has many moves but a definite maximum fixed length of play and only one payoff at the end of play. In the second stage we introduce the possibility that the game may be of indefinite length. In the third stage (discussed in Chapter 10) we consider a game of indefinite length which has payoffs after different moves and a rate of interest which discounts the value of payoffs in the future. Later in Chapter 10 we add certain modifications suggested by Chapter 8.

As a preliminary to the mathematical description that follows in section 2, a simple example is discussed here. In Chapter 1: 2 we define the *normalized form* of a game and note that games which involve several moves by each player can be described by a game in which both players make a single move simultaneously. This move is to pick a strategy. Thus chess can be played (theoretically) by both players telling the referee their over-all strategies. A simple example of the game of matching pennies is presented in Table 1 of Chapter 1. In this game the second player has the advantage of knowing the move of the first player. Here we will compare this game with the game in which neither player knows his opponent's move. The *normalized form* for both games is given, and then the extensive form for both games is presented. From Table 12 we see

Table 12

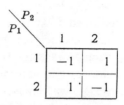

	P_2 1	2
1	-1	1
2	1	-1

that in the game without any information in favor of the second player both players have a choice of two moves and two strategies. In this game a move and a strategy are equivalent. Table 13 indicates that the added information available to the second player gives him four strategies (although each one amounts to a convention for selecting one of the two moves he has available to him). A detailed description of these strategies is given in Chapter 1: 2.

Table 13

P_1 $\backslash$ P_2	$(1,1;2,1)$	$(1,1;2,2)$	$(1,2;2,1)$	$(1,2;2,2)$
1	-1	-1	1	1
2	1	-1	1	-1

Both games can be described by a diagram known as a *game tree* [1]. Figure 36 represents the simultaneous move game, and Figure 37 shows the structure of the game in which the second player is informed of the move of the first before he commits himself to move.

We can represent the position of the first player by the point labeled P_1. The two branches leaving this point at the apex of Figure 36 represent the alternatives he faces. Here his alternatives consist of a choice between his moves 1 and 2. After he has moved

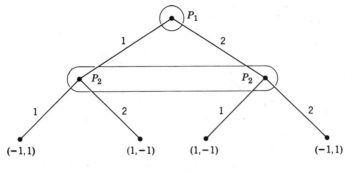

Figure 36

the game will have proceeded to one of two positions from which the second player has to make a choice. In this game the second player will be faced with the same number of choices from either position; he must choose between his alternatives of moves 1 and 2. After he has selected his move, the game will have reached one of four positions at the bottom of the game tree. At any of these positions the game is over and the players obtain their payoffs. These are indicated by the pairs of numbers shown there. The first number of each pair is the payoff to the first player.

In the fair game of matching pennies the second player will not know which move the first has chosen until he has chosen his own move and the *play* of the game is over. In order to indicate this in Figure 36 we circle the vertices marked P_2. This indicates that the second player cannot distinguish between the enclosed vertices. Each group of vertices enclosed in this manner is called an *information set*. It belongs to the player for whom the vertices are labeled. The first information set containing only the vertex of the game tree belongs to the first player. The second set which consists of two vertices belongs to the second player.

By the use of similar diagrams it is possible to describe the anatomy of any game, no matter how complicated the moves or the information conditions may be.

In the second example, since the second player is able to distinguish between the two vertices labeled P_2, we circle them separately, thereby indicating that he has two *information sets* instead of the single one he had in the first example. The selection of his move now depends upon the use he makes of this added

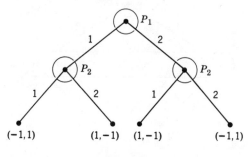

Figure 37

information in his strategy or plan of action. For instance, if the first player used his first or second strategy and the second player used his second strategy, the second player would always win. The added information enables him to take advantage of his opponent.

A game tree is a complete picture of the sequence of alternatives that make up a game. The information sets indicate the structure of information available to every player at every point in the game. For instance, in Figure 36, the referee or omniscient economist will know at which of the two vertices labeled P_2 the second player is .making his choice, but the player himself is unable to distinguish between them.

2. THE MATHEMATICAL DESCRIPTION OF THE EXTENSIVE FORM OF A GAME

In order to describe the many possibilities inherent in a game we make use of a mathematical diagram known as a *tree*. Figures 38 and 39 provide examples of simple game trees. They represent the game of matching pennies. A vertex of the tree represents a *position* in the game; a branch leading away from a vertex represents an alternative which can be chosen from that position; and a path starting from the apex 0 and proceeding in a continuous manner down to an end vertex of the tree is called a *play*. By an end vertex we mean a vertex from which there is no further choice from any set of alternatives to be made. An end vertex signifies the end of

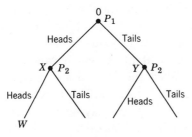

Figure 38

the game. In the game tree for chess the end vertices consist of all positions at which there is a win for black or white or at which there is a stalemate. A path starting from 0 and reaching an end vertex contains a complete description of the way in which a particular play of the game has proceeded from the start to the end. A write-up of a chess game is a description of a play and is equivalent to a single path down the game tree.

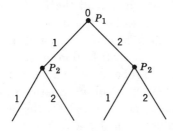

Figure 39

Two distinct plays starting at the point 0 will branch somewhere in the game tree. Each branch point is labeled with the name of the player $P_1, \ldots, P_n$, making the choice at that position, or by P_0, if the choice is made by a chance device. We label the *choices* arising at any branch point in the manner indicated in Figure 39.

Before we can define the extensive form of a game, some general technical terms must be explained:

We identify the vertices of the game tree by the letters X, Y, Z. These vertices are called *positions*. In other words they represent some stage in the play of a game. An example of the meaning of this can be drawn from the game of chess. If the apex 0 represents the board as set up initially, there will be twenty branches leading away from 0. These branches stand for the choices which can be made by White for his first move.

The branches incident at X which can be reached by further play from X are called the *alternatives* at X. In Figure 38, if we continue from vertex X, there will be two branches still accessible. These are the alternatives of playing heads or tails faced by the player P_2 when he has to make his move after the first player has chosen heads as his move.

For each end point or end vertex W we define an n-tuple of numbers; $h(W) = ([h_1(W), \ldots, h_n(W)]$. This function h is called the *payoff function*. In poker the function specifies the monetary awards to each player at the end of any play. It assigns wins, draws, and losses in chess.

The set of all moves can be classified in two ways which will help us to understand the structure of a game. We partition it into sets $A_1, A_2, \ldots, A_j, \ldots$, where A_j contains those moves with j alternatives. We also assign the moves to $n + 1$ indexed sets $P_0, P_1, \ldots, P_n$ which we call the *player partition*. The moves in P_0 are called *chance moves*; the moves in P_i, for $i = 1, \ldots, n$, are called *personal moves* of player i. For each chance move with j alternatives a probability distribution on the alternatives $1, \ldots, j$, which assigns a positive probability to each alternative, must be given.

A specification of the state of information of a player when he is called upon to make a choice completes the description of a game. We identify the information by a function $I(X)$. If the function $I(X) = I(Y)$, i.e., if a player is given the same information when the play has progressed to either X or Y, then we shall say that X and Y belong to the same *information set U*. Figure 40 provides an example which serves to illustrate the meaning of the notation.

The game shown in Figure 40 can portray an economic model of the following sort. The first move is made by chance and determines whether a crop is scarce or plentiful. A probability distribution of $\frac{3}{4}$ and $\frac{1}{4}$ is assigned to these alternatives. The first player is informed of the outcome of the chance moves. He has two information sets. These are shown by the two curves circling a single vertex and labeled P_1. If the crop is low, the first player has two alternatives; he may buy nothing or he may buy everything (which we assume is enough for only a medium inventory position).

If the crop is large, the player has three alternatives. He may buy nothing, enough for a medium inventory, or enough for a large

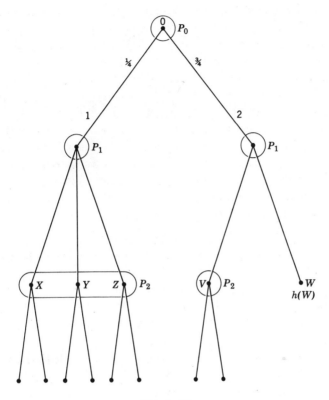

Figure 40

inventory. If the crop is low and the first player buys nothing, then the second player has the choice of buying nothing or buying for a medium inventory. If the crop is low and the first player has bought, then there is nothing left for the second player and the game is over, as indicated by the vertex W and the payoff $h(W)$. If the crop is large, then no matter what the first player does the second player will always have a choice of not buying or buying for a medium inventory position.

We note that when the crop is low the second player is always able to tell what has happened before he moves, even though he may not be directly informed about the choice of the first player.

In other words, the vertices V and W cannot belong to the same information set for the second player. The knowledge that he is faced with a different number of alternatives at V and W enables him to distinguish whether the play of the game has proceeded to V or W. If the crop is plentiful, then the second player is unable to distinguish between the vertices X, Y, and Z unless he is directly informed of the action of the first. Here $I(X) = I(Y) = I(Z)$. There are three vertices, all of which belong to the same information set, indicated by the curve circling them. We note that if any two vertices belong to the same information set then there must be the same number of alternatives at both vertices (otherwise they can be distinguished). Thus, if an information set belongs to a player P_i, all the vertices in that set must also belong to some set of moves A_j.

We are now able to define a game in extensive form.

Definition. An *n-person game* Γ in *extensive form* is a game tree K with the following specifications:

(1)   A partition of the moves into $n + 1$ indexed sets P_0, $P_1, \ldots, P_n$ consisting of *chance* and *personal moves*. This is known as the *player partition*.

(2)   For each chance move with j alternatives, a probability distribution, which assigns a positive probability to each alternative.

(3)   For each play W, a *payoff function* $h(W) = (h_1(W), \ldots, h_n(W))$.

(4)   A partition of moves into sets U so that each U is contained in some P_i and A_j for some i and j, and no U contains two moves belonging to the same play. This partition is called the *information partition*. [3]

An interpretation of this formal scheme is offered. We may imagine that each player (say a corporation) has many agents in his employ. Each agent knows the rules of the game, and there is one agent for each information set. An agent belongs to the ith player if his information set lies in P_i. By considering so many agents we are able to account for any sort of complication in the information conditions. For instance, as seen in subsection 2.1, it is possible for a player to "forget" what he has already done. In a corporation in which there are many decision makers the agent or vice-president in charge of sales may not know what the vice-president in charge of production has done at the time he makes his decision. If we regard the corporation as a whole as a single player, then we can say that when it makes its sales move the information concerning its production move has been forgotten.

A play begins at the vertex 0. If it has progressed to the move X and if X is a personal move with j alternatives, the agent whose information set U contains X chooses a positive integer not greater than j, knowing only that he is choosing an alternative with this index at one of the moves in U. For example, an agent may be a branch manager in control of a particular production process. At some point in the game he is called upon to act. He knows that he has perhaps ten alternative rates of production; hence his action will consist of selecting one of these ten rates. If X is a chance move, then an alternative is chosen by a chance device in accordance with the probabilities assigned to the alternatives at X. In this way a unicursal path starting from 0 is constructed. It leads to a unique play W, at which point P_i is paid the amount $h_i(W)$, for $i = 1, 2, \ldots, n$.

In Chapter 1 we give the meaning of a *pure* and a *mixed* strategy. We are now in a position to make these concepts clearer. Kuhn suggests that we consider a pure strategy as a plan formulated for a player by a strategist in his employ. We phrase this slightly differently. If a player is regarded as a corporation, then the pure strategy is a plan formulated by the directors and officers or executive committee. The choices decided upon by this committee are communicated to the agents, i.e., the different decisionmaking members of the corporation at all levels. This may be done without violating the rules of the game regarding the information possessed by the agents. Imagine that the strategist has a book with one page for each of his information sets U. He gives the appropriate page to the agent acting on that information set. If the agent is called upon during a play, he chooses the alternative indicated by the strategist on the page of instructions. A formal definition of a pure strategy is given in Note 4 at the end of this chapter. Less formally, a pure strategy is a plan such that at any point in the play of a game where a player must select from a set of alternatives the plan specifies an alternative.

For some games—matching pennies, for example—it is not rational to play the same pure strategy on all plays; it is necessary to randomize in some manner to protect against being "found out" by your opponent. Thus a mixed strategy attaches a probability to each book (pure strategy), and before the play begins the strategist chooses the book that he will use by means of a chance device in accordance with these probabilities. The player still follows a fixed plan throughout the course of the play, but this plan is chosen by a chance device before the play begins. The formal definition of a mixed strategy is given in the Note 5.

In some of the examples the players do not know what their opponents are doing before moving themselves. However, many games exist in which they are informed about all previous actions of all players. We can now re-examine the meaning of a game with *perfect information*. It is a game in which the information partition consists of one-element sets. Chess, checkers, and tic-tac-toe are games of this type. Matching pennies with one player moving first and being forced to disclose his move is another example of a game with perfect information. This is shown in Figure 37. We noted in Chapter 1:2 that this game has a solution involving only pure strategies. If a duopoly involves a number of moves by both players at the end of which they obtain a payoff and if one duopolist always makes his move before the other, who is then informed of his opponent's choice, this "leader-follower" situation will have an equilibrium point involving only pure strategies.

There are two theorems which state

(1)   If a two-person, zero-sum game has perfect information it has a solution involving only pure strategies. [6]

(2)   Any general *n*-person game with perfect information has an equilibrium point involving only pure strategies. [7]

Both of these theorems can be proved by "backward induction." Suppose the last player were about to make the last move. As he knows everything that has happened up to this point, his move is determined by picking the maximal alternative. At two moves before the end we know what the last move of the last player will be as a function of the move before, so we can replace the game by a different game with one less move. In this manner we can proceed backward, working out the way in which each player would maximize if he were given complete information at his move. The formal proofs are given in the references.

We have described the extensive form of a game and have drawn some economic analogies. However, although the dynamic overtones have become greater, we still have not achieved a dynamic model of a market. There is only one payoff made to each player at the end of the game. The game ends in a certain specified time. In an economic situation payments are made continuously, and there is usually no definite termination point for the game. Modifications of the extensive form are made in section 3 in order to account for these features of economic life.

2.1. MIXED STRATEGIES AND BEHAVIOR STRATEGIES

It is easy to see that in a game which has several moves and many information sets the number of pure strategies becomes very high. In a game with many pure strategies it is hard to envision that anyone would play a mixed strategy which involves assigning probabilities to many thousands of different strategies. Fortunately, in many cases there is a simplification which can be made to support our economic intuition. This is shown by means of an example.

The example used originally was given by Kuhn [8] and was phrased in terms of a simple card game. It has a direct economic interpretation.

A firm has an excess plant. If it does not utilize this plant it has to pay an overhead charge of 2. It can use the plant to produce an extra product; however, both the cost of factors required for the product and final demand fluctuate considerably. The firm is informed of the factor market prices before it decides to produce or to leave the plant idle. If it decides to buy the raw inputs and produce, its profits will be determined by the factor costs (which it knows) and the final market demand (which it does not know until it has acted). Suppose (to make the analogy complete between this market situation and a simple card game) that there were thirteen different values, 1, 2, 3, ..., 13, which can be incurred as costs and the same array which can be earned as revenue. Then, if the firm decides to produce, its net profit will be positive or negative, depending upon the value of costs and revenue. The game tree of this game is given in Figure 41.

We interpret the game tree in the following manner. The first two moves are made by "nature," the markets, or the outside world P_0. The player is informed about the first move (the prices in the factor markets) before he makes his own decision (to produce

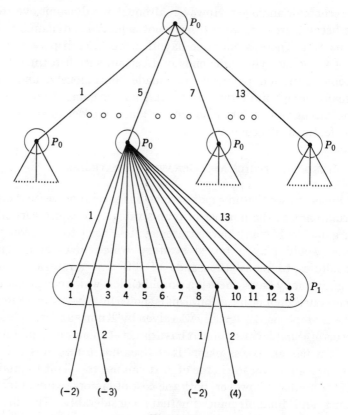

Figure 41

or leave unutilized capacity). He is not informed about the second move by the markets (the selection of the demand which will prevail). There are thirteen information sets for the player; the fifth set is shown in Figure 41. In this example each information set contains thirteen vertices between which the player cannot distinguish. At every one of the vertices the player has two alternatives. This amounts to saying that he has two alternatives at every information set. Hence he has $2^{13} = 8192$ pure strategies. A pure strategy is a plan involving thirteen contingencies with instructions to take one of two actions at each contingency.

If the player wishes to utilize a mixed strategy he will have to select a probability distribution with 8192 numbers. This is far too complicated for such a simple game.

Suppose that we watch the game. All that we can observe is the behavior of the player in thirteen independent situations. We are unable to tell what mixed strategy is being played because we have no way of knowing from his behavior what he would have done had a different contingency arisen. However, we can estimate his behavior independently in each of the thirteen situations, and we can characterize this behavior by a single number for each information set. The numbers will be the probabilities that the firm will not produce, given any one of the thirteen different costs. The complete behavior of a player can be described by a vector $\beta = (b_1, b_2, b_3, \ldots, b_{13})$ in which $0 \leqslant b_k \leqslant 1$. This vector characterizes a behavior strategy.

If the player utilizes a mixed strategy, the behavior observed by the economist watching the market will be

$$b_k = \sum \omega(a_1, a_2, \ldots, a_{13}), \qquad \text{for } k = 1, 2, \ldots, 13,$$

in which $(a_1, a_2, \ldots, a_{13})$ is a pure strategy for the player; a_k has two values, 0 and 1, which signify the actions not to produce or to produce, and $\omega(a_1, a_2, \ldots, a_{13})$ stands for the probability assignment used in a mixed strategy. We note that the b_k implies that we will observe the same behavior being caused by many different mixed strategies. We will not be able to distinguish between many of the mixed strategies.

In the particular example given here it is rational for the firm to produce whenever its expected profit is more than or equal to -2 (the overhead costs). If the thirteen levels of demand are considered equiprobable, this will be whenever costs are 9 or less (the expected revenue is 7). The behavior strategy that is optimal is $(1, 1, 1, 1, 1, 1, 1, 1, 1, 0, 0, 0, 0)$. Expected profit from this strategy is $\frac{10}{13}$, or approximately 0.77.

The result illustrated by this example is that there exists an important class of games for which a player need not be concerned with the complexities of mixed strategies. He can play optimally by deciding what he intends to do at each of his information sets without having to correlate his decision at one with his decision at another.

Kuhn has proved that for all games with *perfect recall* the payoff to a player restricted to the use of behavior strategies will be the same as if he were permitted to use mixed strategies. [9]

A game with *perfect recall* is one in which a player is allowed by the rules to remember everything that he knew at previous moves and all of his choices at every move. If we regard bridge as a two-person game (each pair of partners being counted as one person), then it is a game without perfect recall. As the partners take their moves, each "forgets" the state of information available to the other; i.e., they do not know each other's hand. Most parlor games are games of perfect recall. However, games in which team work is important provide a class of examples in which perfect recall is rare. In a corporation there are often several different decision makers, who act without information as to what the others are doing. The time factors and the complexity of large organizations makes this unavoidable. A game model of such an organization portrays sections of the game tree in which there is no perfect recall. An example is given in Figure 42. The first move by player

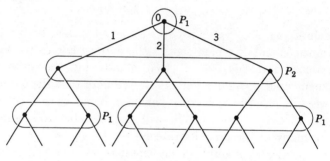

Figure 42

1 is made by the agent in charge of sales, in which he commits the firm to a marketing policy. The next move is made by a competing firm, and, as indicated by the information sets, neither firm knows what the move of the other has been at this stage of the game. The second move by player 1 is made by the agent in charge of production. The game tree indicates that if player 1 chooses his second or third alternative at his first move he will have forgotten this when he takes his second move. If he chooses his first alternative, this will be remembered. This partial forgetting can come about if, say, the first alternative is so drastic that the sales agent immediately informs the production agent, but the choice between the other alternatives is not communicated.

If a game does not possess perfect recall, then, in general, a behavior strategy will not be so good as a mixed strategy; hence we cannot use the considerable simplification obtained by limiting ourselves to behavior strategies (examples are given by Kuhn and Thompson [10]). However, Thompson has obtained a result which is directly applicable to economic models and which still enables us to avoid the complexities of mixed strategies. [11]

Suppose that we had a game which had been played many times over or, at least, a series of games after any one of which had been played the players had perfect recall concerning the previous games. Each game may not possess perfect recall. A market with competing corporations provides an example of such a game. During a single time period the various branches of a corporation may not be informed about the actions of its different sections. At the end of the year the company report more or less brings everyone up-to-date on the actions of both the firm and the market. During the next year a new game is played which, although it may not be identical with, is very similar to the previous game. Thompson has shown that in the composite game obtained by considering this series of games as a single game a *composite strategy* [12] will always yield a player as much as the employment of a mixed strategy. A composite strategy has two components. It is such that the players will use a mixed strategy component in those parts of the game in which perfect recall does not exist and behavior strategy components in everything else.

In Chapter 5 we describe a single-period price game. We obtained a mixed strategy solution for this game. A more realistic market model of the economic structure is dynamic, in which the firms have a financial and asset policy and in which they compete in the market over many periods. The Thompson result implies that in this dynamic game we need not consider the fantastically complicated mixed strategies that are available to the firms, because if they play each market game separately without working out an over-all global strategy they will do as well as if they had. If the demand and production conditions do not change too violently for several periods, then it becomes possible to give a frequency interpretation to the repeated playing of a mixed strategy in each of a sequence of independently treated "subgames" which constitute the over-all game.

3.   GAMES OF INDEFINITE LENGTH

*3.1. THE MATHEMATICAL DESCRIPTION OF AN INFINITE GAME

The bare mathematical description of an infinite game is given here. By infinite we mean that there need not be a time limit on the length of a play. Subsection 3.2 contains the economic interpretation of this type of game. [13]

An *n-person infinite game* Γ is an infinite game tree K with the following specifications:

(1)   A partition of the moves into $n + 1$ indexed sets P_0, P_1, ..., P_n, consisting of *chance* and *personal moves*. This is called the *player partition*.

(2)   For each chance move with j alternatives, a probability distribution which assigns a positive probability to each alternative.

(3)   A partition $\mathscr{U}$ of the moves into information sets U.

(4)   For each path of play up to the tth move $r_t \epsilon R_t$ (the set of all plays up to the tth move), a *payoff function*

$$h_t\,(r_t) = (h_{1t}(r_t), h_{2t}(r_t), \ldots, h_{nt}(r_t)).$$

(5)   For any player i, the sum $\sum_{t=0}^{\infty} h_{it}(r_t)$ is bounded.

3.2. THE ECONOMIC INTERPRETATION OF AN INFINITE GAME

Subsection 3.1 contains a mathematical description of a dynamic game complete with a representation of all strategic possibilities, all states of information, and all consequences of every act. It does not tell us how the game should be played. No pattern of behavior, course of action, or method of solution is given in this formalization. We must specify a goal that each player wishes to achieve, for instance, the maximization of the expected value of his discounted income stream, and then suggest a course of action as a solution. The Cournot duopoly model, the models of Bertrand, Edgeworth, and Stackelberg, the actions under competitive equilibrium, and the monopolistic equilibrium of Chamberlin all imply specific behavioristic patterns which serve to select a path of play down the game tree. The game tree itself is nothing more or less than a complete description of everything that can happen.

By introducing a rate of interest and many income periods and eliminating a specific termination point for the game we obtain a model which begins to give explicit form to the dynamic features of a market. Profits become some discounted function of a series of income payments made in different periods. There are many different ways of formulating profit maximization for unincorporated enterprises and corporations which are owner-controlled or in the hands of managers. The investigation of *games of economic survival* deals with these problems in Chapter 10.

A Cournot duopoly model treated as though the equilibrium adjustment is a truly dynamic process is shown in Figure 43. We

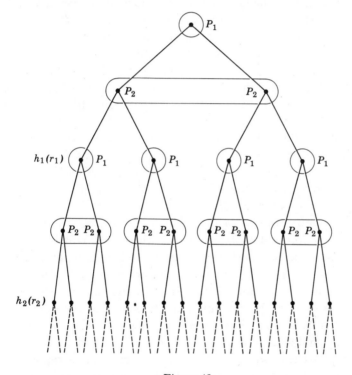

Figure 43

regard every adjustment and counter-adjustment on the part of the entrepreneurs as actually occupying one time period at the end of which they obtain an income from the market.

The interpretation of this game tree is that each of the two players makes his production decisions without knowledge of the action of the other. As a result of these decisions the market price is determined, and both receive their payments and are fully informed as to what the other did in the previous period. They then make simultaneous decisions in the second period, and so on. The discount factor introduced by the existence of a rate of interest in the economy serves to limit the summation of the discounted values of any future income stream even though there is no definite ending point to the game. This satisfies condition 5 in subsection 3.1. It is possible that some play of the game might lead to the elimination of one duopolist, but this possibility presents no extra difficulty. It merely means that the game is terminated for one player, whereas the other may continue to play in the resultant one-person, nonzero-sum game in which he is in a position to maximize monopolistically over all periods.

For simplicity in the foregoing game tree we have assumed that each player is faced with only two alternatives at every production period. Of course, this is a vast oversimplification because we can regard every production rate as a different alternative. We note that any *path* down the game tree describes how the situation is actually progressing. We define a set of functions $h_{it}(r_t)$ which are the payoffs made to the players during the game. If we let R_t be the complete set of possible paths in the game up until the tth move, then the payoff made to the ith player at the tth move of the game is a function of $r_t \epsilon R_t$, the actual path taken by the game, and can be expressed as $h_{it}(r_t)$ for the ith player. This is assumed to be bounded in any period. Because there is a discount factor at work we know that $\sum_{t=0}^{\infty} h_{it}(r_t) \leqslant M_i$ for all players; this is the condition that the sum of all payoffs is bounded. (The M_i merely stand for a set of large, but finite, numbers, so that the summation of the payoffs to any player i never exceeds M_i).

The Cournot theory actually provides a criterion of choice for each duopolist at any point in the game; hence it can be represented as a single path through this general tree representation of a simultaneous-move, dynamic duopoly system. This single path contains all the information concerning information state and payoffs to players at every period in a Cournot duopoly. Given the criterion of choice, the game tree contains even more detail than the arrow diagram method for portraying dynamic systems. [14, 15] This method, as applied to Cournot duopoly, is shown in Figure 44. Here the quantity produced by each duopolist is a function of the price in the last market, which, in turn, is a function of the production of both duopolists in the last period.

We reiterate at this point that the Cournot behavior equations, or, for that matter, any other set of behavior equations, merely provide a method whereby we can make a selection of a single path down a game tree. The game tree itself represents the most general and complete representation of everything that could possibly happen in a dynamic oligopoly or in any other system. Possibly, by looking at a complete game-tree representation of action in a market, some methods of action may appear to be better than others, in which case we will be in a position to suggest methods for playing dynamic games which will be superior to the present set of action assumptions used. But even if this were not the case, then at least we would be left with a method of representation whereby we could examine the aspects of a dynamic oligopoly *in toto*.

Many economists have agreed upon the reasonability of certain modes of action when the individual firms are small and the number of competitors great. For other conditions of competition, various "reaction curve" assumptions have been made. Many conjectural behavior assumptions have been discussed in a half-theoretical, half-descriptive manner (see Fellner [16] or Zeuthen, [17] for instance).

$$q_{1,t} = \mu_1(p_{t-1})$$
$$q_{2,t} = \bar{\mu}_2(p_{t-1})$$
$$p_{t-1} = \psi(q_{1,t-1} + q_{2,t-1})$$

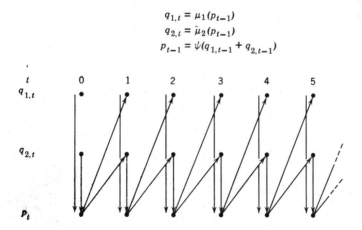

Figure 44

However, the test of the value and relevance of these assumptions is mainly an empirical one. In this chapter no attempt has been made to offer new sets of reaction functions or methods of solution to oligopoly problems. The apparatus erected here is not quite sufficient to capture the major economic features that are relevant to the study of competition or collusion in a market. An attempt is made to build the extra apparatus in the succeeding chapters. Once this has been done we may then have a general method of description for a market form sufficiently complex that when the appropriate measures of demand, asset structure, liquidation values, and other factors noted in Chapter 10 are specified we may obtain a reasonably good picture of a specific market. We may then wish to suggest that certain patterns of behavior may be expected and attempt an empirical verification of our hypotheses.

NOTES

[1] J. von Neumann, and O. Morgenstern, *Theory of Games and Economic Behavior* (Princeton: Princeton University Press, 3rd. ed., 1953), pp. 64–66.

[2] The mathematical description of the extensive form of a game given here follows closely the formalization of Harold Kuhn. See H. W. Kuhn, "Extensive Games and the Problem of Information," in H. W. Kuhn and A. W. Tucker, eds., *Contributions to the Theory of Games*, **II**.

[3] H. W. Kuhn, *op. cit.*, p. 195.

[4] *Definition:* Let $\mathcal{U}_i = (U | U < P_i)$. A *pure strategy* for P_i, for $i = 1, \ldots, n$, is a function π_i mapping $\mathcal{U}_i$ into the positive integers such that $U \subset A_j$ implies $\pi_i(U) \leq j$. [5] *Definition:* A *mixed strategy* for P_i, for $i = 1, \ldots, n$, is a probability distribution μ_i on the pure strategies for P_i, which assigns the probability q_{π_i} to π_i.

[6] J. von Neumann, and O. Morgenstern, *op. cit.*, pp. 112–124.

[7] H. W. Kuhn, *op. cit.*, p. 209.   [8] ———, "Lectures on the Theory of Games," (Reproduced lecture notes Princeton, 1953), p. 102.

[9] ———, "Extensive Games and the Problem of Information," p. 214.

[10] G. L. Thompson, "Signalling Strategies in n-Person Games," in H. W. Kuhn, A. W. Tucker, eds., *Contributions to the Theory of Games*, **II**, p. 268.

[11] *Ibid.*   [12] *Ibid.*, p. 272.   [13] These games have been called pseudo, stochastic, or recursive games.

[14] J. Tinbergen, *Econometrics*, translated by Dr. H. Rijken van Olst (Philadelphia: Blakiston, 1951), p. 38.

[15] H. Wold, *Demand Analysis*, in association with Lars Jureen (New York: Wiley, 1953), p. 13.

[16] William Fellner, Competition among the Few (New York: Knopf, 1949), Chapter 7, pp. 169–174.

[17] F. Zeuthen, "Undetermined Wage Problems," (Unpublished translation by Olaf Helmer, October 1952), *Archiv für Sozialwissenschaft und Sozialpolitik*, Vol. 62 (1929).

A THEORY
OF OLIGOPOLY
(PART 1)

1. INTRODUCTION. ENTRY, EARNINGS, AND ASSETS

In this chapter we integrate the role of entry, asset, and corporate structure into our analysis. Previously, we had implicitly assumed that profits or payoffs were equal to the difference between total revenue and total costs in a single period. However, in the discussion of static models in Part One the obvious inadequacy of this interpretation is not explicitly brought out. We shall see that when we attempt to incorporate entry and asset conditions directly into a dynamic oligopoly model we are forced to deal separately with the profit motives and maximization problems faced by unincorporated individual entrepreneur-owners, incorporated individual entrepreneurs, and corporations operated by directors and managers with ownership scattered among many stockholders. The different goals of maximizing dividends, growth, and chances of survival all play their part with varying force, depending upon the institutional framework of the organization representing the firm.

Before we can construct adequate game models of corporate competition we must engage in a few final preliminaries. *Games of survival* are discussed in section 2. In section 3 the considerations which lead to and the formulation of a *game of economic survival* are given.

2.   GAMES OF SURVIVAL

> Unto every one that hath shall be given,
> and he shall have abundance;
> but from him that hath not
> shall be taken away even that which he hath.
>   *Matthew XXV, 29*

A game of survival [1] is a natural extension of the two-person, zero-sum game when asset structure and dynamic features are introduced. At the beginning of the game each player is in control of a given amount of capital, his assets or "fortune." During every time period a two-person, zero-sum game is played and the appropriate payments are made until one of the players runs out of funds or is "ruined." The goal of each player is to ruin his opponent; hence his payoff consists of the valuation he places upon survival and ruin.

The money or assets in a game of survival play the role of counters or chips. They have no intrinsic value in themselves, although possession of resources enables a player to survive. In a market assets still have this property. The possibility of ruin is important to a firm, but the earnings of the firm also enter into the valuations of the players. This is shown in section 3.

Suppose two players with resources of two dollars each decide to match dollars until one of them is ruined. Furthermore, let the value of being ruined be 0 and the value of surviving be 1. In every period they play the game of matching which has this simple payoff matrix:

$$
\begin{array}{ccc}
 & H & T \\
H & 1 & -1 \\
T & -1 & 1
\end{array}
$$

The value of this game to both players is obviously $\frac{1}{2}$. Each starts with the same resources and in every period plays a "fair game." The expected gain from the game of matching played in each period is zero. Each player has the same chance as his opponent to survive. Furthermore, it can be shown [2] that the expected duration of this game of survival is four periods.

More generally, suppose that the players started with resources X and Y, respectively. The probability that the first player would win is given by

$$
v_1(X, Y) = \frac{X}{X + Y},
$$

and the expected duration of the game is

$$
E(t) = XY.
$$

This particular example is a special case of the well-known "Gambler's Ruin Problem"; the general problem is analyzed at length by Feller. [3]

Hausner, [4] Peisakoff, [5] and Shapley and Milnor [6] have investigated games in which the players start with different resources X and Y, but instead of playing the simple game of matching pennies every time they play a two-person, zero-sum game having a payoff given by the general matrix $||a_{i,j}||$ whose only properties are that there are no zeros or rows with only positive entries or columns with only negative entries. A reason for the two qualifications is that the resulting problem would be mathematically uninteresting if they did not hold. [7] One of the players would be able to play a pure strategy which would cause loss to the other at every play; hence the game is trivial to solve, and the length of play is given by the length of time it takes to exhaust the losing player's assets. Although a game not conforming to these restrictions is trivial mathematically, there are closely related problems which arise in cutthroat competition that are of interest to economists. Before they can be discussed adequately we must investigate *games of economic survival.*

3. GAMES OF ECONOMIC SURVIVAL

3.1. THE ANATOMY OF A GAME OF ECONOMIC SURVIVAL

The games of survival described are *strictly competitive* games. The interests of the players are diametrically opposed. A solution to a game of survival is obtained by finding optimal strategies for both players and calculating the value of the payoff to both if they play their optimal strategies. This gives a minimax condition similar to that discussed for two-person, zero-sum games in Chapter 1. Markets cannot usually be represented by zero-sum games, since there is no pure opposition of interests. However, in order to demonstrate some of the financial aspects of competition as simply as possible we first construct a model in which the game played by the players is zero-sum as long as both survive, but there is a bonus to the survivor. We consider a duopoly in which two firms are struggling for an oversaturated market. For instance, by using advertising and styling they may attempt to bid customers away from each other. The success of one firm will cause losses to the other; hence a zero-sum matrix serves as a crude approximation to the market. Suppose, for simplicity, that the payoff matrix when both firms are competing were the same as in the example in section 2. A firm wins or loses a unit every period. Up to this point the game is identical with a game of survival. Now the differences appear. If one firm is ruined, the survivor is left with the market. Although the two competitors were unable to make a profit jointly, there may be room for one to do so. We assume that the surviving firm obtains an income the value of which we identify as A.

The aim of the players in the game of survival is to survive. In a game of economic survival their aim may be to maximize income subject to some considerations of survival. In this example it is assumed for simplicity, that each player wishes only to maximize his expected monetary income.

Before the game can be completely defined two further economic considerations must be introduced. The income of a firm is not necessarily the same as the income of its owners, if they decide to "plow profits back" into the firm's account to increase earned surplus instead of paying out dividends to themselves. This distinction is made by distinguishing between two accounts, the enterprise or *corporate account* and the dividend or *withdrawal account*. In this example it is assumed that the players wish to maximize the value of their withdrawal accounts.

As the money entering the withdrawal account of a player comes in a stream over time, it is natural that we discount it in order to evaluate its present worth. Let the rate of interest be r, then the discount rate $\rho = 1/(1 + r)$.

After every period one player suffers a loss and the other makes a gain of 1. We assume that the gains or losses effect the players' *corporate accounts*. After every period each player must decide whether he wishes to make a payment to his *withdrawal account* or to keep all his corporate assets in his corporate account. If he pays out the money instead of building up assets, then he personally is able to benefit from present consumption, but he does so at the expense of accepting a greater probability of ruin for his firm. Although it may happen that when a corporation is pressed for funds its owners produce them from their own resources, or it borrows, we assume that once money has been paid out to the withdrawal accounts it is no longer available for use in the corporate account and that the firm cannot borrow. A firm or a player is ruined when the corporate account is zero. Suppose that both firms had two units initially in their corporate accounts. If the income obtained by the surviving firm were sufficiently high, neither firm would find it profitable to pay out money into its withdrawal account until its opponent was ruined; i.e., until the war was over each player would endeavour to keep his war chest as full as possible. [8]

We note that until a player is ruined the game played is the same as the gambler's ruin described in section 2. Each player will still have an expectation of $\frac{1}{2}$ of winning; however, the payoff will depend upon the length of the game. In order to calculate the expected payoff we must find out the probability of the game ending at every possible time and the value of the payoff associated with the time at which the game ends. We can do this by observing that the game can end only at an even number of plays, and we can list the number of ways this can happen. Let L stand for a loss of one unit and W stand for a win of one unit. There are two ways in which the game can end in two plays:

$$LL$$
$$WW$$

There are four outcomes after two plays, the two given, at which the game ends, and the two possibilities of WL and LW, in which case the game continues. Following this analysis we observe that there are four ways in which the game can end at the fourth period:

$$LWWW$$
$$WLWW$$
$$LWLL$$
$$WLLL$$

There are, however, four other outcomes after four plays in which the game will continue. In both of these cases the probability that a player will win if the game lasts two or four periods is $\frac{1}{2}$. The probability that the game will end in exactly two periods is $\frac{1}{2}$. The probability that it will end in exactly four periods is $\frac{1}{4}$. In general, the probability that the game will end in period $2t$ (it can end only in an even number of periods) is

$$(\tfrac{1}{2})^t, \quad t = 1, 2, \ldots.$$

In order to calculate the expected value of the game we must sum the different discounted payoffs multiplied by their probability of occurring. Thus, if A is the value of the income obtained by the survivor as soon as his opponent is ruined, the value of the game is

$$\sum_{t=1}^{\infty} \frac{1}{2^t} \cdot \frac{1}{2} \cdot \rho^{2t} A = \frac{A}{2} \sum_{t=1}^{\infty} (\rho^2/2)^t.$$

The summation of this geometric series yields a value of

$$\frac{A}{2}\left(\frac{\rho^2/2}{1 - (\rho^2/2)}\right).$$

Suppose, for instance, that the rate of interest were 10 per cent and $A = 20$. The discount rate is $\rho = 0.9$, and the value of the game to each player is

$$v_1(2, 2) = v_2(2, 2) = 6.7.$$

Let us examine a similar game in which the players have only one unit each to start with. It is obvious that this game will last only one period because one player is bound to be ruined after the first play. The probability of winning for either player is $\frac{1}{2}$. and the reward is A which is obtained after one period. Thus the value of the game to each player is

$$v_1(1, 1) = v_2(1, 1) = 9.$$

We note that the return to capital is greater for the game in which the assets of the players are smaller! This has a simple economic interpretation. In an industry with overcapacity, if the firms are financially weak and they do not co-operate, rationalization will take place quickly because someone will be ruined almost immediately. If the firms are financially strong and non-co-operative, the fight and the period of unprofitability may last longer.

3.2. FINANCIAL POLICY AND EXIT FROM COMPETITION

In the examples given in subsection 3.1 there are several details of economic importance which were not made explicit. The value of the income to the surviving firm at the time of its victory is denoted by A. Actually there are two components which must be distinguished. The surviving firm can pay all of its future earnings into its withdrawal account, and the discounted value of these is A; but it may also be able to pay out some of the money that is in its corporate account at the time of its victory. For instance, if both firms start with assets of two units in their corporate accounts and make no payments to the withdrawal accounts until the struggle is over, the survivor will have four units in his corporate account at that time. These units which were needed for financial strength during the fight may no longer be needed if there is no entry threat by a third firm. As soon as the fight is over the survivor may be able to reduce his corporate assets and make an extra payment to the withdrawal account (in this example we are ignoring the possibility of expenditure for plant expansion). We can completely characterize a two-person game of economic survival by the numbers X, Y, ρ, A_1, A_2, and the *market matrices* $\|a_{i,j}\|$ and $\|b_{i,j}\|$. X and Y are the initial values of the players' corporate accounts and ρ is the discount rate. A_1 and A_2 are the values of the "prize" to the surviving player at the period at which one player is ruined or has withdrawn from the market.

The two *market matrices* describe the revenues which are paid into the players' corporate accounts as a result of their market actions. For purposes of clarity we distinguish the financial and the market actions of the players. After the players have made their moves in the market and obtained their revenues, their strategies call for a financial move by which they decide upon the size of their payments to the withdrawal accounts.

In the examples in subsection 3.1 we assume that the game played between the two players before the ruin of one is zero-sum. When this is so we do not need the extra matrix $\|b_{i,j}\|$, since it is the same as $\|a_{i,j}\|$ with signs changed.

The explicit (non-co-operative) solutions of the game identified by

$$X, Y, \rho, A_1, A_2, \text{ and } \begin{pmatrix} 1 & -1 \\ -1 & 1 \end{pmatrix}$$

are given elsewhere [9]. However, without solving it explicitly here we can examine some of the economic problems it poses.

If the rate of interest is high and the value of having the market to oneself is low, it may not appear worthwhile to stay in a market if a player has to fight for survival. On the other hand, if his opponent voluntarily leaves the market, there may be sufficient gain to merit staying. A simple example in which each player has only one unit of assets serves to illustrate this. Suppose that the discount rate is 50 per cent and that the market matrix is

$$\begin{pmatrix} 1 & -1 \\ -1 & 1 \end{pmatrix}$$

Furthermore, we assume that the value of the income from the market at the time of the exit of one of the firms is $\frac{3}{2}$ to the survivor, i.e., $A_1 = A_2 = \frac{3}{2}$. When a player is the only survivor in the market we assume that he needs to keep only one unit in his corporate account.

For simplicity, it is assumed that a player is able to withdraw without liquidation losses; i.e., if he has X in his corporate account and he withdraws immediately, he is able to pay X into his withdrawal account.

If both players stay in the market, their expectation of winning is $\frac{1}{2}$ each. The value of the market to the survivor at the end of one period is $\frac{3}{2}$. He will also be able to pay out one unit from his corporate account at that time; hence the total value of the game is $\frac{3}{2} + 1 = \frac{5}{2}$ to the winner, if both firms compete. The discounted value of this "prize" is $\frac{5}{4}$, for a player must wait one period before he can obtain it.

If one player withdraws his funds immediately, the value of the game to him is 1. If one player withdraws immediately and the other does not, the latter obtains the prize immediately, and the value is $\frac{3}{2}$. When examining this game in the normalized form (see Chapter 1: 2 and Chapter 9: 1) we need consider only two strategies for each player. A player either leaves the industry immediately or he stays and plays optimally in the market. The payoff matrix (i.e., the discounted expected values of the withdrawal accounts) is

	Player 2	Out	In
Player 1	Out	$(1, 1)$	$(1, \frac{3}{2})$
	In	$(\frac{3}{2}, 1)$	$(\frac{5}{8}, \frac{5}{8})$

There is a mixed strategy equilibrium at which each player withdraws from the market immediately with a probability of $\frac{3}{7}$ or stays in with a probability of $\frac{4}{7}$. The value of the payoff to a player at the equilibrium is

$$v_1(1, 1) = v_2(1, 1) = \left(\frac{3}{7}\right)(1) + \left(\frac{4}{7}\right)\left(\frac{3}{2}\right) = 1.$$

This game is very similar to that analyzed in Chapter 6: 2.5. The value of the game to each player is his maximin value. If they were able to co-operate, one would leave the market immediately and the other would be able to compensate him.

In many situations it may not be possible for a firm to withdraw all its assets immediately without loss. A more realistic example than the one given would have a penalty or a liquidation cost to the firm withdrawing. In an industry which finds itself with excess capacity caused, perhaps, by a change in taste or discovery of a substitute the firms will either rationalize co-operatively, or, if they have a heavy fixed investment, they will find it cheaper to fight to the death than to withdraw.

An example in which the first player has two units and the second has one illustrates a financial policy in which the added capital in the corporate account of the first player is worth less than if it were paid out immediately. Suppose, as in the last example, that the discount rate were 50 per cent per period. The value of the income obtained by the survivor at the time he obtains it is $\frac{3}{2}$. Furthermore, suppose that the survivor, at that time, needed to keep only one unit in his corporate account in order to operate at optimum technical efficiency. For instance, if the first player won and had three units in his corporate account, he would be able to withdraw two.

We calculate the payoff for the first player if he adopts any one of three strategies against two strategies of his opponent. The strategies are (1) keep all money in the corporate account until the ruin of the opponent; (2) pay out one unit to the withdrawal account immediately but stay in the market; (3) withdraw from the market immediately by paying two units into the withdrawal account. The strategies we consider for the opponent are (1) keep all money in the corporate account until the ruin of the opponent; and (2) withdraw from the market immediately. There are many more strategies in this game but these suffice to show the nature of the financial considerations. If both players use strategy 1, there will be a fight, with all money staying in the corporate accounts until one player is ruined. There is only one way in which the game can end in any period; this is shown in the following table, in which W and L stand for a single win or loss by the first player:

$$W \qquad \frac{1}{2}$$

$$LL \qquad \frac{1}{4}$$

$$LWW \qquad \frac{1}{8}$$

$$LWLL \qquad \frac{1}{16}$$

The first player can win the whole game in any odd period, and the second player can win in any even period, if he wins. These numbers are the probabilities with which a player may win at any period.

If the first player loses, his payoff is zero. If he wins, his payoff is

$$(2 + \tfrac{3}{2}) \sum_{t=1}^{\infty} (\tfrac{1}{2})^{4t-2} = (\tfrac{7}{2}) \left\{ \frac{(\tfrac{1}{2})^2}{1 - (\tfrac{1}{2})^4} \right\} = \frac{14}{15}.$$

The $\tfrac{7}{2}$ consists of the income worth $\tfrac{3}{2}$ at the time of victory plus a transfer of two out of the three units in the corporate account at that time. The tth occasion at which the first player can win occurs at the $2t - 1$ period, his chance of winning then is $(\tfrac{1}{2})^{2t-1}$. Since the discount rate is 50 per cent, the value of any income obtained then must be discounted by the factor or $(\tfrac{1}{2})^{2t-1}$. Summing the geometric series, we are able to obtain the total expected value of the payoff to the first player, which is $\tfrac{14}{15}$.

The other payoffs are easier to calculate. If the second player withdraws immediately, the first player obtains an income worth $\tfrac{3}{2}$ immediately and in the next period can pay out one unit from his corporate account, which contains two units. Discounting this unit, the total payoff becomes 2. The payoff matrix for the first player only is

Player 1	Player 2	(1)	(2)
	(1)	$\frac{14}{15}$	2
(2)		$\frac{7}{4}$	$\frac{5}{2}$
(3)		2	2

We observe that both the second and third strategies dominate the first.

One further example illustrates an important feature about the length of a struggle. Suppose that the market matrix of a game had four strategies for the first player and two for the second, as shown here:

$$\begin{pmatrix} -1 & 1 \\ 1 & -1 \\ 2 & -3 \\ -3 & 2 \end{pmatrix}$$

Furthermore, suppose that the discount rate were high, say 50 per cent, that the first player had at the start of the game ten units, and the second player had only two. In a single-period market game the optimal strategy for the first player, which gives him his maximin value, is to use his first two strategies with a probability of $\frac{1}{2}$ each. This yields him an expected value of zero. However, in this ruin game it is more profitable for the player to use the last two strategies with a probability of $\frac{1}{2}$ each, even though the expected value is $-\frac{1}{2}$. The reason is that despite the expected value of a single play being less and because of the greater stakes involved the first player has a chance of ruining his opponent much faster by employing the latter strategy. If the income he receives as the survivor is sufficiently great, the value of receiving it sooner more than offsets the extra expected loss incurred by not playing the first two strategies. Suppose that the prize were 10, then if the first player employs the first two strategies he has only a $\frac{1}{4}$ chance of winning in two periods; hence with the high discount the prize must be worth less than $(\frac{1}{4})\,(10) = \frac{5}{2}$. If he employs the last two strategies, he has a $\frac{1}{2}$ chance of winning in one period, and this alone is worth $(\frac{1}{2})\,(\frac{1}{2})\,(10) = \frac{5}{2}$. If we add the value of winning later, the total payoff will be greater than $\frac{5}{2}$.

The general economic point illustrated by this example is that if a fight for survival must take place it may be cheaper in the long run for a powerful firm to indulge in an intense but quick war rather than one which costs less per period of fighting but enables both sides to survive for a protracted struggle.

3.3. The Description of a General Game of Economic Survival

The examples in subsections 3.1 and 3.2 have all had zero-sum market matrices which were the same during every period of the game. There are two major oversimplifications caused by using a fixed zero-sum market matrix. First, as we have already noted, if market models are to be a realistic reflection of economic conditions, they will, in general, call for subgames which are nonzero-sum. Second, by using a fixed matrix during every period we imply that the firms are unable to expand their production beyond a limit, which is always the same regardless of their corporate asset positions, and that they are unable to expand or increase operational efficiency by plant improvement. In order to rid ourselves of these limitations we start with a very general description of factors that we would like to consider in a general game of economic survival, after which we give further specifications for the economic models we wish to investigate further.

An *n-person game of economic survival* Γ is an infinite game tree K with the following specifications:

(1)   A partition of moves into $n + 1$ indexed sets V_0, V_1, V_2, ..., V_n consisting of *chance* and *personal* moves. This is called the *player partition.*

(2)   For each chance move a probability distribution which assigns a positive probability to each alternative.

(3)   Let M_t be the set of all plays up to the tth move. $m_t \epsilon M_t$ is a specific play up to the tth move. To each play m_t there are associated the following arrays of numbers:

$R_{i,t}$ in which $i = 1, 2, 3, ..., n$; these are the short-run or *positional revenues.*

$C_{i,t}$ represent the *corporate asset positions.*

$w_{i,t}$ are the *withdrawal payments* or the positional payoffs. The relation

$$C_{i,t} = C_{i,t-1} + R_{i,t} - w_{i,t}$$

will always hold.

$\omega_{i,t}$ are the *ruin or bankruptcy levels* of corporate assets.

$\lambda_{i,t}$ are the *liquidation values.*

$\rho_{i,t}$ are the *discount rates.*

(4)   There is a partition $\mathcal{A}$ of the moves into *information sets* $A_{i,\beta}$ in which β is the index of the information set and i is the index of the player.

(5)   For each player i, there is a bounded *utility function*

$$P_i = P_i(w_{i,0}, \rho_{i,0}, \ w_{i,1}, \rho_{i,1}, \ ..., \ w_{i,\tau}, \rho_{i,\tau}, \ \lambda_{i,\tau}),$$

where τ is the index of the move at which the ith firm liquidates.

The moves of the players consist of actions involving production, financing, payment of dividends, advertising, research, expansion, and other actions of a firm. The chance moves may be associated with fluctuations in national income, changes in taste, the probabilities of success in advertising and in innovation, and other variables which involve risk or uncertainty and which are exogenous to the players. It may be very difficult to assign probabilities to some chance moves. However, we will assume at this time that in most cases crude approximations can be made.

The positional revenues are a more general form of the revenues obtained from the market in the examples given in subsections 3.1 and 3.2. The positional revenue for a firm is its net income during some period (which is often conventionally picked as a quarter of a year or a year). Net income has to account for all income sources, some of which may have little to do with the market in which the firm primarily operates; thus income from bond holdings or stock interests in other firms is included.

As a first approximation we use a single number to represent the asset position of a firm. This is, in essence, an aggregation of the information contained in a balance sheet.

The withdrawal payments represent the income received by ownership. The relationship between corporate asset position, positional revenue, and withdrawal payments is given by an accounting condition that will always hold true, provided the firm does not borrow, sell stock, or finance in some other manner. Practically, there are considerable difficulties in imputing depreciation. This must be done in order to compute the corporate asset position and positional revenue.

At any time a firm will run some risk of being forced out of competition. The excess of the capital asset position over the bankruptcy index gives the losses that must be suffered by a firm if it is to be forced to close.

The utility function in specification 5 indicates that the function maximized by a corporation is some general expression involving the discounted value of the amounts paid out to ownership, plus a liquidation value that is paid out when the firm terminates its operations. More structure can be given to this function, and this is done in subsection 3.4.

Within this broad sketch of the elements that make up a game of economic survival it is possible to introduce side payments between players as actual moves in the game. The many different information conditions that are brought about by industrial secrecy may be reflected by the information conditions on the game tree. However, for specificity we limit our analysis to games of economic survival which can be best described as composed of single-period games played many times over. In this manner we are able to bring about a natural extension of the type of game discussed in Part One. Later in this chapter we discuss more general conditions in which changes in demand, innovation, and other secular forces play their role.

Following the line of development used in Part One, we first consider a market in which there are a fixed number of firms in existence and no potential entrants. Later in section 9 we extend the analysis to firms-in-being and entry.

The initial position of a firm is given by the size of its corporate account. The initial value of the corporate account of the ith firm is

$$C_{i,0} = a_i.$$

The formulation given here is for any number of players; however, when we discuss solutions to a game of economic survival in this chapter we limit ourselves at most to two-person games.

The size of the withdrawal account at period t^* is denoted by

$$W_{i,t^*} = \sum_{t=0}^{t^*} \rho^t w_{i,t}$$ for the ith player. This is the cumulative function of all discounted payments until time t^*. Initially, we may assume $W_{i,0} = 0$. This convention is quite general. It merely indicates that past withdrawals are not relevant to the present maximization problem of a firm. The value of a firm depends upon present and future income streams.

In general, the actions available to a firm in any market period depend upon the assets it has available. In a world with capital restrictions and severe limitations on the financing of production even if a firm has the physical plant to increase its scope of activity it may still lack capital. The importance of the asset position can be stressed by assuming that in any subgame, i.e., any single period, the ith firm has a set of market strategies $S_{i,t}$ available at time t; and, further, the size of this set of strategies depends upon the size of its corporate account:

$$S_{i,t} = S_{i,t}(C_{i,t}); \qquad S_i = \bigcup_{t=0}^{\infty} S_{i,t}.$$

Furthermore, we assume that if $C_{i,t} > C_{i,t}^1$ then $S_{i,t} > S_{i,t}^1$. This states that as the assets of a firm grow so do its strategic possibilities. If two firms differ only in the amount of money they happen to possess, then the richer is in a position to take any action that the poorer can afford, as well as some extra actions. Usually, when firms differ in wealth this difference is soon reflected in a different asset structure, i.e., different plant, inventories, and fixed-to-liquid asset ratios. However, in this simple first approximation to dynamic corporate competition we do not distinguish the detailed differences in corporate asset structure. The market matrix for a two-person game indicates the relation between the

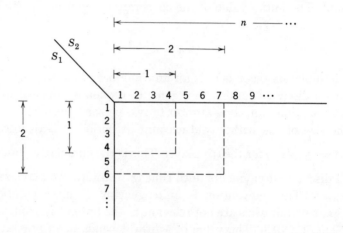

asset condition and the availability of strategies. The different asset positions of the firms are represented by the numbers in the overlapping intervals at the top and left-hand sides of the matrix. The numbers on the borders are the strategies for the players. Thus, if player 1 has assets of 1 and player 2 has assets of 1, they play a game in the market that is represented by a 4 x 4 matrix as shown. If the second player has assets of 2 and the first has assets of 1, then the game is played on a 4 x 7 matrix in this example.

We have called this matrix the market matrix; it can also be called the net revenue matrix. This indicates the revenue that is obtained by the firm at the end of a period. With no change in technology or taste

$$R_{i,\,t}(S_{1,\,t},\,S_{2,\,t},\,\ldots\,S_{n,\,t}) = R_i(S_{1,\,t},\,S_{2,\,t},\,\ldots\,S_{n,\,t}).$$

As soon as the net revenue is obtained, a payment is made to the withdrawal account:

$$C_{i,t} = C_{i,t-1} + R_{i,t} - w_{i,t}.$$

Two factors of importance to corporate competition are the *ruin* or *bankruptcy* conditions and the *liquidation value* of a firm.

A firm will be ruined at time τ if at that time its assets reach or fall below some critical value for the first time:

$$C_{i,\tau} \leqslant \omega_i.$$

In general, when a firm is bankrupted it may be forced to liquidate. The liquidation value is usually less than the assets carried on the firm's books, even if liquidation is voluntary.

$$\lambda_{i,t} = \lambda_i(C_{i,t}),$$

where t is the period when liquidation takes place.

There is a discount rate $\rho = 1/(1 + r)$, where r is the long term rate of interest which operates on the withdrawal account but not on the corporate assets. The reason for this is that the alternative employment of the money entering the withdrawal account will yield the rate of return r, whereas the yield from the employment of the corporate assets is already shown by the net revenue.

Finally, we can describe the over-all payoff to a player i as a function of the payments to the withdrawal account and the value of liquidation at some time t.

$$P_i = P_i(w_{i,0}; \ w_{i,1}\,\rho; \ w_{i,2}\,\rho^2; \ \ldots w_{i,t}\,\rho^t; \ \lambda_i(C_{i,t})).$$

Different specifications of this function are discussed subsequently.

3.4. Motives for Profit Maximization

The utility functions for the players in the games of economic survival discussed in subsection 3.3 are very generally described. We noted that they are a function of the paid out earnings or withdrawals and the value attached to the liquidation of the firm. We offer three specifications of the utility functions which approximately reflect different motivations that may arise from different legal and financial structures. There may, of course, be many more, but we shall limit ourselves to these for now.

3.4.1. THE INDIVIDUAL ENTREPRENEUR. The traditional pre-sentation of the theory of the firm is applicable to an individual entrepreneur trying to maximize the money income from his business. Even at this simple level of abstraction two difficulties are faced. The first concerns the treatment of the role of chance or uncertainty. If the future income of a businessman is uncertain, he can no longer maximize the present value of a known income stream but must act so as to maximize some function of income expectation.

A second difficulty is brought about by the possible distinction between the asset position of the entrepreneur and that of his firm. Our formalization of a game of economic survival in subsection 3.3 highlights this problem. Its resolution calls for explicit consider-ation of the legal and institutional framework in which a firm operates.

First, let us consider the unincorporated individual businessman. Legally, there is no difference between his business and his per-sonal accounts for the most part. However, our distinction is still a useful one to make. The money he spends to live represents his withdrawals. If he is bankrupted, his personal assets which are not distinguished from his firm's assets are liable. A small shopkeeper or farmer who is unincorporated and operates with unlimited liability may place a high value on his "freedom" or independence. His aim may be to maximize his survival in business, subject to the side condition that he can pay himself a wage large enough to compensate for the wage he could obtain by seeking other employ-ment. The precise mathematical formulation involves the definition of probability of survival. This is discussed in subsection 3.4.2.

Our second example is that of the owner of an incorporated enterprise. He may be quite prepared to be bankrupted if the promise of gain is high enough. If his risk preferences are more or less linear for money (i.e., if he is willing to take "fair gambles"), then he will try to maximize the expected value of the sum

$$\sum_{t=0}^{\tau} w_{i,t}\rho^t + \lambda_{i,\tau}\rho^\tau,$$

where the $w_{i,t}$ are his withdrawal payments for every period he is in business and the $\lambda_{i,\tau}$ is the monetary payment he obtains upon liquidation. Examples in subsections 3.1 and 3.2 assume this.

In some businesses in which, for instance, there may be a temporarily unsatisfied demand caused by a delay in production by a large firm it may be perfectly consistent for a small firm to enter into competition even if there were a certainty of ruin; i.e., even if the owners knew that they would eventually have to liquidate or be wiped out.

3.4.2. THE CORPORATION AND MAXIMIZATION.   Most of the firms which fall within the domain of study of the theory of oligopoly are corporations. They have boards of directors whose members may hold positions on other directorates, they have managers who may hold little or no stock in the firm and whose interests may vary from keeping their jobs in a live and growing firm to winning their way up the general corporate heirarchy or eventually going into business for themselves. The corporations often have stockholders whose only interest is the market value of the stock and the size of their dividends. Who maximizes what and how are the various desires reflected in the decisions made by a corporation?

We note as an example one possible set of motivations which serves to define the goals or utility function for an officer-dominated corporation. If we consider that the directors and officers are in actual control (in the United States officers often occupy many, if not a majority, of the directorships; see Chapter 12: 4 and 5, for instance), then we may study their desires in the context of the desires of the other interested parties. The management group may wish to stay in control of a strong corporate entity, subject to the condition that it "has discharged its responsibility" to the stockholders, employees, and public. This imprecise expression of goals may have one manifestation in a policy which calls for the maximization of the growth of the firm, subject to the payment of some percentage of the profits of the firm in dividends and some profit-sharing scheme for the employees. The bonuses and salaries of the management may be intimately related with both the size of the firm and its profitability.

We still have not included risk in this discussion. When corporations are young their probability of survival is poorest (see Chapter 12: 2); hence they may not be in a position to risk large fluctuations in expected revenue. Even when survival or failure is not the problem, as is the case when a firm has the choice of obtaining different positive revenues with different risks, this feature must be introduced into the payoff.

The probability of survival of a firm over any period of time depends upon its asset position, the strategies of all players, and the payoffs. If, for instance, the payoff matrix has no negative terms (as might be the case in a boom market with few supplying firms and no new entrants), then the probability of survival of any firm is 1. In the example given in subsection 3.1, in which both firms have assets of 1, their probability of survival for one period is $\frac{1}{2}$. When they have assets of 2 each their probability of survival for one period is 1 (they could not be ruined in that time), but their probability of survival for two periods is $\frac{3}{4}$.

In a market in which one player has the resources and ability to cause losses to an opponent, no matter what he does, until his assets are exhausted, the long run probability of survival for the second player (see subsection 5.1.1) is 0 if a policy of destruction is used by his opponent. Without a knowledge of the strategies of the opponents, a firm can calculate the set of policies it must restrict itself to in order to have a contingent probability of survival above any level it wishes. The contingency is based upon the actions of its opponents. If the strategies of its opponents are known, then the firm may make a specific calculation of the restriction needed to its actions in order to maintain a probability of survival of any specified level over a given period of time.

4. SOLUTIONS OF A TWO-PERSON GAME OF ECONOMIC SURVIVAL

4.1. Co-operative and Non-Co-operative Solutions?

In section 3 in our example of a game of economic survival we observed that the sum of the revenues to the firms in any period when they both were in the market was zero and side payments between the firms were forbidden. A reasonable solution was a non-co-operative one in which they fought until one firm was forced out of the market. However, as we have already noted, the payoff in a market is rarely zero-sum. Suppose that we have a game in which in every period the players obtain the following payoffs:

| | s_2 1 | 2 |
s_1		
1	(5, 5)	(2, 6)
2	(6, 2)	(3, 3)

If this game were played only once, then the co-operative solution calls for each of the players to use his first strategy, jointly maximize, and obtain 10 between them. The Nash non-co-operative equilibrium is such that each player will use his second strategy and each will obtain 3. This is obviously minimal! But the incentive to double-cross the other player if he can be persuaded to use his first strategy makes this outcome plausible when the game is played once.

Suppose that this game were to be played twice, or any specific number of times, perhaps t times. With no discount, i.e., $\rho = 0$, if the players insist upon using their second strategy in each of the games, their payoffs will be $3t$ each, whereas by co-operation they can obtain $5t$ each. The difference between the reward for non-co-operative behavior and co-operative behavior is great. If we are to put much faith in the non-co-operative equilibrium point theory, we hope that in a game of this variety, in which the period-by-period reward of the players can vary so drastically, there will be an equilibrium point which yields more than the joint minimum. We can show, however, that this is not so. We do this by means of a "backward induction."

Consider that the players have evolved some other method of playing than to use their second strategies at each period. If either player is committed to using his first strategy in the game to be played in the tth period, it will pay his opponent to use his second, since this will yield him a higher profit, and the game will be over before reprisals can be taken. This implies that for the strategies of players to be in equilibrium in the last period both must use their second strategies. But both can calculate this and can carry the argument one step back to the $t - 1$ period. If either player is committed to using his first strategy, it will pay his opponent to use his second, in which case it is foolish for a player committed to using his first strategy to do so.

We end up with an equilibrium point which consists of both players always using their second strategies and obtaining a jointly minimal outcome. This might be a simplified model of price cutting, in which case the interpretation would be that the players never learn and by their own cupidity jointly harm themselves. When we add the basic features that turn this example of a two-person, nonzero-sum game played over t periods into an economic ruin game we are able to resolve the paradox of non-co-operation and observe that in general the clear-cut distinction between co-operative and non-co-operative behavior begins to blur.

Suppose that at the end of every period the firms paid out all the money they obtained into their withdrawal accounts. In this model there is no motivation to do otherwise because the firms never lose money, hence are in no danger of ruin; on the other hand, there is no possibility of using the extra assets to increase their scope of action or profitability. We assume that the game is of indefinite length and that there is a discount rate of ρ effective on the withdrawal accounts. The goal of each firm is to maximize the discounted value of its withdrawal account.

In a game which has a specified number of periods the chiseller may be able to double-cross his partners, violate "trade ethics," or strike against the cartel and make a greater profit than if he had kept the faith, i.e., if he waits until the time that reprisals cannot cost him more than his gain. If the game is of indefinite length, then an individual may obtain a temporary gain by deviating from a jointly favorable strategy, but the reprisals of an opponent may cost him more than his short-run gain.

For all intents and purposes, both a market and a corporation have an infinite or at least an indefinite life which makes this model a better approximation to economic conditions than the game which is played over a fixed number of times t. We can show that in this game of economic survival the players have strategies which can enforce the joint maximum with an income of 5 each per period as an equilibrium.

Suppose that player 1 announced the following strategy:

$$s_{1,0} = 1$$

$$s_{1,\tau} = 1, \text{ if } s_{2,t} = 1; t = 0, 1, 2, \ldots, \tau - 1$$

$$s_{1,t} = 2, \text{ for } t = \tau + 1, \tau + 2, \ldots, \text{ if } s_{2,\tau} = 2.$$

This states that the first player will use his first strategy initially and will continue to do so as long as he is informed that his opponent has been doing likewise. As soon as he discovers that his opponent has utilized his second strategy, then the first player will switch to his second strategy in all succeeding games.

If the second player decides to utilize his first strategy during every period, he will obtain an income stream of 5 every period. This has a discounted value of

$$5 \sum_{t=o}^{\infty} \rho^t = 5 \left(\frac{1+r}{r} \right),$$

where $\rho = 1/1 + r$. If the second player switches to his second strategy in the game that is played in the τth period, then he makes a temporary gain, but this may soon be wiped out by the first player's reprisal. Given the strategy of player 1, the discounted value of the income stream to player 2 will be

$$5 \sum_{t=0}^{\tau-1} \rho^t + 6\rho^{\tau} + 3 \sum_{t=\tau+1}^{\infty} \rho^t.$$

It can be easily verified that the second payoff is always less than the first, unless the rate of interest is greater than 200 per cent per annum! For any reasonable rate of interest it will not pay a firm to risk a price cut if it knows that its opponent can retaliate successfully.

If the second player uses the same type of over-all strategy as the first, then neither will ever depart from playing the strategy 1 during each period because of the cost of reprisal. Thus the joint maximum becomes an equilibrium point!

In general, we observe that the threat of reprisal in a game of economic survival creates equilibria which do not exist in the subgames of finite duration. It may even be possible to have a joint maximum enforced non-co-operatively, as in the example given. Whether or not this can happen depends upon the willingness and the ability of firms to take "police action" against those who "break the faith." The police action may take the form of a price cut, an increase in advertising, a refusal to extend credit, or a cutting off of supplies. The effectiveness of the action will depend upon the flexibility of the firms. It will, in general, be easier to carry out reprisals against a firm with high fixed costs than to punish a trader who can be out of one market and into the next before his maneuvers have been noticed.

4.2. EQUILIBRIUM POINTS GALORE

If we assume that all firms are likely to play every strategy that is within their power, we can see that a non-co-operative equilibrium point yielding almost every imputation of wealth between two firms can be achieved by some pair of strategies. The more paranoid the players are, the more distributions there are which can be non-co-operatively enforced. This is because a player can use a strategy which commits him to carry out a violent and possibly self-destructive threat in order to retaliate against any violation of the *status quo*. Under usual business conditions it is unreasonable to expect that the result of one firm cutting a penny off the price of one of its thousands of products will be an industrial war caused by an all-out retaliation of an industrial opponent. However, we may expect some type of retaliation limited to a few product lines.

In order to prevent our theory from becoming so vague and general that almost all imputations of wealth can arise from non-co-operative equilibria we will consider restrictions on the type of threats that a firm may use. The restrictions on the strategies are "co-operative" in nature and limit the "competitive" or non-co-operative equilibria that can be enforced by the use of permissible strategies. For instance, in war conventions regarding the treatment of medical personnel represent co-operative restrictions on the strategy spaces of the participants. Agreements to follow certain conventions in bridge or the outlawing of "sandbagging" in poker [9] provide examples of this type of restriction.

Before we can apply these considerations to the study of competition in the market, we must establish a formal basis for the somewhat nebulous discussion presented here in subsection 4.2 and in 4.1.

4.3. STRATEGIES, STATIONARY STRATEGIES, THREATS, AND VIOLATIONS

4.3.1. STRATEGIES. A strategy in a game of indefinite length, as in a game of finite length, is a general plan of action which tells the player what to do under every contingency at any time during the game. The fact that there may be no definite stopping point for the game does not prevent a strategist from issuing instructions which tell the player what to do at his tth move for t of any size. For instance, the Cournot behavior condition may be regarded as a complete (even if rather foolish) strategy in a dynamic game. It specifies the action to be taken under all contingencies. It states:

Regardless of any information you have received, always assume that your opponent will repeat his last move and maximize your immediate short-run profit on this assumption.

We need only be concerned with pure strategies and behavior strategies (see Chapter 9: 2.1) in the games we discuss because we have assumed that after every market period the players are informed about the actions which were taken by their competitors. This is not strictly true, but it appears to be a good approximation. Although it may take several years for a new automobile model to be developed, as soon as it is brought on to the market all the previously classified information becomes available.

In the following subsections we single out two special classes of strategies for our attention. They are not mutually exclusive as one class is contained in the other, but the distinction is useful to our concept of solution.

4.3.2. CONSTANT MARKET STRATEGIES AND STATIONARY STRATEGIES. In any subgame or single-period game to be played in the tth period the ith player or corporation will have a set $S_{i,t}$ of strategies available to him. A strategy in a single period involves action with regard to market, asset, and dividend policy. It is a plan of the following sort:

I will utilize my mth market move; as soon as I obtain the net revenue from the operation of the firm, I will divide this sum between the asset and the withdrawal accounts in some manner depending upon its size.

The examples given in subsection 3.2 indicate the way in which the strategies of a firm depend upon its assets and show the distinction between the market and financial component of the strategy. We denote a particular strategy in the set $S_{i,t}$ by $s_{i,t}$. It comprises two moves, the market move which determines the actions of the firm in the market and the financial move which divides the net revenue into the two different accounts. We identify the moves by $m_{i,t}$ and $f_{i,t}$.

An over-all or complete strategy for a game of economic survival is called a *constant market strategy* for player i, if and only if

$$m_{i,t} = \bar{m}_i \qquad \text{for } t = 0, 1, 2, \ldots,$$

in which $\bar{m}_i$ is a market move available to player i during every period. Such a move will always exist unless a player has liquidated and is no longer in the game.

A complete strategy for a game of economic survival is called a *stationary strategy* for player i, if and only if

$$s_{i,t} = \bar{s}_i, \qquad \text{for } t = 0, 1, 2, \ldots.$$

In other words, a stationary strategy is one in which both the market move and the financial move of a player are repeated every period. Such a strategy may not always be feasible. An economic interpretation of the unfeasibility of a stationary strategy is given in section 5.

4.3.3. THREAT STRATEGIES. Suppose that one player were satisfied with a division of a market that could be maintained if each utilized a specific constant market strategy or stationary strategy. The player may realize that if he were committed to his strategy it would be to the advantage of his opponent to deviate. He may be able to prevent this deviation by utilizing a strategy which, though allied to his constant market or stationary strategy, contains a "threat" component. This indicates the action he is prepared to take if his opponent departs from the desired stationary state. The strategies used by the players in the example in sub-section 4.1 are threat strategies. In general

$$s_{i,0} = \bar{s}_i,$$

$$s_{i,t} = \bar{s}_i \text{ if } s_{j,\tau} = \bar{s}_j \qquad \text{for } \tau = 0, 1, 2, \ldots, t-1,$$

$$s_{i,t} = \chi(s_{i,1}, \ldots, s_{i,t-1}, s_{j,1}, \ldots, s_{j,t-1}),$$

$$\text{for } t = \tau + 1, \ \tau + 2, \ \ldots, \text{ if } s_{j,\tau} \neq \bar{s}_j.$$

This states that player i is willing to maintain his stationary strategy as long as he is informed that player j is maintaining a stationary strategy that is consistent with i's actions. As soon as i is informed that j has departed from this strategy, he follows some general course of action as indicated by the function χ.

We note that the threat strategies include the stationary strategies as a special case. A threat strategy is a stationary strategy if the function χ, which describes the course of action to be followed after an opponent has deviated, tells the player to repeat his previous action.

The formalization of a threat is carried out with respect to a stationary strategy. The same type of formalization can be given for a constant market strategy.

4.3.4. MIXED STRATEGIES AND INFERENCE.   In the examples in subsection 3.2 the players utilized mixed strategies in the market games played in every period. These strategies are constant market strategies and formally satisfy the requirements in subsection 4.3.2. However, in the discussion that follows in section 5 we limit ourselves to pure strategies in every period. The reason for doing this is that although there may be many pairs of mixed strategies which satisfy equilibrium conditions a theory of inference is required to explain how one player is able to infer from the actions of his opponent that his opponent has departed from his stationary strategy, if it involves a probability mix. This is not so when both employ pure strategies in the stationary state. Possibly firms exhibit behavior which amounts to "testing the market." For instance, they may maintain a stationary strategy that involves a small random component (the occasional sale or price reduction). The explanation of such behavior requires knowledge about learning and inference that we do not possess. By limiting ourselves to pure strategies (in subsection 6.3 we introduce chance moves made by nature, such as fluctuations in demand or varying degrees of success in advertising, we narrow the scope of the theory. However, it still serves to investigate the basic features of multiple equilibria, price stickiness, and the problems of entry and exit in an ologopolistic market.

4.4. SOLUTIONS TO A TWO-PERSON GAME OF ECONOMIC SURVIVAL

4.4.1. CONSTANT MARKET STRATEGY AND STATIONARY STATE SOLUTIONS.   We define a stationary state solution to a two-person game of economic survival as the set of stationary state outcomes which can be enforced as equilibrium points by pairs of threat strategies. The meaning of this is demonstrated by a simple 2 x 2 nonzero-sum game. [10] Let us replace the complete game of economic survival by a game in which each player has a choice of only two strategies. One is a threat strategy (see subsection 4.3.3) designed to enforce some state of the market as an equilibrium state, and the other is any other strategy which maximizes against the threat strategy of the opponent.

By identifying the two strategies for each player by T^1, V^1, and T^2, V^2, we can describe the game by the matrix

$$
\begin{array}{ccc}
 & T^2 & V^2 \\
T^1 & P_1(T^1, T^2),\ P_2(T^1, T^2) & P_1(T^1, V^2),\ P_2(T^1, V^2) \\
V^1 & P_1(V^1, T^2),\ P_2(V^1, T^2) & P_1(V^1, V^2),\ P_2(V^1, V^2)
\end{array}
$$

If there is no other strategy for either player which yields more than his threat strategy when played against the threat strategy of his opponent, then the two threat strategies form an equilibrium pair. The possibility of threat action prevents both players from departing from the stationary state. Without the threat potential it might pay a player to depart.

As we have already observed, almost every imputation of wealth could become an equilibrium point if we consider all possible threats. However, if we take into account the cost to a player of carrying out his threat, we may be able to introduce some criteria for accepting or rejecting certain threat strategies. Thus, if one firm wishes to maintain a certain level of profit in a market, it might be able to do so by threatening to enter into a fight-to-the-death struggle with its opponent if the market is "disturbed." This threat would be quite plausible if the firm is in a position to win a war, wipe out its opponent, and then go on to recoup its costs. Such is the position of a dominant firm. If, on the other hand, the threat of the firm is suicidal, i.e., by carrying out its threat it ruins itself, then the threat may be quite implausible.

If absolute precommitment took place (i.e., if announced threats were *always* carried out) in a dynamic oligopoly setting or in power politics, then a case could be made out for evaluating all threats only in terms of the amount of damage done to the violator. Thus a threat even by a small country to precipitate an atomic war, if the *status quo* were violated, might be sufficient to guarantee the *status quo*, even though the cost of carrying out the threat were suicidal, provided the country was precommitted to carrying it out.

Without precommitment we must try to introduce some measure of the plausibility of a threat being carried out. We can do this and then examine solutions enforceable under restricted subclasses of threats.

There are at least four natural qualifications which can be attributed to threats in a game of economic survival. A threat is *killing* if it ruins the opponent regardless of any action he may take. It is *suicidal* if the opponent has at least one course of action which will bring about the ruin of the threatener under every possible circumstance.

Up to this point no assumption has been made about the comparability of the value of money between the two firms. If we assume that money has the same value to the players, we can distinguish between *strong* and *weak* threats. A threat is *strong* if the loss suffered by the threatener, measured by the difference in profits obtained by maintaining the stationary state and by utilizing the threat, is not greater than the loss suffered by the opponent. A threat for player 1 is strong if

$$P_1(T^1, T^2) - P_1(T^1, V^2) \leqslant P_2(T^1, T^2) - P_2(T^1, V^2).$$

A threat is *weak* if the converse holds, i.e., the threatener loses more than the violator if he carries out his threat.

If restrictions are made upon the strategy spaces of the players by limiting the type of threats which may be employed, this may limit the number of stationary state positions which can be enforced as equilibria. For instance, we may limit the *threat* strategies to the class of *stationary* strategies. In certain dynamic models, as might be expected, there is only one stationary state equilibrium, which is the Cournot equilibrium point replicated through time (see section 5).

We shall see in sections 5, 6, and 7 that the economic conditions imposed by entry costs, time lags, capital structure, finance, product mix, demand, advertising, and innovation are often sufficient to modify the model of a game of economic survival. This is done to such an extent that with very weak assumptions concerning the behavior of the firms in the market results concerning the likelihood of different degrees of competition or collusion can be obtained without having to delve very deeply into psychological theories of learning.

4.4.2. RUIN SOLUTIONS.   It may happen that a pair of repeated market moves or a stationary state which can be enforced as an equilibrium does not exist. We note that if one player has no threat strong enough to prevent his opponent from departing from some stationary state it implies that the opponent is in a position to drive the firm out of competition and to gain sufficient profits later to the extent that the long-run profit is more than that offered by the stationary state. In this case the solution will consist of the optimal path of exit for the weaker firm.

5.   A DYNAMIC DUOPOLY MODEL

5.1. AN EXAMPLE COMPUTED

The nature of the solution concept presented in this chapter is illustrated by examining a duopoly model of competition between firms by quantity variation. It might be desirable to consider a model in which the market move of a firm is more complicated than the selection of a rate of production. In Chapters 5 and 7 we examined one-period models in which price, quantity, advertising, inventories, and product were the independent variables. The results of that analysis can be applied to the dynamic models, but for simplicity we limit ourselves to the easiest duopoly model, that of quantity variation. We stress here that although we make the unrealistic assumption that the firms merely offer a quantity of goods to the market at every time period and that the market mechanism determines a price at which no inventories remain actually the more realistic assumption would reinforce the type of result obtained.

The model presented here is closely related to the model given in Chapter 4.

Physical Conditions

1. *Demand Conditions.*   At any time period t there is a demand function $p_t = \phi_t(q_t) = \phi(q_t)$, where $\sum q_{i,t} = q_t$, $q_{i,t}$ is the output of the ith firm in the tth period.

The above condition implies that the demand is regenerated in the same way every time period and that the price obtained during any period depends only upon the quantities produced by all the firms during that period. In other words, inventory carry-overs are not taken into account here. Specifically, for purposes of illustration, we assume there is a demand of

$$p_t = 10 - 2q_t,$$

where $\quad\quad\quad q_t = \Sigma\, q_{i,t}, \ i = 1, 2.$

2. *Average Variable Costs.* The average variable cost to player i of producing the quantity q_{it} in period t is $\gamma_{it}(q_{it}) = \gamma_i(q_{it})$. This implies that the average variable costs of production for each player remain constant through time. In our example we assume

$$\gamma_{1,t} = \gamma_{2,t} = 5 - q_{i,t} + q_i,^2{}_t.$$

3. *Fixed Costs.* If an entrepreneur owns a plant but does not produce during any period t, he loses a sum $k_{it} = k_i$ during that period. In this case overhead charges are taken to be 1 per production period (this amounts to approximately 20 per cent at Cournot equilibrium).

4. *Liquidation Value.* If, for any reason, a firm is forced to or wishes to liquidate, there is a (positive) difference between its corporate asset account immediately before liquidation and the amount transferred to the withdrawal account upon liquidation; i.e., there is a cost to liquidation. This cost is assumed to be 10 in the example.

Time Lags

1. *Entry.* The problem of entry is not dealt with until section 7. Here we assume that both firms initially possess plants.

2. *Exit.* If a player liquidates, we assume that the survivor is left in sole control. In the example a player is assumed to sell his plant and cease production in one period when he liquidates. This assumption ties in with item 4 of *Physical Conditions* because if we further assumed that a player could use any method to liquidate there would be more than one liquidation value, depending upon the amount of time available and the circumstances under which liquidation takes place.

3. *Production Conditions.*   A player can change his production rate by any amount in one time period. (This, in general,, is highly unrealistic.) In the example we assume that there are six production periods per annum.

4. *Information Conditions and Moves.*   Each subgame may be regarded as a game with a single simultaneous move. As previously noted, a strategy in a subgame has both a market and a financial component. After every period the players are completely informed about the progress of the game.

Financial Conditions

1. *Corporate Account.*   We assume that initially the ith player has the amount $C_{i,0} = a_i$ in his corporate account. At this level of simplification we are not going into detail about the asset structure of the corporations. We assume no long-term debt and two simple balance sheets:

Balance Sheet for Corporation 1

Assets		Liabilities	
Current assets	40	Current liabilities	10
Fixed assets	20	Net worth	50
Total Assets	60	Total liabilities and net worth	60

Balance Sheet for Corporation 2

Assets		Liabilities	
Current assets	20	Current liabilities	10
Fixed assets	20	Net worth	30
Total Assets	40	Total liabilities and net worth	40

2. *Withdrawal Account.*   We assume that initially the ith player has the amount $W_{i,0} = 0$ in his withdrawal account. This assumption will have to be modified when we wish to discuss entry conditions. The initial condition for a firm-in-being is such that it starts with a corporate account of zero but has money in the withdrawal account which can be transferred. This corresponds to the initial financing condition of a corporation just before formation. Once again we stress that the choice of $W_{i,0} = 0$ is not **arbitrary** but indicates that (leaving stockmarket expectations

aside) past payments are not germane to the measurement of present profitability of a firm.

3. *Forced Liquidation Point or Ruin Level.*   If the net worth of the corporate account ever drops down to, or below, an amount g_i, the ith firm will be ruined and forced to liquidate.

For the example we make the simple assumption that if current liabilities ever exceed current assets the firm will be ruined and will have to liquidate.

4. *Long-Term Rate of Interest.*   We assume that there is a long-term rate of interest r_i for any player i. He may earn this rate on any money in his withdrawal account, but any money in his corporate account cannot be tied up in long-term financing. (Even if it were, this is reflected in the net revenue of the corporation: for instance, the product dealt in by a financial corporation may be regarded as being a long-term investment; its income may then consist of interest or dividend payments.) The long-term rate of interest in the example is assumed to be 6 per cent. The discount factor $\rho_i = 1/(1 + r_i)$.

5. *Short-Term Rate of Interest.*   There is a short-term rate of interest r_i' for the ith player, who may earn this rate on funds available in his corporate account. As a simplification we assume that $r_i' = 0$. The assumption is that these earnings are shown implicitly in the net revenue and/or the financial costs of production and are such that the costs of very short-term financing, such as banking charges, brokerage fees and charges for overdrafts, offset the yield of the short-term investment.

6. *Money Markets and Financing.*   There is no major outside financing available to a firm. Thus when its assets approach the ruin level it cannot go into the financial market to stave off disaster. Here we make the simplifying assumption that this also excludes transfers from the player's withdrawal account to the corporate account.

Motivation.

We assume the simplest of the maximization motivations discussed in subsection 3.3. Each entrepreneur wishes to maximize the discounted expected value of the income paid into his withdrawal account, regardless of whether his firm is ever forced into liquidation.

The Payoff Functions

Let $R_{i,t} = q_{i,t}\phi(q_t) - q_{i,t}\gamma_i(q_{i,t})$ be the revenue function of the ith firm in the tth period.

$C_{i,t}$ is the size of the corporate account of the ith firm in the tth period.

$w_{i,t}$ is the size of the payment from the corporate account into the withdrawal account by the ith player in the tth period.

P_i is the discounted value of the total payoff paid to the individual account of the owner of the firm until it liquidates.

At the tth period the corporate account is determined by

$$C_{i,0} = a_i \text{ and } C_{i,t} = C_{i,t-1} + R_{i,t-1} - w_{i,t-1}.$$

The discounted value of the total payoff is

$$P_i = \sum_{t=0}^{\infty} w_{i,t}\,\rho_i{}^t,$$

if the firm never liquidates, and

$$P_i = \sum_{t=0}^{\tau} w_{i,t}\,\rho_i{}^t + w^1{}_{i,\tau}\,\rho_i{}^\tau,$$

if it liquidates at the end of the τth period, in which $w^1{}_{i,\tau}$ is the liquidation payment to the withdrawal account.

5.1.1. THE DOMINANT FIRM SOLUTION. In the example given we have two firms which face identical production and demand conditions. There is an asymmetry in the financial structure which will prove to be highly relevant when we examine the ability of the firms to withstand a war for the control of the market.

The revenue function to each firm at any period t is

$$R_{i,t} = q_{i,t}(10 - 2(q_{1t} + q_{2t})) - q_{it}(5 - q_{it} + q_{it}{}^2).$$

We first carry out an analysis of the one-period game in order to obtain the information necessary to solve the many period situation. Using the methods given in Chapter 4: 3, we compute Table 14:

Table 14

	q_1	q_2	R_1	R_2	p
Monopoly solution	1.000	0.000	2.000	0.000	8.000
Joint maximal	0.633	0.633	0.709	0.709	7.468
Cournot	0.786	0.786	0.591	0.591	6.856
Efficient point	1.000	1.000	0.000	0.000	6.000

These points are indicated in Figures 45 and 46 as M_1, J. M., C, and E, respectively. The two curves in these figures are the joint maximal surface production and profit curves and the threat production and profit curves, respectively. They were obtained by solving for points on each curve. Figure 45 indicates that the Cournot production level is well above that of the joint maximum production but well below the rate at the efficient point.

The Nash threat point and the efficient point coincide in this symmetric example. The threat point is obtained for player 1 by

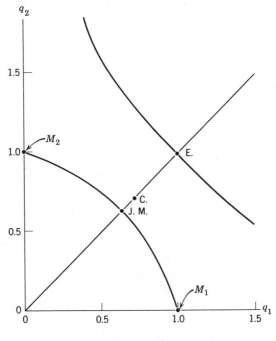

Figure 45

finding the production rate that makes the maximum of $R_2 - R_1$ a minimum for any action by player 2 (see Chapter 4: 3.6). We can interpret this type of threat in terms of an attrition rate. In a quantity-variation model it can cost the individual who starts a war more per period to inflict damage upon an opponent than the opponent loses. This may still be worthwhile if the opponent's resources are slim and he can be driven out of competition.

The upper limit to the damage that can be done to an opponent is to cause him to lose his overhead costs in a single period. This is computed on the minimax assumption that if he knows that an all-out attack is being launched in any particular period he can always insure that damage to him will not go above his overhead costs by shutting down his plant in that period. In this particular example player 1 would have to produce 2.5 in order to inflict a loss of $R_{2,t} = -1$ on his opponent. The cost of doing this is $R_{1,t} = -10.375$, which makes it prohibitive in most cases. This serves as a bound for the threat curve.

If a stationary state exists in the dynamic game, both firms can compute their long-run returns by summing the discounted value of the revenue paid out every period.

Suppose that the stationary-state production rate for player i were $\bar{q}_i$ per period and that all revenue were paid into the withdrawal account. The long-run returns would be

$$\bar{P}_i = \sum_{t=0}^{\infty} \bar{R}_{i,t}(1.01)^{-t}.$$

(The long-run rate of interest is 6 per cent, but there are six production periods per annum; hence for one production period the discount is approximately 1 per cent.)

$\bar{R}_{i,t}$ is a function of both $\bar{q}_i$ and $\bar{q}_j$. It is evident that the ith player will not accept any long-run equilibrium if it is possible to drive out the jth player and then recoup more than enough to equal the suggested stationary-state income. The lines labeled a_1 in Figure 46 give the stationary-state profit that player 1 can enforce by means of a strong killing threat against player 2, i.e., if player 2 were to attempt to increase production it would be cheaper for player 1 to fight than to fail to react.

On the assumption that the first firm will start a war immediately, its long-run payoff will consist of two components, the withdrawals made during the fight and the withdrawals obtainable after a successful war in which the survivor obtains the market for himself. During the fight the incomes of both firms must be negative, as shown by the shape of the threat curve in Figure 46; hence no payments will be made until one firm has succumbed. The survivor may proceed to pay out all revenue from then on into the withdrawal account. Table 14 lists this amount as 2.000 per period.

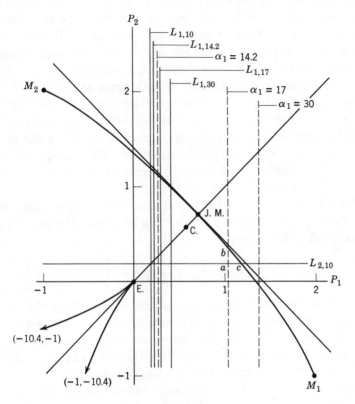

Figure 46

$$P_i^* = (2.000) \sum_{s=\tau}^{\infty} (1.01)^{-t},$$

where τ is the period during which player j is ruined, computed on the assumption that j wishes to minimize the payoff to i (this is a very pessimistic expectation for player i; he will make a profit at least as large as this).

We must make one further distinction here. Although the payoff represents the amount paid into the withdrawal account, the corporate account of the firm will have been depleted somewhat by the end of any fight. Should these losses be taken into account in the profit calculation? The answer to this depends upon a not completely defined feature of the asset structure of the firms. We were faced with a similar problem in the example in subsection 3.1. How much of the assets is needed to offset threat power of an opponent and how much is needed for production? If there is no possibility of further entry into the market, when one firm succumbs it may not matter to the other firm that it is barely solvent because it no longer has to fear attack. If both firms are in a stationary state equilibrium, part of this equilibrium includes having war chests of the right size to counteract each other. In this very simple model a phenomenon resembling overcapitalization is one of the features caused by that type of competition! Of course, a perfectly competitive capital market would remove this effect. However, this is usually not the case.

If we evaluate the asset losses at their replacement value, then the stationary-state profit yield that can be enforced by player 1 can be calculated by solving

$$\sum_{t=0}^{\infty} P_i(1 + r)^{-t} = \sum_{t=\tau+1}^{\infty} R_{i,t}^*(1 + r)^{-t} + \sum_{t=1}^{\tau} R_{i,t}(1 + r)^{-t}.$$

The number τ is determined by calculating how long the ruined firm can last against an optimum ruin strategy, on the assumption that it attempts to make its demise as costly as possible to the opponent. In the example given here the optimum ruin strategy and the number τ were obtained by approximation. The optimal threat for player 1 is to commence production at the rate of $q_1 = 1.63$; no matter what player 2 does he cannot cut his losses to below $P_{2,t} = -0.505$ per period. Hence, player 1 can ruin player 2 within twenty periods. His long-run payoff is

$$P_1 = (2.000) (1.01)^{-21}(101) - (0.505) \sum_{t=1}^{20} (1.01)^{-t} = 137.56.$$

This is equivalent to a steady-state payoff of $P_{i,t} = 1.363$; hence the first player need never accept a market equilibrium yielding him less than this amount.

The second player, by producing 0.498 per period, can reduce his losses per period to -0.505. In order to calculate player 1's optimal threat we must not only take into account the possibility that player 2 merely minimizes his losses per period until he goes bankrupt, but we must also compute the maximum amount of damage he can do to player 1, regardless of how long he stays in the game. Thus we are actually computing

$$\min_{q_{2,t}} \quad \max_{q_{1,t}} \quad P_1$$

In this example the optimal minimizing action of player 2 against player 1's payoff is to survive for as long as possible. Thus the action of producing 0.498 every time period if his most damaging alternative.

Table 15 gives an analysis of this dynamic duopoly for three different net liquid asset relations:

Table 15

α_1	α_2	$\bar{q}_{1,t}$	$q_{2,t}$	$\bar{q}_{2,t}$	$R_{1,t}$	$R_{2,t}$
30.0	10.0	1.630	0.498	1.000	−1.462	−0.505
17.0	10.0	1.300	0.574	1.000	0.121	−0.140
14.2	10.0	1.200	0.656	1.000	0.258	−0.007

$\bar{R}_{1,t}$	$\bar{R}_{2,t}$	τ	P_1	L_1	L_2	θ_1
−3.10	−1.26	20	137.56	0.400	0.200	27.51
−0.99	−0.60	72	104.26	0.270	0.2	28.18
−0.568	−0.40	1.429	26.02	0.242	0.20	7.57

$\bar{q}_{i,t}$ is the threat production rate used by player 1. $q_{2,t}$ is the production rate used by player 2 on the assumption that he would attempt to maximize $P_{2,t}$, given the other production. $\bar{q}_{2,t}$ is the production rate used by player 2 on the assumption that he wished to maximize the damage exchange rate or the attrition $R_{2,t} - R_{1,t}$. $R_{1,t}$ and $R_{2,t}$ are the profits per period under the first of player 2's actions. $\bar{R}_{1,t}$ and $\bar{R}_{2,t}$ are the profits under the second. τ is the maximum number of time periods it takes player 1 to ruin player 2. P_1 is the long-run profit that player 1 can enforce for himself against any action by player 2. θ_1 gives the percentage earned by player 1 on his net investment or net worth.

The values L_1 and L_2 represent the income each player could obtain by liquidating his plant immediately and investing at the long-run rate of interest. The asset values chosen indicate the range of the effect of difference in assets. When $\alpha_1 = 30$ there is no possible steady-state production level that is stable with both firms in the market. This can be seen in Figure 46. The line for $a_1 = 30$ is the lower bound on the profit player 1 can accept without ruining player 2, but there is no production level for both players which will yield player 1 a profit equal to or greater than this amount at the same time that player 2 obtains a profit of $P_{2,t} = L_{2,10}$, which is the amount he can obtain per period by liquidating.

When $a_1 = 17$ the possible steady-state equilibria which can exist consist of the triangular area bounded by the line $a_1 = 17$, the line $L_{2,10}$, and the joint maximum curve M_1M_2. (If side payments are permitted, then this area is extended to the triangle encompassed by the first two lines and the line passing through the point J. M.)

When $a_1 = 14.2$ the first player has just enough assets to ruin the second player. This can be seen is Table 15 by observing that if the second player tries to maximize the rate of attrition he will be ruined in twenty-five periods; the first player will just survive. by means of the very weak assumption that an individual prefers more income to less income with the same risk when he is given a If the second player tries to maximize his profit subject to the first player's production, it will be just slightly negative; hence he too eventually will be ruined. The ruin of the second player takes so long that the first player is able to enforce a profit for himself only slightly above his liquidation return (as indicated by lines $a_1 = 14.2$ and $L_{1,14.2}$).

5.1.2. MARKET EQUILIBRIUM AND BEHAVIOR IN THE DOMINANT FIRM SOLUTION. In the example computed in subsection 5.2.1 the only behavioristic assumption made was that the firms wished to maximize their discounted income values. When the two firms had sufficiently different asset structures the economic factors were strong enough to restrict the competitive possibilities in the market, *without having to consider the behavior patterns* of the rivals except by means of the very weak assumption that an individual prefers more income to less income with the same risk, when he is given a choice between the two. The financial dominance of one firm can be enough to entitle it to the lion's share of a peacefully divided market if its opponent cannot obtain enough financial support to make a threatened fight unprofitable. When the asset values of the firms in subsection 6.2 were $a_1 = 17$ and $a_2 = 10$, respectively this was enough to limit possible equilibria to the narrow triangle shown by *abc* in Figure 46. When the asset structure was more asymmetric ($a_1 = 30$) there was no longer room for both of the firms in competition. This does not imply that a war would have to be fought to drive the weaker firm out. It merely suggests that the economics of maximization require that the weaker firm be bought out, merged, or fought. In actual situations noneconomic goals may modify the action taken. For instance, fear of government action may stop the more powerful firm from driving out the weaker, whereas the law may forbid a merger as "tending to restrict competition." Thus "competition" is preserved by the powerful firm distorting its economic motivation to conform with legal and social restraints.

No suggestion is made here as to which of the many equilibrium points in the area *abc* (for the case in which $a_1 = 17$ and $a_2 = 10$) will actually be arrived at. This is not determined by the gross economic factors but depends upon detailed features of the market and the behavior patterns of the firm. In order to make useful assumptions about this behavior we need a combination of specialized knowledge of the market under examination and a theory of "learning."

We note in this example that if the initial assets of both firms are sufficiently close to each other it may not be possible for either one to ruin the other. In this case every distribution between the Pareto-optimal surface in Figure 46 and the appropriate lines L_1 and L_2 is available as an equilibrium distribution, provided the financial policies accompanying the market policies are such that the assets of the firms stay in the appropriate relationship to each other.

5.1.3. Other Solutions and the Behavioristic Assumptions. If we limit the threat strategies to stationary-state strategies alone, i.e., strategies of the form $s_{i,t} = \bar{s}_i$ for $t = 0, 1, 2, \ldots$, and if the asset conditions of the firms are not too dissimilar in the example given, the Cournot equilibrium point repeated through time will be the only equilibrium point. This has the value

$$\bar{P}_i = (0.5910) \sum_{t=0}^{\infty} (1.01)^{-t} = 59.69.$$

This result can be established generally. Suppose that in a

dynamic game the management of each firm knew that the opposing firm was committed to a steady-state strategy, i.e., that it would not change its production rate in any of the periods ahead. In a quantity-variation game played under this behavioral assumption the Cournot equilibrium strategies played through time give rise to the only equilibrium point (or points, if those is more than one Cournot equilibrium point) in the dynamic game, unless the asset conditions are such that it is profitable for one firm to ruin the other. Consider the strategy of player i given by $s_{i,t} = \bar{s}_i$ for $t = 1, 2, 3, \ldots$, where $\bar{s}_i$ is the component of the Cournot equilibrium in a single market period. Player j will be motivated to play a strategy other than his Cournot equilibrium strategy if and only if

$$\max P_j(\bar{s}_i, s_{j,1}, \bar{s}_i, s_{j,2}, \ldots \bar{s}_i, s_{j,t}, \ldots) > P_j(\bar{s}_i, \bar{s}_j, \bar{s}_i, \bar{s}_j \ldots),$$

where $\bar{s}_j$ is the component for player j of the Cournot equilibrium in a single market period.

If player j does not ruin player i, then in any single period his optimum strategy will be that which produces the Cournot equilibrium. This gives a player the maximum revenue he can obtain in any period as long as player i is active. The optimum revenue for the whole game will be obtained by j if he maximizes his income per period; this entails maintaining the Cournot equilibrium.

$$P_j = \sum_{t=1}^{\tau} R_{i,t}^* \rho^t + \rho^\tau A_j < \sum_{t=1}^{\infty} R_{i,t}^* \rho^t,$$

in which $R_{i,i}^*$ is the revenue in the tth period obtained from the use of the optimum ruin strategy of player j against player i, ρ is the discount rate, $R_{i,t}$ is the stationary-state revenue, and A_j is the value of the market to the survivor, the stationary Cournot equilibrium will dominate any ruin strategy. Given that similar conditions hold for player i against Player j, the Cournot equilibrium (if unique in the single-period game) will be the unique equilibrium in the game of economic survival.

6. DIFFERENT TYPES OF TWO-PERSON GAMES OF ECONOMIC SURVIVAL

6.1. CONSTANT SUM MARKET CONDITIONS

In subsection 3.2 we noted that a two-person game of economic survival can be completely characterized by the corporate assets X, Y, a discount rate ρ, the numbers A_1, A_2 representing the value of the market to a surviving firm at the time of exit of its competitor, and the market matrices $||a_{i,j}||$ and $||b_{i,j}||$. There are several different types of solution which can be considered for these games, depending upon the structure of the market matrices, the initial assets, the discount rate, and the rewards to the survivor upon the exit of his opponent. In this section we categorize some of the different types of games of economic survival and discuss various solutions.

Suppose that the market game, i.e., the game played every period, were constant sum $a_{i,j} + b_{i,j} = c$ for all i and j. Furthermore, suppose that $c \leqslant 0$. If there exists a row with only positive entries or a column with only negative entries in the market matrices, there may be a trivial solution in which one player can enforce a fixed loss on his opponent at every play of the market game. In such a case the financial policy for the losing player is to withdraw his assets as fast as possible, and his market policy is to minimize losses.

It may happen, as illustrated in the following example, that even though there is a sure way of eliminating the opponent it takes so long that a strategy which is less advantageous in a single market game is employed. Consider the game characterized by corporate assets of 1000 and 98, respectively, and a discount rate $\rho = 0.8$. We use the notation

$$1000, \ 98, \ 0.8, \ 1{,}000{,}000, \ 1{,}000{,}000, \ \text{and} \ \begin{bmatrix} 1 & 1 \\ -100 & 99 \\ 99 & -100 \end{bmatrix}.$$

In this notation $A_1 = A_2 = 1{,}000{,}000$, if player 1 or 2 wins. We assume that the market is zero-sum, hence we note only one market matrix. It is easy to observe that the first player can play his first strategy and win one unit every period. If the second player fails or is unable to withdraw from the market, it will take the first player 98 periods to ruin him. The prize to the survivor is 1,000,000, but discounted at the rate of 0.8 per period (equivalent to an interest rate of 25 per cent) it becomes virtually worthless. If the first player uses a mixed strategy of $(\frac{1}{2}, \frac{1}{2})$ over his second and third pure strategies, his short-run expectations in the market game are less than before, but he has a 50 per cent chance of winning 1,000,000 in a single period, and even at the high discount this is still worth 400,000.

Suppose that the market game were constant sum and that $a_{i,j}$ and $b_{i,j} > 0$ for all i and j. In such a game it is impossible for the players to ruin each other. If the players have a linear utility for money, then both will play an optimal strategy in the two-person, constant-sum game played every period. Their financial policy will be to pay out all winnings immediately.

If the players are able to co-operate, there may be a solution involving side payments in which they are made jointly better off by having one firm withdraw while the other extracts a monopoly profit. The following example is an illustratation:

$$10,\ 10,\ 0.9,\ 60,\ 60,\ \begin{pmatrix} 1 & 3 \\ 3 & 1 \end{pmatrix}, \text{ and } \begin{pmatrix} 3 & 1 \\ 1 & 3 \end{pmatrix}.$$

Without side payments, both players can enforce an expected income of two units per period each. At a discount of 0.9 the discounted value of their joint income is 36. If one player leaves the market, the survivor can obtain an income worth 60.

6.2. Nonconstant-Sum Market Conditions

Given constant-sum market conditions, there is, in general no way that two firms can work out any level of co-operation except by merging or having one firm bought out by the other. If the market is variable sum, there is considerable scope for co-operation, as shown in the example in section 5.

If both $a_{i,j}$ and $b_{i,j} > 0$ for all i and j, then neither firm can be ruined. There will, in general, be many stationary states which can be enforced as equilibria by the employment of threat strategies. This is discussed in section 4.

If there is a negative row in $b_{i,j}$ or a negative column in $a_{i,j}$, it may be possible for one firm to ruin the other by exhausting its assets. This will hold true only if the firm employing the strategy of exhaustion does not suffer from a loss which would put it out of the market first (see subsection 4.3.3). If it is possible for one firm to ruin another with certainty, this strategy will be employed only if it dominates all stationary states. If not, it will serve to limit the possible equilibria. This is shown in the dominant firm example in subsection 5.1.1.

6.3. CONDITIONAL EQUILIBRIA

In subsection 5.1.1 we constructed a solution to a game of economic survival which consisted of a set of stationary states. The size of the set was determined by the strong killing threat of one player and the liquidation value of the other. The stationary states did not involve chance. They were obtained by repeating the same pure strategy at every period. If there is a chance element involved in the outcome, the long-run stability of a stationary-state equilibrium may depend upon chance. The example given illustrates this. First we consider the game

$$12, \ 12, \ 0.9, \ 80, \ 80, \ \text{and} \ \begin{pmatrix} (6, 6) & (0, 8) \\ (8, 0) & (1, 1) \end{pmatrix}.$$

We have written the market revenues to both players together rather than in two separate matrices. The market revenues which yield both players 6 or both players 1 can be enforced as equilibria (see subsection 4.1). Each player can use a constant market strategy (see subsection 4.3.2) combined with any financial policy, as funds are never needed to prevent ruin. We now examine a game in which the expected value of the payoff during any period is the same, but chance plays a role. The game is

12, 12, 0.9, 80, 80, and

$$\begin{pmatrix} \{\frac{1}{4}(-12, 0)+\frac{1}{2}(18, 18)+\frac{1}{2}(0, -12)\}\{\frac{1}{4}(4, -4)+\frac{1}{2}(8, 0)+\frac{1}{4}(12, 4)\} \\ \{\frac{1}{4}(-4, 4)+\frac{1}{2}(0, 8)+\frac{1}{4}(4, 12)\} \qquad \{\frac{1}{4}(-2, 0)+\frac{1}{2}(3, 3)+\frac{1}{4}(0, -2)\} \end{pmatrix}.$$

Each of the resulting market revenues has the same expected value as before, but now they all involve risk. If both firms have considerable assets in their corporate accounts, it will be possible for them to maintain the joint maximum as an equilibrium, but its permanence as a stationary-state equilibrium depends upon the financial policies of the firms.

Suppose, for example, that the firms were corporations that wished to maximize the growth of their corporate accounts. First, we assume that they would be forced to pay dividends (i.e., make payments to the withdrawal accounts) at the rate of $\frac{1}{3}$ of any (positive) revenue; second, we assume that they would be forced to pay out $\frac{2}{3}$ of any positive revenue.

If both firms utilize their first move in the single-period market game and pay out $\frac{1}{3}$ of any gains as dividends, then each has a chance of $\frac{1}{4}$ of losing 12 and a chance of $\frac{1}{2}$ of winning 18, of which 12 will be kept in the corporate accounts. The state of the corporate account of a player at any time period can be calculated by solving a *random walk* [12] problem in which the assets increase or are depleted by twelve units every period with probabilities of $\frac{1}{2}$ and $\frac{1}{4}$, respectively. It can be shown [13] that there is a probability of $\frac{1}{9}$ that neither firm will ever be ruined and that the equilibrium will continue undisturbed through time.

If the firms are forced to pay out $\frac{2}{3}$ of their positive revenues as dividends, then the random walk has jumps of -12 and 6. It can be shown (see Appendix C for proof) that there is a probability of 1 that eventually one firm will be ruined and the equilibrium will be destroyed. These models reflect the role that hazard plays in competition. The asset and market policies of the firms give them some control over chance, but there is always the chance that a run of "bad luck", such as the failure of an advertising campaign or a change in tastes, may be sufficient to ruin a firm that is being run in even an optimal manner.

The market equilibrium with the risk features described here can best be described as a conditionally stationary equilibrium. As long as both firms are strong enough, they can enforce the equilibrium. However, there is always a possibility that sooner or later chance will weaken one competitor to the extent that the equilibrium will be destroyed. This will happen if the asset ratio exceeds some critical value. Consider the game

$$11, 10, 0.9, 15, 15, \text{ and } \begin{pmatrix} [0.2(-1)+0.8(1), 0.2(-1)+0.8(1)] \\ (-1, -1) \end{pmatrix}.$$

The first player has two strategies and the second player has one.

Initially, it does not pay the first player to use his second strategy because it takes ten periods to ruin the second. This gives the prize of 15 the discounted value of

$$(0.9)^{10}(15) = 5.22,$$

but if he plays his first strategy his expected income is 0.6 per period, which is worth approximately 5.4 (the value of a certain income stream of 0.6 discounted at 0.9 per period). If the assets of the second player become depleted, there will be a point at which it will pay the first player to switch to his second strategy.

7. ADVERTISING, STYLING, EFFICIENCY, INNOVATION, PRICE, AND OTHER COMPETITION

The strategic interlinkage between competitors is shown by the effect of the actions of one competitor upon the payoffs to another. In the market models studied earlier in this chapter the short-run strategic interlinkage is illustrated in the market matrices. These serve to indicate the amount of damage that one firm could inflict upon another in a single period. The long-term profits are affected not only by market action but also by financial policy. It is well known that oligopolistic competition may be carried on by product differentiation, advertising, styling, the introduction of innovations, and by other means, as well as by pricing. The considerations governing the form of competition are brought out by examining the different degrees of strategic interlinkage between firms.

7.1. Market Structure and Decision Variables of the Firm

Strategic interlinkage and the effect of this interlinkage are the dominant factors in determining the nature of competition in the market. A fruitful study of oligopoly must depend upon the understanding of the many market forms encountered. In this section we refer to some of the features of the market which are too often ignored by economic theorists and yet play an important role in the shaping of competition.

The distribution and the retailing systems do much to modify the possibilities of competition between manufacturing firms. Our models up to this point have not distinguished between competition in manufacturing, distributing, or retailing, between producer's goods or consumer goods, and so forth. In the study of oligopoly these considerations are of importance. The time lags and inflexibilities caused by their presence radically reduce the myriad psychological possibilities that are feasible from a priori considerations.

A detailed study of market forms and an understanding of the roles of the different decision variables calls for much empirical work and eventually for experimentation by simulation with high-speed computers. At this time we must be limited to an example of how a consumer's good market may be structured in order to indicate the forces modifying strategic interlinkage.

Figure 47 shows three major manufacturers and half a dozen minor competitors aggregated into one. The largest manufacturer

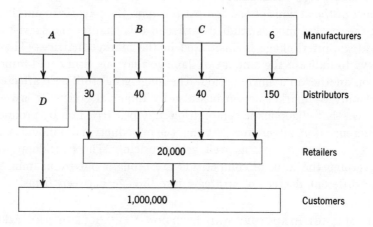

Figure 47

sells part of his output to a large distributor-retailer and the rest to thirty independent distributors. The second manufacturer sells to forty owned distributors, the third to forty independents, and the remainder to another 150 distributors. In turn, the distributor-retailer sells directly to the market, and the distributors sell to around 20,000 retailers, many of whom buy from two or three distributors. The retailers and the large distributor-retailers sell to one million customers. The three large manufacturers and the large distributor-retailer are probably multiproduct corporations, so that their fates and resources do not depend solely upon the outcome in this market. Strategically, the firms A, B, C, and D are of primary importance. Their flexibility and interlinkages vary considerably because of the structure of the distribution system.

The shape of the market and the properties of the product traded help to determine which decision variables are dominant in competition. The following is a list of some of the more important ones:

Pricing
Advertising
Production and inventory scheduling
Styling (involving few changes in the factory)
Model change (requiring considerable changes in the factory)
Innovation
Capital investment
Financing

Depending upon the specific structure of a market, some subset of these decision variables will dominate the competition. A brief discussion of some of them follows.

7.2. Price Competition in an Oligopolistic Market

In a market in which there is a combination of some or all of these features, few competitors, high overhead costs, high entry costs, limited flexibility of short-run production rates (possibly job shop production), high inventory charges, relatively inelastic demand for the products of the firms as a group, relatively high cross-elasticity of demand between similar products of different firms, open information on prices, technical difficulties in spreading information about frequent price changes (catalogues for instance), or consumer resistance to recurrent price adjustments, it is plausible to expect that any perceptible price cut by one firm will at least be met by its competitors. If it is more profitable for a firm to meet an opponent's price reduction than to maintain a higher price, the reduction will at least be met. In general, with the foregoing qualifications as to the type of market, this will hold true.

If we consider price competition, then *ceteris paribus* almost any price that is not too high to cause new entry will be a potential equilibrium price. The mere threat of each firm to meet a price cut is sufficient. A plausible threat strategy that we may assume would be employed by each firm can be expressed as follows:

I will maintain the stationary price if I observe that my opponent has done so; if he cuts price, I will meet the cut; if he raises price, then, depending upon my analysis of market cross-elasticities, I may follow him.

The only violation short of total war that should be attempted against such a strategy is an upward testing of the market.

Ceteris paribus (i.e., leaving out advertising, plant expansion, styling, etc.), aluminum, steel, automobiles, rayon, and other heavy manufacturing fit closely into this pattern of price competition. We see that in markets of this structure we may expect similar prices and even upward movements *without* there being any explicit communication between firms or any collusive intent. It is almost meaningless to talk about collusive price behavior in such a market because the structure implies that almost any price level within a range can be enforced as a non-co-operative equilibrium under very plausible assumptions concerning an opponent's threat.

7.3. ADVERTISING AND STYLING

Even in cases in which price competition is so jointly suicidal that it will be ruled out by non-co-operative firms there still may be areas of strategic flexibility in advertising and styling. We distinguish several cases, depending upon costs of advertising, effect upon "industry" demand, effect upon consumer tastes, brand loyalty and product differentiation, and the asset structure of the firms.

For example, we assume that the firms have roughly equal resources and the expected effect of any pair of advertising strategies (i.e., one strategy for each player) can be predicted.

Case 1. As long as the "industry" demand is expanded at a rate which more than offsets the marginal costs of advertising and of satisfying the new demand, then both firms will find it to their advantage to advertize. A simple suggestive example is given in this 2 x 2 matrix:

$$
\begin{array}{ccc}
 & N & A \\
N & (8, 8) & (9, 12) \\
A & (12, 9) & (10, 10)
\end{array}
$$

The two strategies are to advertise or not to advertise. If one firm does so and the other fails to do so, the advertiser will increase its profits considerably. Even though the nonadvertising firm benefits (from general expansion of demand), it can improve its position by advertising as well.

Case 2. If the "industry" demand shifts at a rate which just covers the marginal costs of advertising and satisfying the extra demand, then the payoff matrix to the players will be constant sum! The players are involved in a market game of strict opposition: neither gains by advertising but neither can risk not advertising. [14]

Case 3. If the "industry" demand does not expand sufficiently to cover extra costs, then the firms are involved in every time period in a nonzero-sum game in which the equilibrium point is unfavorable to each, as shown in this 2 x 2 matrix:

$$
\begin{array}{ccc}
 & N & A \\
N & (5, 5) & (2, 6) \\
A & (6, 2) & (3, 3)
\end{array}
$$

The equilibrium point in this game is at (3, 3). We observe that this is apparently the same situation discussed in subsection 4.1. The payoffs of the firms are so interlocked that they may be able to attain many different equilibrium levels of advertising expenditure. Each firm knows that any increase would result in an opposing increase; hence it would be unprofitable.

The main reason why case 3 is not strategically identical with price competition is due to the variance in the expected result of an advertising campaign. In general, there may be a high level of uncertainty as to the outcome of an advertising campaign (for instance, the Lucky Strike campaign). [15] If advertising is successful or a new styling "takes," an opponent may not be able to make a strategically successful countermove. If a price cut is successful, an opponent can counter by also cutting prices. The effect of risk is illustrated in the example given in subsection 6.3. We reiterate that equilibrium in a market in which chance fluctuations can influence the payoffs to the players may have a stability which is conditional only upon there being no run of misfortune against one of the players. If there is, then the asset structure of the industry may be sufficiently changed to destroy the stationary state. Firms in competition are masters of their fates to the extent that they can exert some control over the random processes which effect them. A firm may not be "lucky" with an advertising campaign, but there will be relation between its probability of success and the amount of money expended. It may not be able to avoid the occasional failure of a product line, but the effect of the failure will depend upon the previous financial policy.

If an active opponent or a potential entrant (i.e., a firm-in-being) is short of resources, then advertising and style changes will serve as extra weapons to use with pricing in efforts to exhaust assets, block entry, or control growth.

Cigarettes, detergents, automobiles, and other consumer durables provide examples in which competition must be waged heavily via advertising and style.

7.4. INNOVATION

Innovating offers another way in which competition between a few can be carried on in a less damaging manner than price cutting. The effect of one firm's innovation upon the profits of an opponent will depend heavily upon whether the new product is a complement to, substitute for, or only slightly competitive with a competitor's product line.

As with advertising and styling, the incertainty in innovating is greater than in price cutting. The major impact of competition via research and innovation makes itself felt on the asset positions of firms. If the results are uncertain, the risk of disaster through financial difficulties or bankruptcy will, in general, decrease for any fixed percentage of research expenditure to assets, as the assets of the firm increase. Thus it is riskier for a small firm to engage in research than a large firm. The disparity in risk may be made even wider when tax positions and diversification of product are taken into account.

One way in which the disparity in risk may be reduced is for small firms to purchase research work from independent research enterprises and thus make use of the insurance obtained from large numbers.

Once a corporation has become large enough as a financial entity and a bureaucracy it is in a position to purchase talent, innovations, and small innovating firms before they attain an independent existence of an importance sufficient to constitute a competitive threat.

Professor Schumpeter [16] has suggested that profits come about in a dynamic economy by the introduction of innovation. The innovator manages to be a step ahead of the mob and obtains a relatively short-lived monopolistic return which is soon whittled away by the others who close in. It appears to this writer that in our economy an innovation can help the innovator entrench himself ahead of his competitors. The several score original automobile manufacturers who started together competed until very few remained. The few who are still in business have plants valued in the billions of dollars. The innovations served as a tool whereby the individual innovators could leave behind them corporate structures of such size that the latter-day innovators are more likely to be working within these corporate structures than trying to raise an independent 100 million dollars to "try out a new idea".

The formal apparatus erected in subsection 3.3 is not adequate to account for innovations or changes in efficiency. It is not difficult to modify the structure of the theory to include these extra possibilities. This involves dividing the corporate account into fixed and liquid assets. The financial action for a firm at any period then must specify not only the payment into the withdrawal account but also the division between the liquid- and fixed-asset accounts. Depending upon this division, the market matrix faced by the firm in a subsequent period will vary. Computational difficulties limit our developing this approach at this time. Empirically, it appears that, in general, it may be cheaper to fight a price war by improving efficiency and then lowering price than by making an attempt to use a liquid-asset advantage with an old plant.

7.5. Production and Inventory Scheduling

One of the primary contentions made here is that the eventual understanding and development of a fruitful theory of oligopoly will depend upon a detailed investigation and an interpretation of the influence of time lags in decision processes. These are induced by the behavior patterns of individuals, by physical indivisibilities, and inflexible features of the firm and/or market.

The viability of a firm in the market place may easily be the dominant factor for its survival. Flexibility in manufacturing firms depends heavily upon production and inventory scheduling. Flexibility among retailers and distributors is dependent on their ability to solve their inventory problems. There appear to be markets in which the major problems of strategy are more concerned with the ability to adjust to the vagaries of fortune than to do battle with competitors. In a market in which pricing strategies are not advisable, advertising and style changes are heavily employed, major innovation is unlikely, and demand is subject to fluctuations due to the effects of a volatile taste caused by advertising and styling, viability may be the key to survival.

The ability to minimize the cost of a blunder or a run of misfortune is a defensive virtue, yet one which can outweigh pricing or advertising. During recent years there has been a considerable growth in the literature on inventory theory and scheduling. Unfortunately, this has not yet been integrated with theories of competition. We will not pursue this topic further here, except to draw the biological analogy in which the eventual survival of one of two competing species depends not only upon its ability to damage the other but upon a favorable combination of successful combat and adjustment to the rest of the environment.

7.6. Parameters Affecting the Solution to a Game of Economic Survival

7.6.1. Liquidity and the Money Markets.
We have limited our duopoly models to situations in which firms were assumed unable to borrow outside money. If it were always possible to borrow money in unlimited quantities at the "going" rate of interest, no competitive threat involving a possibility of ruin could

ever have effect because, in essence, there would never be any capital problem facing any firm. If a small firm is able to obtain support from the money market, its ability to withstand industrial war or other adversity is considerably improved.

Various references have been made to the liquidation value of a firm's corporate account. These emphasize an important feature of any theory of oligopoly. Assets may be highly illiquid. Thus, if a firm is caught in an industry in which for some reason, technical or tactical, it finds that its yield has been cut to below the return given by the long-run rate of interest, multiplied by its net worth, it may not shift assets out in any other manner than by depreciating its plant over a long period. The reason is that its return to investment is still greater than the amount earned by obtaining the long-run rate of interest on the capital obtained through immediate liquidation. If we permit ourselves to talk about perfectly liquid assets, then, again, as with the money-market conditions, we can wipe out much of the central core of the problems of the theory of oligopoly.

7.6.2. THE RATE OF INTEREST. The solutions described in the examples given are all sensitive to a change in the long-run rate of interest, inasmuch as the lower the rate of interest, the greater is the discounted value of future profits, hence the more profitable wars to drive an opponent out of competition become, *ceteris paribus*. Coincident with this effect is the lessening of the size of the alternative income stream obtained by liquidating and then reinvesting the proceeds. This implies that the lower the interest rate, the more feasible it becomes for a financially strong firm to dominate the market (provided that outside financing for small firms is difficult to obtain). This may be regarded as the type of situation which exists in a stagnant economy. The most profitable outlet or use for the surplus funds of a firm may be their employment as a backing for a threat or a war to obtain a larger share of the market.

7.6.3. CHANGES IN DEMAND. If demand becomes more inelastic, the cost of inflicting a certain level of damage by a threat becomes less (because it requires less change in production than before and the production is obtained at increasing marginal cost).

When there is an upward shift in demand (say, a linear shift of the demand function) the cost of inflicting a given level of damage on an opponent rises. There is a shift of the joint maximal surface (the curve M_1M_2 in Figure 46) in a northwest direction. It becomes more difficult to maintain a killing threat against an opponent; hence the area of possible steady-state equilibria increases.

8. MONOPOLISTIC COMPETITION REVISITED

The kinked demand curve models and the Chamberlinian small group equilibrium model were introduced into economic theory in order to explain price rigidities in the face of a shift in demand and the possibility of the multiplicity of equilibria in an oligopolistic market. The analysis in this chapter extends these investigations in the sense that the financial and corporate structure behind oligopolistic competition is made explicit. The examples dealt with in this chapter indicate the possibility of price rigidities which will be disturbed only when a complex of financial and technological conditions is not satisfied. In the Chamberlin and kinked demand discussions the composition and magnitude of the assets of the firms being examined are not specified. The possibility of ruin of some of the competing firms and, in general, the importance of time lags, fixed costs, liquidation, and entry conditions are mentioned only *en passant*. In short, most of the obvious economic information which the empiricist uses and which gives considerable structure to any market form is not explicitly utilized in these theoretical discussions.

In common with the discussants of the kinked oligopoly demand, Chamberlin has implicit in his diagrammatic and verbal treatment an amalgam of assumptions concerning the objective features of demand, the behavioristic assumptions of the competitors, the time lags in the market, and the profit motivation of the competitors.

Both of the theoretical constructions appear to be helpful to economic analysis inasmuch as they point out that if dynamic considerations are introduced, even only implicitly, we can expect rigidities and multiple equilibria. Other than that, in this writer's opinion, they are unable to provide more than a very limited insight into the forms of oligopolistic competition because they fail to make explicit use of the considerable amount of information available on the structure of enterprise.

9. ENTRY INTO COMPETITION

The description of a game of economic survival in section 3 can be extended to account for entry. To do this we must introduce one more type of account. We call it the *investment account*. This contains the funds that a firm-in-being or a would-be entrant has at its disposal. We may also equate this account with the withdrawal account if we regard the initial position of a firm-in-being as one in which it has assets in its withdrawal account but none in its corporate account. Thus we denote a two-person game of economic survival in which one firm is actively in the market and the other is a firm-in-being by

$$O, X, Y, O, \rho, A_1, A_2, \text{ and the matrices } ||a_{i,j}|| \text{ and } ||b_{i,j}||.$$

The first two numbers stand for the assets in the investment account and corporate account of the firm in the market. If we do not fix the amount in the first account as zero, this implies that the firm is able to obtain extra financing. The second two numbers indicate that the firm-in-being has resources in its investment account but has not entered actively into the market and has no assets in its corporate account. As in section 3, the ρ is the discount rate and A_1 and A_2 are as before.

9.1. INDIVIDUAL AND CORPORATE ENTRY

The amount of capital required to enter into competition, the specialized knowledge needed to be able to start up in business, and the degree of competence necessary for survival varies immensely. The entry problems of the shoeshine boy and the builder of a new oil refinery require different characterizations. Even the mere presence of different forms of legal structure can result in a different allocation of resources for firms which are physically identical. Consider a partnership in which the partners have the opportunity of entering into a new market. There is a chance that they may be ruined and a chance that they make a large profit. Depending upon their risk preferences and the probability of making a profit, they may decide to risk entry. The selfsame individuals with the same risk preferences for their own money, when seated as officers of a corporation in which they hold little or no equity, even though the corporation's plant is physically identical with the plant of the partnership and the amount of money tied up is the same in both cases, may decide not to enter. The officers may claim that they do not like to risk their stockholders' money (and their corporate posts) in the same way as they would risk their own money. In a partnership the prospects of failure may be bad, but the dividends of success are high. This gross oversimplification of different motivation from the same individuals is offered only as an example to show the effect of different business forms on the allocation of resources. In order to illustrate the result we compute an example.

*9.1.1. THE SOLUTION TO A ONE-PERSON GAME OF ECONOMIC SURVIVAL. The model to be examined is a very simplified one-person game of economic survival applied to a problem of entry and investment. We describe the game with the following notation:

$$X, 0, 0, \infty, \rho, A_1, \begin{pmatrix} -1 & 1 \\ 1 & -1 \end{pmatrix}, (p, 1-p).$$

The X is the amount of money in the firm's investment account, the first 0 indicates that there is no money in the corporate account. The 0 and the ∞ are used to indicate that the player's opponent is nature, who has 0 in her investment account and infinite resources in her corporate account. The A_1 indicates the prize to the player if he loses (he never wins in the sense that he remains the only survivor because he can never ruin nature).

The market matrix and the strategy of nature are given. With all this information, the problem that remains is more closely related to probability theory than to game theory. However, it is a degenerate form of game that is of economic interest.

As before, ρ is the discount rate. Furthermore, we assume that if the firm enters the market, it will be forced out if its corporate account reaches the size K where $K < X$. If a firm is ruined or otherwise liquidates, the "prize" $A_1 = -K$; in other words, if a firm leaves the market, its liquidation losses are K (in the simplest example we assume $K = 0$).

Suppose that a group of individuals with resources X wished to enter the market with the object of maximizing the size of the expected discounted income paid into the withdrawal account of their firm. We can see immediately that they will not enter if $p = q = \frac{1}{2}$. We assume that $p > \frac{1}{2}$. It is also evident that there will be no incentive to enter if the discount rate is greater than the expected gain in a single period. For instance, if the expected gain from the investment of a unit is 0.05 in one period and the discount rate is greater than 0.05, there is no incentive to invest. Let $v(X)$ represent the expected value of entering into the market with initial assets of X. Suppose that the group adopted the following financial strategy: If it entered the market, then it would plow back all earnings into the firm until a certain safety level Z had been established. Any amount above Z would be paid out in dividends. The proof that this is the optimal policy for the firm is given elsewhere. [16] The group wished to determine the optimal value for this number Z and then to determine the value of entering $v(X)$ if they adopted their optimal financial policy. We can portray the problem by this set of equations:

(1) $\qquad v(X) = \rho p v(X + 1) + \rho q v(X - 1) \qquad$ for $X < Z$

(2) $\qquad v(0) = 0$

(3) $\quad v(Z + 1) = v(Z) + 1$

Equation 1 establishes a relation between the value of the position of the firm at a given time t and the discounted value of the firm one period later if it enters the market. It states that the value of the firm at time t equals the expected discounted value of the firm in one period later, after it has made a profit, plus the expected discounted value of the firm after it has made a loss. Equation 2 states that the value of the firm when it has no assets is zero (this is a special case in which $K = 0$). Equation 3 specifies the boundary condition at which the firm begins to pay dividends. The value of the firm, when it is operating under the rule that it pays dividends if it makes a profit, equals the expected discounted value of the firm with less assets caused by taking a loss, plus the expected discounted value of the firm with the same assets as previously, plus the expected discounted value of the dividends.

In order to solve the difference equation 1 we set

$$v(X) = a^x.$$

Equation 1 becomes

$$\rho p a^{x+1} - a^x + \rho q a^{x-1} = 0,$$

hence
$$\rho p a^2 - a + \rho q = 0,$$

and
$$a = \frac{1 \pm \sqrt{1 - 4\rho^2 pq}}{2\rho p};$$

denoting the roots by a_1 and a_2,

$$v(X) = A_1 a_1{}^x + A_2 a_2{}^x.$$

From (2) and (3) we obtain

$$A_1 = -A_2$$

and

$$A_1 = \frac{1}{(a_1{}^{z+1} - a_2{}^{z+1}) - (a_1{}^z - a_2{}^z)}.$$

The value of the investment to the firm is a function of both X and Z, so we can express it as

(4) $$v(X, Z) = A_1(Z)\{a_1{}^x - a_2{}^x\}.$$

If we restrict payments to integral quantities, then we can calculate $v(X, Z)$ for different assets, policies, and probabilities directly by machine using equation 4.

Several values are given in Table 16:

The numbers in boxes represent the values of the largest investment that will be made under the appropriate optimal policy. We note that in each case the incremental value of an extra unit invested drops until it yields a return of less than a unit. The optimal amount called for by the optimal policy is determined by the point at which the increment of capital added has the same value as its cost. For example, we note that when $\rho = 0.995$ and $p = 0.99$, under the policy $Z = 3$, the value added by increasing investment from $X = 2$ to $X = 3$ is $194.99 - 193.99 = 1$.

In general, the optimum policies call for small values for Z. Only if there is a very low discount rate and a small favorable bias in the odds, will Z become large.

The withdrawal policy depends upon the discount rate, the probability of success, and the size of the liquidation loss. In the example calculated we simplified the calculations by assuming that there was no liquidation loss. Thus we used equation 2, $v(0) = 0$. If we wish to examine how the size of liquidation losses

Table 16

$\rho = 0.7, \quad p = 0.99$

Z X	1	2	3
1	2.26	1.59	1.10
2		2.29	1.60
3			2.29

$\rho = 0.995, \quad p = 0.99$

Z X	2	3	4
1	191.34	195.08	195.08
2	194.21	198.02	198.02
3		199.04	199.04

$\rho = 0.99, \quad p = 0.55$

Z X	7	8
1	1.95	1.93
2	3.57	3.55
3	4.97	4.94
4	6.20	6.16
5	7.33	7.27
6	8.38	8.32
7	9.39	9.32
8		10.31
9		
10		

$\rho = 0.995, \quad p = 0.55$

Z X	7	8	9	10
1	2.66	2.84	2.97	3.06
2	4.86	5.18	5.42	5.59
3	6.71	7.1ς	7.48	7.71
4	8.82	8.83	9.24	9.52
5	9.65	10.28	10.75	11.09
6	10.85	11.57	12.10	12.47
7	11.94	12.73	13.32	13.72
8		13.80	14.43	14.87
9			15.48	15.95
10				16.98

effect the solution we must solve the system using equation:

$$(2') \qquad\qquad v(K) = 0.$$

This indicates that as soon as the firm's assets fall to K it is ruined and loses these assets. When there is no liquidation loss and the probability of gain is greater than the discount factor it will always pay a firm interested in maximizing expected discounted income to enter the market. This will not be true when there is a liquidation cost.

The analysis used was based on the assumption that the firm wished to maximize the expected discounted value of funds withdrawn from the corporation. Suppose, instead, that the investing firm were a corporation controlled by officers whose fortunes are linked to the assets as well as the earnings of their corporation. If they are forced to pay out to the stockholders at least as much as q/p of any unit earned, there will be no incentive for the directors to invest because it is certain that eventually the investment will be lost and the total assets of the corporation diminished, even though the stockholders may have benefited.

Our discussion was limited to a market in which the firm could win or lose one unit in any period. This restriction can be relaxed and an explicit solution is obtainable for "jumps" of $+\lambda_1$ and $-\lambda_2$ when the λ_1 and λ_2 are of any size. The optimal policy becomes slightly more complicated as financial indivisibilities appear. For a discussion of this the reader is referred elsewhere. [18]

The type of problem posed by a one-person game of economic survival is closely related to problems in dynamic programming [19] and inventory theory and involves the study of the theory of random walks.

9.1.2. THE VALUE OF A FIRM AND THE ENTRANT'S ASSETS. The formula in equation 4 depends upon four financial features: the rate of discount, the liquidation conditions for the firm, the size of the initial investment funds available, and the disbursement policy adopted by the entrant.

We note that as the initial assets of the entering firm are raised, i.e., X becomes larger, the value of entering becomes greater. In other words, the value of a firm is a function of the amount of money possessed by the individuals who buy it. The meaning of this becomes more evident when we examine entry into an oligopolistic market. Suppose an individual were offered an industrial plant for a sum that tied up almost all the money that his financial group could obtain credit lines for. Given a weak capitalization the other firms might be able to wipe out the entrant within a brief period and more than recoup their battle losses as compared with the loss they would otherwise suffer through sharing the market. In this case the firm is not worth its price to the prospective purchaser. Suppose now that the price of the firm were still the same but that the purchasing group controlled larger resources than before. The time it would take the others to drive the entrant out and the losses incurred in doing so might make it more economical to allow the newcomer to take a share of the market without resorting to destructive tactics. The mere presence of the entrant's extra reserves could be sufficient to change a poor buy into a worthwhile investment.

9.2. A Rise in Demand Which Helps to Block New Entry

It is usually assumed that if there are no institutional blocking factors a rise in the demand for a product will attract new entrants (unless the existing firms were previously operating in an area of decreasing average costs and were not in a competitive equilibrium). The contrary may in fact be true. Consider a group of firms which have relatively flat average costs, high overhead, a massive fixed plant, and at least some flexibility to expand production a few per cent in the short run before a new plant can be built. Possibly they may also have an inventory to utilize. Suppose also that, as is often the case, a high capitalization were required for any firm. Before the rise in demand we assume that the firms were at some type of equilibrium. No new firm entered because a profit computation would show that the difference between possible profits and possible losses was not great enough to merit entry. After the rise in demand the outside firm-in-being might observe that its potential profits had risen. However, the existing firms were able to take immediate advantage of the situation (leaving aside the feature that they would usually be able to block the would-be entrant from obtaining supplies merely by having ordered new equipment from the suppliers first). Their added profits might easily be such that if applied to their asset positions instead of going to stockholders they would be in a sufficiently stronger position to fight a new entrant so that his incentive to enter would be lowered by the rise in demand.

9.3. Quick Profits and Certain Ruin: "Hit-and-Run Entry"

If you look up my Bradstreet, I'm Dunn.
Old American folk saying

Be it ballpoint pens or television sets, it is easy to see the logic behind the actions of the small "independent" entrepreneur who can act fast in getting in and out of competition in markets before the full force of aggregations of either liquid capital or machinery or both can make themselves felt. Here Schumpeter's innovators and the arbitrageurs are in their element; quick action, fast results, and often a speedy retreat as soon as the others close in are called for. The small firms may not even expect to grow old (at least not under the same name or incorporation). A new market with rising demand prior to "stabilizing" may give scope to entrants whose expected profit is still sufficient to merit entry, even though their long-term chances of survival are small if not nonexistent.

The formal mechanism for dealing with situations of the type described here and in subsection 9.2 is sketched in subsection 3.3. It is necessary to investigate games of economic survival in which the market matrices faced by the players change in every period. The changes in the market matrices reflect changes in demand and asset structure. A detailed examination of the many varieties of games of economic survival must be delayed until more mathematical technique for dealing with them and more empirical information are avilable.

NOTES

[1] M. Hausner, *Games of Survival, The Rand Corporation, RM–776*, February 12, 1952; *Optimal Strategies in Games of Survival, RM–777* February 18, 1952; M. P. Peisakoff, *More on Games of Survival, RM–884*, June 20, 1952; H. Everett, "Recursive Games," mimeographed, Princeton University, 1954. See also R. D. Luce, and H. Raiffa, *Games and Decisions* (New York: Wiley, 1957).

[2] W. Feller, *An Introduction to Probability Theory and its Applications*, **I** (New York: Wiley, 1950), p. 282.

[3] *Ibid*, pp. 282–288.

[4] M. Hausner, *loc. cit.*

[5] M. P. Peiskaoff, *loc. cit.*

[6] J. W. Milnor, and L. S. Shapley, *On Games of Survival, The Rand Corporation, RM–1320*, August 10, 1954.

[7] There are also difficulties of analysis which arise if there are "traps" present, i.e., situations which permit the game to be repeated indefinitely without any possibility of ending.

[8] This decision is a function of the discount rate and the value of the prize to the players. If the discount rate is very small and the value of the prize is considerable, then even if a player has a very small probability of winning in a game which will probably last a long time it will pay to keep all assets in the corporate account.

[9] M. Shubik, and G. L. Thompson, "Games of Economic Survival," Naval Logistics Research Quarterly, forthcoming, 1959.

[10] Sandbagging in poker is a manner of play in which a player checks his hand initially and then raises on the bet of the opening bettor. It is a legitimate manner of playing that is sometimes regarded as "unethical."

[11] The writer is indebted to G. L. Thompson, who suggested this way of formulating the "test" for a stationary state equilibrium.

[12] W. Feller, *op. cit.*, Chapter 14.

[13] *Ibid.*

[14] M. Shubik, "The Uses of Game Theory in Management Science," *Management Science*, **II**, No. 1 (October 1955), pp. 40–54.

[15] R. B. Tennant, *The American Cigarette Industry* (New Haven: Yale University Press, 1950), p. 83.

[16] J. A. Schumpeter, *The Theory of Economic Development* (Cambridge: Harvard University Press, 1934), Chapter IV.

[17] M. Shubik, "and G. L. Thompson Games of Economic Survival."

[18] *Loc. cit.*

[19] See R. Bellman, "The Theory of Dynamic Programming," *Proceedings of the National Academy of Science*, **38** (1952), pp. 716–719.

A THEORY
OF OLIGOPOLY
(PART 2)

1. SOLUTIONS TO AN n-PERSON GAME OF ECONOMIC SURVIVAL

1.1. $\{k_i\} - \{r_j\}$ STABILITY OF EQUILIBRIUM UNDER A GIVEN SET OF THREATS

1.1.1. STRATEGIES IN AN n-PERSON GAME OF ECONOMIC SURVIVAL. In Chapter 10 we limited ourselves to markets with one or two firms. We observed that with only two firms present the threat structure in a market was of considerable importance and could be examined by making use of economic information on assets, overheads, and finances, as well as demand, product, and advertising. When we consider situations involving more than two firms the notion of a threat becomes more difficult to define. We have to account not only for the effect of the action of one firm on another and the latter's reaction but also the reaction of the rest of the competitors. This is done by extending the previous analysis.

As in Chapter 10, we restrict our analysis to a specific type of n-person *game of economic survival*. In each time period the players are assumed to play in a game that is repeated from the last period (i.e., as a first approximation, the market is assumed to be the same in every period; there is no change in demand, tastes, or technology). If a player is ruined, the "prize" obtained by the remaining players (if there are two or more) consists of a position in a new game with fewer players. Making use of the results of Chapter 6 and 10.9, we note that some of the players in this n-person game may be firms-in-being. These firms may be regarded as consisting of entrepreneurs who are not actively engaged in competition but have enough assets to be able to enter.

As before, we define a strategy S^i of player i to be a stationary strategy if the move $s_{i,t}$ of the ith player at time t is such that

$$s_{i,t} = \bar{s}_i \qquad \text{for } t = 0, 1, 2, \ldots .$$

A threat strategy T^i for player i now contains a plan of action involving the moves of all n players. It is described as follows:

$$s_{i,0} = \bar{s}_i;$$

$$s_{i,t} = \bar{s}_i \qquad \text{for } t = 1, 2, \ldots, \text{ if } s_{j,\tau} = \bar{s}_j,$$

$$\text{for } \tau = 0, 1, 2, \ldots, t-1, \qquad \text{for all } j \neq i;$$

$$s_{i,t} = \chi(s_{j,1}, s_{j,2} \ldots s_{j,t-1}) \qquad \text{for } t = \tau + 1, \qquad \tau + 2, \ldots,$$

$$\text{and } j = 1, 2, \ldots, n, \text{ if for any } j \neq i \; s_{j,\tau} \neq \bar{s}_j$$

This states that the ith player is committed to maintaining the *status quo* at every time period, provided his information does not tell him that some other player has departed from the stationary state. If his information indicates that at least one other player has departed from the stationary state, then his strategy calls for the ith player to follow some plan of action as is indicated in $\chi(s_{j,1}, s_{j,2}, \ldots, s_{j,t-1})$.

1.1.2. SOLUTIONS TO AN n-PERSON GAME OF ECONOMIC SURVIVAL. Suppose that we wished to examine the stability of some market structure on the assumption that some specified pattern of behavior exists. In order to be specific suppose we wished to know whether or not one firm were in a position to stop another firm from departing from a steady state on the assumption that all other firms were utilizing steady-state strategies. Call the two firms i and j. We now formulate a 2×2 matrix game in which players i and j each have a choice between two strategies: a threat strategy which attempts to enforce the steady state and some other strategy which maximizes against the threat of the opponent on the assumption that all other players maintain their stationary-state actions. The following notation is used: S stands for a vector of n stationary strategies $(S_1, S_2, \ldots, S_n)$. (S, T^i, T^j) stands for the vector of strategies in which players i and j use strategies T^i and T^j, and the remainder use their stationary strategies. V^i is the optimal strategy of i against T^j, excluding T^i. V^j is similarly defined.

$$
\begin{array}{ccc}
 & T^j & V^j \\
T^i & P_i[(S, T^i, T^j)],\ P_j[(S, T^i, T^j)] & P_i[(S, T^i, V^j)],\ P_j[(S, T^i, V^j)], \\
V^i & P_i[(S, V^i, T^j)],\ P_j[(S, V^i, T^j)] & P_i[(S, V^i, V^j)],\ P_j[(S, V^i, V^j)].
\end{array}
$$

If the pair of strategies (T^i, T^j) defines an equilibrium in this 2×2 game in which all players except i and j are assumed to be maintaining their stationary strategies, then this equilibrium is defined to be $\{1_i\} - \{1_j\}$ and $\{1_j\} - \{1_i\}$ stable. The threat of i against j and the threat of j against i is sufficient to prevent either from departing from the stationary state, given that all other players maintain the stationary state.

In general, we can divide the players into three sets containing k, r and $n-k-r$ individuals, respectively. A market equilibrium is defined to be $\{k_i\} - \{r_j\}$ stable [1] (in which $\{k_i\}$ is a specific set of players, k in number, and $\{r_j\}$ is a specific set of players, r in number), if no joint action by the r players yields them more than maintaining the steady state, on the assumption that each of the k players is committed to a threat strategy and that each of the $n-k-r$ players is playing a steady-state strategy.

The scheme outlined and the definitions given here lead *in abstracto* to great complications for games with even as few players as ten. For instance, there are $\dfrac{n!}{(n-k-r)!\,k!\,r!}$ different sets of players, which would be relevant to an exhaustive study of

$\{k_i\} - \{r_j\}$ stability for any k and r. However, if we wish to investigate the state of competition between a group of firms, we can utilize economic information to limit the combinatorial possibilities which need to be considered. The discussion of different market forms makes this clear.

1.2. THE DOMINANT FIRM

1.2.1. DISCUSSION.   We examined a model of a dominant firm in competition in Chapter 6: 2.6. We use the term "dominant" loosely in the sense of "much larger than the rest." Here we wish to examine the conditions under which the size of the large firm can enable it to dominate the market by exerting control over price, production, and entry. In the model in Chapter 6: 2.6 the dominant firm had 50 per cent of the capacity of the active firms. It was assumed that no new firms could enter into competition. The remaining industrial power was divided among fifty other enterprises, each with 1 per cent of the plant. In its efforts to use its monopolistic power the dominant firm was willing to settle for 38.6 per cent of the controlled market (allowing the small firms to take advantage of its restrictive policy), even though it had 50 per cent of the plant (see Table 9, Chapter 6). In the dynamic setting of a game of economic survival we can make our entry and behavior assumptions explicit and to some extent realistic.

Physical and Financial Conditions.   Suppose that the goods being sold were fairly close substitutes (although advertising, styling, and other forms of product variation may play a role). There are entry time lags, sufficient fixed plant, and sufficient capital required to limit flexibility and maneuverability. In this type of market the size of the capital commitment is such that a certain amount of skill and "creditworthiness" is required of prospective entrants. Although the entrants may not be so well informed and may not have the same degree of knowledge as the dominant firm's control group or even as much as the experienced small operators, their investment decision is sufficiently large that at least some attempt is made to apprise themselves of an accurate objective picture of the nature of the market.

Behavioristic Assumptions.   The would-be entrants, or at least their bankers, are aware that if the large firm finds its pricing policy unsuccessful because of the influx of new firms and gives up trying to control price there will then be too many firms in the market and some will succumb.

Under these assumptions our model computed in Chapter 6: 2.6 is now complete. In this market, at the equilibrium indicated, the dominant firm is in a position to use its power to obtain extra profit. There need be no implicit or explicit collusion present in the market and no particular behavioristic pattern aimed at monopolistic aggrandizement *per se*. If we assume that the directors of the dominant firm prefer more money to less money, then because of the technological and financial features of their market structure they are in a position to obtain it. An analogy with poker may be given. If your opponent has three aces showing on the table, you may be perfectly free to enter the next round of competition with your pair of twos; however, neither the kibitzers nor your bankers are going to be willing to finance your venture, and if you have a modicum of sense you will stay out of harm's way.

If entry into competition can be achieved quickly, with little financial backing, no legal restraints, no heavy plant commitments, and no vital need for special skills or ability, then, as suggested in Chapter: 2.6, any restrictive action of the major corporation or syndicate will merely cause new firms to enter. The corporation will find that the price will drop to approximately the efficient point price (there was no product differentiation in the model) and that its profits will be lower than before it attempted to exercise control (see Chapter 6: 2.6). This may cause it to abandon its attempt to control the market through its price and production policy.

In the penumbra of oligopolistic competition two different types of behavior can be distinguished which prevent a powerful firm from utilizing its power to control price. If technological conditions are right, there may be room for the intelligent small operator (see Chapter 10: 9.3). He will be able to effect a "hit-and-run" entry with a profit if any attempt is made to control price. In this manner he serves as the classical arbitrageur, "scalper," or chiseler. The soft-goods industries, notions, and import trades apparently still have some small businessmen who fit into this category. They may have to change their "lines" many times, and on some

occasions their offices may be their home addresses, an extra telephone, and a letter head. On the other hand, it is possible that the
technological conditions may be such that the intelligent small
entrepreneur would not enter, but, if entry costs are low and skill
requirements minimal, new entrants may blunder into a market
without realizing the true extent of the danger. Family grocery
stores, restaurants, and small service shops [2] fall for the most
part under this category. Entry rate is high, and failures are frequent. However, a plentiful supply of unintentionally suicidal
entrants serves to prevent a large firm from exerting its control
in a way that would be feasible against more rational competitors.

1.2.2. $\{1_i\} - \{r\}$ STABILITY, AN INDEX OF DOMINATION.   Suppose that we wished to examine a market with one dominant and
many small firms. Is there, at least theoretically, a measure to
indicate the degree of control exercised by the dominant firm?
We suggest the following scheme: A market is $\{1_i\} - \{r\}$ stable
if the dominant firm is in a position to enforce the equilibrium
against any joint action by as many as r players. ($\{1_i\}$ stands for
the set consisting of the dominant firm; $\{r\}$ stands for *any* set of
r players not including the dominant firm; and since we do not
need to distinguish between different sets of r players we do not
use a subscript with the $\{r\}$. The weakest control of a dominant
firm comes in a market with $\{1_i\} - \{1\}$ stability. It is completely
dominant in a market with $\{1_i\} - \{n - 1\}$ stability. Symbolically,
the condition of $\{1_i\} - \{r\}$ stability can be expressed as follows:

(1) $$\max_j P_j((\mathbf{S}, T^i, V^j)) = P_j((\mathbf{S}, T^i)).$$

(2) $$\max_j \max_k [P_j((\mathbf{S}, T^i, V^j, V^k)) + P_k((\mathbf{S}, T^i, V^j, V^k))]$$
$$= [P_j((\mathbf{S}, T^i)) + P_k((\mathbf{S}, T^i))], \qquad \text{for all}$$
$$j, k = 2, 3, \ldots n; \; j \neq k.$$

and so on up to and including the r player coalitions.

In this scheme we still have not completely specified the stability. What keeps the dominant firm at the equilibrium? We must
add an index of $\{k_j\} = \{1_i\}$ stability:

(3) $$\max_{v^i} P_i((\mathbf{S}, \mathbf{T}^{k_j}, V^i)) = P_i((\mathbf{S}, \mathbf{T}^{k_j})),$$

where the $\mathbf{T}^{k_j}$ stands for the threat strategies used by all players belonging to the set of k players denoted by k_j. We assume that a specific group of k players uses a threat strategy and the remainder uses a stationary strategy. As the n players include not only active firms but also firms-in-being, a threat may be a threat to enter. By adding condition 3 the maximizing actions of all players including the dominating player are constrained by the threat of retaliation from some individual or group.

Characteristically, we might expect that if a dominant firm is in powerful control of a market then the market will be $\{m_j\} - \{1_i\}$ stable where m is close to n in size (i.e., almost all the other players are required to enforce stability). Such a situation is met with under price leadership. The dominant firm sets the market price, and equilibrium comes about with the others adjusting to this price. The major firm will have no motivation to change its price if the small firms are expected to follow suit, expand production, and/or new entries open plants. These represent the threats of the small firms. On the other hand, at equilibrium it is unlikely that a small firm will engage in price cutting or other disturbances of the equilibrium for fear of retaliation.

Once more we wish to stress that *per se* an n-person game in extensive form does not supply us with very much a priori information upon which to base a theory of solution. When we limit our consideration to *games of economic survival* (see Chapter 10: 3) economic information may serve to suggest a concept of solution useful for economic applications of game theory.

Abstractly, the threat component of a threat strategy can be almost any function and can involve very complex behavior. "Reaction functions" and patterns of conjectured behavior serve as possible examples. Practically, it may be possible to obtain useful results while restricting oneself to very simple behavioristic assumptions. Thus we may examine a market for stability while restricting the threat action of firms to meeting price cuts. Since firms often are forced to meet price cuts or go out of business, this is not a very complicated or far-fetched behavioristic assumption. Combined actions involving price, advertising, distribution, and product variation must be examined eventually. Unfortunately, at this time economic science is not sufficiently advanced to be able to do so fruitfully.

1.3. EQUILIBRIUM POINTS, REACTION FUNCTIONS, AND "LEARNING STRATEGIES"

> I can call spirits from the vasty deep.
> Why, so can I, or so can any man; but will
> they come when you do call for them?
> *King Henry IV, Part I*

In general the solutions to the two-person and the many-person games of economic survival contain many equilibrium points. No attempt has been made to choose between different equilibria if they are enforceable under the same power structure. Our interest has been to avoid making complex behavioristic assumptions but to utilize structural and financial information in order to limit the "indeterminacy" present in oligopolistic markets as much as possible without being forced to make assumptions about behavior which could be verified only by psychologists. Thus the criteria of stability suggested are only of use in telling us what we can infer from an equilibrium state if it exists. In general, no analysis of motion from one particular equilibrium to another is given. In order to do this we would need a detailed knowledge of the behavior and reaction processes of individual entrepreneurs in different markets. Apart from a few fairly obvious behavior patterns (such as meeting price cuts of an opponent in certain markets), little is actually known about the psychology behind these processes. It is trivially easy to concoct different reaction functions with a thousand and one portrayals of bargaining procedures. It is phenomenally difficult to demonstrate that many of the models so constructed have any realism or relevance or at least add sufficiently to the body of theory to merit their construction.

The basic thesis in this book is that useful theory and applications can be found for oligopoly analysis without having to enter into the occupation of constructing extra, untestable models of learning psychology.

There is a purely formal connection between the game theory concept of strategy and learning behavior, for there will always be a strategy associated with any form of learning behavior. Thus, if we had a psychological theory of how individual businessmen react to certain stimuli in the market, we could investigate models in which the players were limited to using strategies that were equivalent to the postulated learning behavior.

The reasons why it does not appear to be too fruitful for economists to follow this approach at this time are (1) there is no body of scientifically analyzed observations upon which to base any but a very few simple theories of learning in economic situations, and (2) the mathematical difficulties are considerable. [3]

1.4. Pure Competition Revisited

An equilibrium point will be purely competitive, in the sense used in economics, if it is {0} — {1} stable, i.e., if it *needs no policing* by any group of players. If all players are using a steady-state strategy and no player is motivated to change his strategy, then a competitive equilibrium exists.

We are now able to construct a measure for the strength of a competitive equilibrium. It is {0} — {r} stable if no coalition of r or less players possesses a joint strategy that improves the profit of its members. An immediate connection can be seen between this measure and the *inessentiality* of a game. If an equilibrium point in an n-person game is {0} — {n} stable, then the game is inessential. No group of players acting jointly can improve their returns.

An immediate interpretation of the meaning of {0} — {r} stability in terms of market structure is given. A group of market gardeners surrounding a town and a mass of unorganized farm laborers may be in market structures in which individual action against the existing state of affairs does not pay. However, it may require an agreement between only five or six market gardeners to launch a successful program of collusion, whereas many thousands of laborers must be organized before a union has a chance of success. The second market has a higher degree of {0} — {r} stability than the first.

We noted in Chapter 10: 5.2.2 that if the asset conditions of two firms were not too dissimilar and the firms were similar in productive efficiency then the Cournot equilibrium maintained through time is an equilibrium point. This point is {0} — {1} stable. The Chamberlinian large group equilibrium will also be {0} — {1} stable if we add the appropriate conditions on assets, entry, and interest rates. In Part One we showed in Chapters 6 and 7 that as the number of players in a non-co-operative quantity (Cournot) or price game became large and the product differentiation small then the equilibrium point converged to the pure competition equilibrium. Utilizing the results of Chapters 6, 7, 10, and 11, this can be shown to hold true in the dynamic setting of an n-person game of economic survival as described in subsection 1.2.1.

1.5. Trade Associations, Industrial Ethics, and Codes of Behavior

The concept of $\{k_i\} - \{r_j\}$ stability suggests a method whereby certain objective levels or "benchmarks" concerning the degree of collusion in a market could be established if the strategies available to the players and the payoff functions were known. The greater the number of firms required to take police action or the more costly the police action to enforce an equilibrium, the more collusive is that equilibrium.

Trade associations serve the purpose of keeping the level of information high among members of a trade. An association may supply the research work and the statistics that an individual firm may not be able to afford to procure by itself. At the same time, without any overt intention to collude, codes of behavior or tables of industrial ethics [4] may be formulated. The result of a given code of behavior may be the establishment of some degree of collusive control over the market by the members of the association. This may not be bad *per se*. The code of ethics for competition among medical doctors serves as an example of a professional code that some members of society will regard as desirable.

The existence of a code of behavior can be translated into the enforceability of some degree of $\{k\} - \{r\}$ stability. Any firm or group of firms is aware of the prevailing sentiment of the other members of the association toward certain competitive acts. Given this information, a group of firms contemplating a certain policy is in a position to evaluate the degree of reprisals that may be called forth.

1.6. Absolute Competition and Complete Collusion

We call an equilibrium which is $\{0\} - \{n\}$ stable an absolutely competitive equilibrium; and an equilibrium which is $\{n - 1\} - \{1\}$ stable a completely collusive equilibrium. In the first case the game is inessential (as noted in subsection 1.5). The structure of the market is such that even if the players wished to collude there would be no gains to be obtained from collusion. In the second case the equilibrium is enforced only if all the remaining $n - 1$ players carry out a threat action against any single individual who wishes to depart from the equilibrium. The first case depends purely upon market structure and is rarely found in economics or in society in general, where most situations are nonconstant sum and where inessential games seldom occur. The second case is behavioristic; i.e., the existence of an equilibrium of $\{n - 1\} - \{1\}$ stability depends not only upon the payoff but on whether or not the members of the firms or of a society are willing to take joint police action against any individual who deviates from the *status quo*; these cases are discussed further in subsection 3.4.

2.   MODELS OF AN OLIGOPOLISTIC MARKET

2.1. A MARKET WITH TWO LARGE ACTIVE CORPORATIONS, A FINANCIAL SYNDICATE INTERESTED IN ENTRY, AND MANY SMALL FIRMS

Chapter 10: 5 is devoted to the construction of a dynamic duopoly model without entry. Here we use the same data for the two active firms as given in Chapter 10: 5.1. We add to the model a third competitor which is nothing but a financial syndicate with liquid assets of 30. We include many small firms with severe capacity limitations on their output and with capital limitations such that they are unable to weather more than a very few periods of industrial war. It is assumed that there are a number of small groups which would enter the market if it appeared profitable.

2.1.1. TREATMENT OF SMALL FIRMS AND ENTRANTS IN AN OLIGO-POLY MODEL.   A precise numerical formulation and computation of solutions to the market form described involves a considerable amount of mathematical and computational work. Instead of carrying out such a program here, we will discuss the nature of the solutions, making use of a minimum of computation. As a first step we discuss the method for treating the effect of small firms and entrants.

If we have a game in which there are a few dominant players and the rest is very small by comparison (say, at the Cournot equilibrium point the two large active firms control 60 per cent of the market, whereas no other player has more than $\frac{1}{10}$ per cent), then, from the viewpoint of the large industrialist, the economist, or the government investigator, it may be quite reasonable to approximate the actions of all the small players by an aggregated statistical model rather than to treat each firm as a player. For example, each large player may account for the small firms by assuming that expected entry is related directly to price and duration of price and inversely to the number of bankruptcies. When this is done the large n-person game can be replaced by a three-person game between the two large firms in production and the large syndicate. The small firms represent a drag or friction, which limits the "tightness" of collusive action, but they do not take the role of players. Such a treatment may also reflect the information conditions in the market. The information levels between the three large contestants are apt to be high, whereas the small firms are too small either to afford to have and process a great amount of information or to be the subject of close individual study by the giants.

2.1.2. A COMPETITIVE SOLUTION $\{0\} - \{1\}$ STABILITY. If the syndicate has the opportunity to erect a plant and enter into the market, then there is no competitive equilibrium in which it fails to enter, provided its plant is sufficiently efficient (for instance, identical with the others). There may be several equilibrium points that are competitive, and they will be the Cournot equilibrium for the major three active players and possibly a few small firms. The method for calculating the equilibria is outlined in the note on Chapter 6: 2.3 in Appendix C.

2.1.3. $\{1_i\} - \{1_j\}$ AND $\{1\} - \{1\}$ STABILITY. We reiterate that a stability of $\{1_i\} - \{1_j\}$ means that a market division is stable against any action of a specific single player, say j, because the threat or retaliation by another specific single player, say i, is large enough to dissuade j from disturbing the *status quo*. This does not imply, however, that player j is also able to force player i to maintain the status quo. $\{1\} - \{1\}$ stability means that any player can enforce the *status quo* against any other single player. In the example given here the position at which the syndicate stays out of the market and the two active firms produce at Cournot equilibrium can be enforced as an equilibrium of $\{1\} - \{1\}$ stability. There will be many other equilibria which have this property.

2.1.4. SOLUTIONS WITH $\{1_i\} - \{2_j\}$ AND $\{2_i\} - \{1_j\}$ STABILITIES. The existence of market states with $\{1_i\} - \{2_j\}$ stability implies that one firm is in a position to enforce an equilibrium against the joint actions of the other two. The threat of entry by the syndicate may be sufficient to prevent a joint action to monopolize beyond a certain point by the active firms. The joint threat of retaliation by the active firms may be sufficient to prevent entry by the syndicate. Hence a market state may be stable under a threat of two firms against the third and vice versa.

Even with three firms the complexities become considerable, and a priori it is not always possible to deduce a unique pattern of the structure of collusion or co-operation from the existence of a market equilibrium. However, by utilizing specific market information it may be feasible to narrow down the possibilities as to the level of collusion or co-operation in the market. For instance, when dealing with firms of approximately the same size and structure it may be possible to limit our consideration simply to $\{k\} - \{r\}$ stability, i.e., a stability which depends only upon the size of the policing and "chiseling" sets of players not upon their specific membership.

2.1.5. THE $\{2\} - \{1\}$ STABLE OR COMPLETELY COLLUSIVE SOLUTION. In subsection 1.7 we define complete collusion to be a limiting case under which, in order to prevent independent action by *any* individual, all the remaining members of the group must take joint police action. In this example, without side payments, there is no possibility for a completely collusive solution. If side payments were allowed, then such a state could be achieved. A scheme involving the distribution of stock and the awarding of some directorships would serve the purpose.

3. THE STATE OF INFORMATION IN AN OLIGOPOLISTIC MARKET

The theory presented in this chapter has been based upon the formulation of the class of games called *games of economic survival*. Strictly speaking, these games are defined in terms of complete information, i.e., every possible state is known to every player at every period. In reality, we are well aware that large gaps in knowledge are common. The existence of these gaps raises many empirical problems. The importance of the problems depends heavily upon the uses to which we wish to put our theory. If we wish to make a definite prediction about the future development of some specific market, our imprecise knowledge of the rate of innovation, demand fluctuations, general business conditions, and the varying degrees of ignorance manifested by the competitors may render a prediction just about as useless (or useful) as other economic predictions. If we are interested in analyzing markets *ex post* for purposes of control of industry or preservation of some sort of politically or legally defined "degree of competition", then the fact that there is uncertainty in a market may not hamper our analysis too much. Using our historical knowledge, we may be able to demonstrate that although in some markets collusion cannot be proved either collusion or excessive conservatism in the face of uncertainty exists. The word "excessive" calls for a political definition. Given any definition for it, the problem of the economist is to see whether at least an approximate measure for a degree of conservatism or a degree of collusion can be obtained (see subsection 4.3).

In general, the implicit assumptions made in this book, when talking about dynamic market situations involving a few large firms, are that the firms are usually approximately equally informed about the market and have relatively good knowledge about each other's general financial and physical structure, although certain costing and inventory processes and style or product innovations may not be known by competitors. On the whole, businessmen read the same journals, and, if there is any such thing as a state of over-all business confidence, they have roughly the same responses, since they are all exposed to the same stimuli. In industries in which the cost of entry is very high the entrants are usually well informed and technically competent. When entry costs and plant are negligible and competitors are many and small entrants may be neither well informed nor technically competent. We assume, for instance, that fewer unskilled individuals blunder into competition in the steel, automobile, or tire industry than into family grocery stores. [5]

4. STRUCTURE OR BEHAVIOR?

4.1. THE EFFECTS OF SIZE, INTEGRATION

In this section we discuss some specific problems faced in the study of oligopolistic markets.

Inventory theory teaches us that as the volume of trade increases in a market with random fluctuations in demand the inventories required in order to maintain a given level of safety increase at a lesser rate. [6] We can apply the same type of analysis to problems of horizontal integration.

Consider n markets, each for a different product. In each market we assume that there are two firms. Both firms in any market are identical in efficiency and capital structure. In particular, with both firms in the ith market there is associated a number k_i, the amount by which the assets of a firm in that market can be depleted before the firm is ruined and forced into bankruptcy. Suppose that the demand in each market were described by a random variable η_i and that the demands in different markets were uncorrelated. Let us assume that initially all the firms are in some symmetric equilibrium. The policy of the firms in the ith industry is described by the symbol $\mathscr{F}_i$. This policy includes a manner of production and a financial and dividend plan. If both firms in the ith industry are committed to the same plan (collusive or otherwise) and they are identical in all respects, then the expected profits of either firm, hence its value, is the same as that of its competitor. In particular, the probability that either firm will be ruined can be described by a number p_i which depends upon three factors: the policy of the firm, the demand, and the bankruptcy level. Thus we can write $p_i = p_i(\mathscr{F}_i, \eta_i, k_i)$. Let us now suppose that one of the two firms in every one of the markets agreed to join in a horizontal integration. The $2n$ firms are replaced by a corporation with n plants and n remaining independent firms. We can see immediately that on the assumption that nothing else has changed, i.e., each plant of the corporation still uses the same market and dividend policy, the probability that a plant of the corporation will be ruined has decreased and the probability that an independent firm will be ruined has increased. By the process of integration all retained funds are paid into a common corporate account, and thus ruin for all plants can be averted as long as the total assets of the corporation do not sustain a loss greater than $\sum k_i$. We observe that the insurance effects of horizontal integration come about in this case by mere size. It is easy to see that each plant in the integrated firm could afford to be slightly less efficient than its unintegrated competitor and yet still have a larger profit expectation on account of the extra security brought about by integration.

If it were possible for the independent firms to buy insurance at actuarial cost with no extra overheads, then, of course, there would be no difference in the two markets. This is not usually the case.

This example is given merely to call attention to a situation in which there may be no question whatsoever of intent. The integrating firms may not change their individual market policies. The only feature that will have changed is that the firms will be integrated into a mutual low-overhead insurance scheme. This by itself may be sufficient to establish a competitive advantage over otherwise equally efficient or more efficient competitors.

4.2. The Effects of "Fewness": "Conscious Parallelism"

The analysis in Chapter 10 and here in Chapter 11 has been developed in terms of threats against those who depart from an equilibrium. A measure of plausibility for a threat was suggested by comparing the effect upon revenues of maintaining the stationary strategy with the effect upon revenues caused by carrying out a threat. Both of these quantities are well defined because we have carried out our analysis in terms of strategies or complete plans of action employed by all players.

When there are very few players in a market with a high structure of overhead, a considerable financial barrier to entry or exit (high liquidation losses), and a large cross-elasticity of demand between the product lines of the competitors then the market revenues of one player will be highly sensitive to the actions of any competitor. In particular, the profits of all players will depend upon all prices in such a manner that it would be almost suicidal to allow a competitor with large capacity (or the means to expand quickly) to undercut price more than some amount determined by product differentiation.

A complete generation of economists has pointed out the idiocy of the charge of conscious parallelism (i.e., implicit collusion). In terms of the analysis offered here almost any price is stable under a very plausible system of threats. This can include strategies which permit the upward testing of a market. It does not take a very intelligent board of directors to realize that unless a price increase in a narrow oligopolistic market is followed the instigator of the price change will have to bring his price down again. A straightforward calculation will indicate whether or not the extra profits that can be made by obtaining a larger share of the market, while an opponent is engaged in maintaining a price raise, will be more than the gain in profits to be made by meeting that raise and thus establishing a new equilibrium at a higher price. In the first case the firms can be assured that if they do not meet the raise the firm instigating the price raise will cut prices sooner or later (see for instance the price raise by Lucky Strike [7]).

4.3. Conservatism or Collusion? Ex Post and Ex Ante Risk

In the definitions of solution to a game of economic survival given in Chapter 10: 4 the restrictions permitting the use of certain feasible threats can be defended only on empirical grounds. It appears to be a reasonable assumption that if one firm departs from a stationary state another firm will not go to the extent of inflicting a much larger long-run damage on itself than on the violator, possibly to the extent of committing suicide, in order to teach the violator a lesson. On the other hand, a threat which costs the enforcers less than the violator and which might be cheaper to carry out than to maintain their stationary strategies is more plausible. Thus when we speak of a market as being $\{4\} - \{1\}$ stable under strong threats we mean that any violator believes at least some four firms will take joint action against him, and he knows that among them they have a strong threat.

If we are trying to measure the level of collusion present in a market from an *ex post* viewpoint, then, if there were no stochastic elements involved in the model, we would have no (theoretical) difficulty in being able to compute the possible stability patterns for the market. However, in practice there may be many random elements involved. If we observed, for instance, in the example given in section 2 that the syndicate never entered the market, then, if the active corporations were accused of being in collusion to block entry, they could claim that the potential entrant did not really fear a joint threat action but was, in fact, acting conservatively under the fear of exogenous random variables such as the expected instability of demand. Practically, in a trade with a high rate of innovation it might be difficult to establish the existence of collusion; however, in trades with a market pattern less susceptible to violent random fluctuations it may be possible to establish the alternative hypotheses that either there must be a certain level of collusion or there must be a very high level of risk aversion, the need for which is not borne out by the *ex post* observations. The problem confronting the administrator then becomes that of determining whether or not legislation is aimed at a state of affairs or at a state of mind. If the legislation is aimed at correcting actions and if a state of affairs could have been caused by collusion or extreme caution on the part of the participants, action is called for in both cases (although not necessarily the same action).

4.4. STRUCTURE AND BEHAVIOR

Does the law wish to distinguish between structure and behavior? Do legislators want to rule upon intentions or upon actions? The very nature of size and structure will be able to bring about a set of closely parallel market policies between a few large oligopolists without calling for any conferences between boards of directors or the writing of incriminating letters. The same parallelism of action between several hundred medium-sized firms belonging to a trade association will be less likely to occur without a conscious effort towards organization.

The presence of many small firms in a market usually implies *individual strategic weakness*. The individual acts of the small firm are of little importance. Joint action must provide stength when structure is such that the individual is weak.

Size in itself usually implies strategic power. This power is not necessarily most usefully described by a single number. It manifests itself in the range of the strategy space of a firm. The battery of forces that can be brought to bear upon a market may include pricing, advertising, rebate policy, financing terms, extra services, and insurance. Whatever they may be, the test of their importance is to be found by examining the range of maneuverability they give a player and by measuring the effect of the use of any of these weapons upon the payoffs of an opponent. If the behavior of a Gulliver is especially restrained, he will not kill any Lilliputians. If he is even slightly careless *without any intention* to do harm, he may cause considerable damage.

NOTES

[1] For a closely related concept see R. D. Luce, "Chi-stability: A New Equilibrium Concept for n-Person Game Theory," *Mathematical Models of Human Behavior*, Proceedings of a Symposium (Stanford: Dunlop and Associates, Inc., 1955) pp. 32–44.

[2] "Competition and Monopoly in American Industry," *Monograph No. 21, Temporary National Economic Committee* (Washington: U.S. Government Printing Office, 1940), pp. 59–63.

[3] See, for instance, M. M. Flood, "On Game-Learning Theory and Some Decision Making Experiments," and W. K. Estes, "Individual Behavior in Uncertain Situations: An Interpretation in Terms of Statistical Association Theory," in *Decision Processes*, R. M. Thrall, C. H. Coombs, and R. L. Davis, eds. (New York: Wiley, 1954).

[4] Carl F. Taeusch, *Professional and Business Ethics* (New York: Henry Holt, 1926), pp. 279–284.

[5] See A. R. Hutchinson, and M. Newcomer, "A Study in Business Mortality," *American Economic Review*, 28 (1938), pp. 497–514.

[6] T. M. Whitin, *The Theory of Inventory Management*, Chapter III.

[7] R. B. Tennant, *The American Cigarette Industry* (New Haven: Yale University Press, 1950), pp. 393–396.

THE STRUCTURE
OF THE MARKETS

1. INTRODUCTION

The game theory analysis of competition and/or collusion in an economy is carried out in strategic terms. The clash and coincidence of interests in the market are formalized in models dealing with players, strategies, and payoffs. In the course of development we have incorporated the financial and other asset features of the structure of a firm directly into our analysis. By doing this, the relationship between models of games of economic survival and the balance sheets and income statement of firms becomes apparent. The relationship between different forms of maximization, dividend policies, and survival has been noted. In this chapter a brief sketch of some of the salient features of American industry, utilizing information from the last decade, is given in order to indicate the economic background that has motivated the theory presented earlier.

Two sketches of specific industries are presented mainly to demonstrate the connection between the models of games of economic survival and the empirical study of market forms. These brief studies together with a market interpretation in terms of $\{k_i\} - \{r_j\}$

stability are given as a suggestion for the type of empirical development envisioned by the previous analysis.

2. THE STRUCTURE OF AMERICAN INDUSTRY

If, in fact, the major part of the economy were run by many individual businessmen, each in control of his own firm, with few resources and high liquidity, and if there were no credit restrictions, entry frictions, liquidation losses or information lags, the market models presented here would approximate that of pure competition, and there would be no necessity for the elaborate superstructure.

In order to obtain an approximate description of the structure of business enterprise in the economy a selection of statistical information is given here.

Table 17 presents a breakdown of the number of firms in the United States in 1948 according to size measured by number of employees. [1]

Table 17

Number of Firms (1000)	Employees	Employment (1000)	Per Cent of Firms	Per Cent of Employment
3,771.1	0–19	8,445*	95.1	20.2
160.7	20–99	6,257	4.0	15.0
28.7	100–499	5,712	0.7	13.7
3.3	500–999	2,287	0.1	5.5
4.1	1,000 up	13,749	0.1	32.9

* 5,201,000 proprietors should be added to this group. 133,000 proprietors should be distributed among the remaining groups.

A. D. H. Kaplan has given a classification of these firms according to industry and size of firm. This is reproduced in Table 18. [2] We note that the major proportion of large firms is concentrated in manufacturing and that the majority of small firms is in the retail trade or service industries.

The size and control of assets are important factors in determining the behavior of the firm. Kaplan notes that in 1948 3595.9 thousand small incorporated and unincorporated firms (with assets under 500,000 dollars) had total assets of 76 billion dollars;

Table 18

	All Size Classes	0–19	20–99	100– 499	500– 999	1000 or more
All industries	3966.8	3771.1	160.7	28.7	3.3	3.1
Mining	34.4	29.4	3.8	1.0	0.1	0.1
Construction	312.4	295.4	14.9	1.8	0.1	0.1
Manufacturing	329.3	255.5	54.7	15.3	2.0	1.8
Transportation communications, and other public utilities	186.5	175.7	8.1	1.9	0.3	0.4
Wholesale trade	201.4	183.2	16.2	1.8	0.1	0.1
Finance, insurance, and real estate	345.8	336.2	7.8	1.4	0.2	0.1
Service industries	852.8	830.7	19.5	2.4	0.2	0.1
Retail trade	1704.2	1665.0	35.5	3.1	0.3	0.3

33.6 thousand corporations of intermediate size (assets 500,000 to 50 million dollars) had total assets of 82 billion dollars; and 361 large corporations (assets of 50 million dollars or more) had total assets of 72 billion dollars. [3] These figures serve to stress the importance of the intermediate and large corporations as controlling entities in the economy.

The nature of the control of most firms with more than 500,000 dollars in assets is such that any description of behavior based upon the assumption of the maximization of income by an individual is inadequate. Almost all firms with assets above 500,000 dollars are corporations. As we can see from the information given on assets, approximately 34,000 corporations controlled 67 per cent of the assets of those firms classified as industrial enterprises, of which there were 3.6 million.

Corporate policy is, in general, an amalgam determined by the aims of the directors, officers, employees, and stockholders. There is a considerable overlap between directors and officers, and multiple directorates are frequently held. [4] Among the larger corporations ownership is so fractionated that direct stockholder power is of little importance. Table 19 shows the number of stockholders and employees and the assets of the twenty-two firms whose sales were over one billion dollars in 1954. [5]

Table 19

Manufacturing Corporations with Sales over $1,000,000,000 in 1954

Rank	Company	Sales ($1,000)	Assets ($1,000)		Stockholders		Employees	
1	General Motors	9,823,526	5,130,094	2	487,639	1	576,667	1
2	Standard Oil (N.J.)	5,661,382	6,614,743	1	297,000	2	155,000	6
3	Ford	4,026,300	2,083,500	4	—		171,019	4
4	U.S. Steel	3,250,369	3,348,695	3	275,833	4	268,142	2
5	General Electric	2,959,078	1,691,980	10	295,945	3	210,151	3
6	Swift	2,510,805	495,264	44	65,000	33	78,000	13
7	Chrysler	2,071,598	1,034,592	20	89,307	20	167,813	5
8	Armour	2,056,149	469,915	50	20,000	111	60,000	23
9	Gulf Oil	1,705,329	1,969,052	8	69,140	31	46,800	29
10	Socony-Vacuum Oil	1,703,575	2,256,691	6	174,627	6	72,000	16
11	Du Pont (E.I.) de Nemours	1,687,650	2,747,404	5	149,414	8	84,494	12
12	Bethlehem Steel	1,667,377	1,613,444	12	100,549	18	135,784	7
13	Standard Oil (Ind.)	1,660,343	2,187,358	7	122,100	9	51,270	28
14	Westinghouse Electric	1,631,045	1,329,120	13	111,107	14	117,143	8
15	Texas Co.	1,574,370	1,945,509	9	119,532	10	41,630	37
16	Western Electric	1,526,231	1,073,600	17	—		98,141	9
17	Shell Oil	1,312,060	1,041,886	19	18,669	118	35,275	47
18	National Dairy Products	1,210,329	446,465	54	63,177	35	45,733	33
19	Standard Oil of California	1,113,343	1,677,849	11	114,607	13	35,354	46
20	Goodyear Tire & Rubber	1,090,094	668,664	29	41,152	47	95,727	10
21	Boeing Airplane	1,033,176	252,643	95	18,451	119	65,054	21
22	Sinclair Oil	1,021,461	1,186,771	15	101,285	16	23,746	75

Table 20

Percentage Surviving in 1946 of the Population in Specified Years

Year	Number Surviving in 1946	Per Cent of Population	Year	Number Surviving in 1946	Per Cent of Population
1945	418,689	99.2	1934	220,414	43.5
1944	378,739	87.9	1929	154,684	29.9
1943	358,178	80.7	1924	105,366	24.9
1942	343,912	73.5	1919	73,055	22.6
1941	331,384	67.4	1914	53,124	16.9
1940	314,745	63.2	1909	37,234	15.0
1939	297,226	59.9			

Distribution of Industries by Size and Concentration ratio, 1947

Industry Size (Value of Shipments)	Number of Industries	Value of Shipments	Concentration ratios (first 4 companies)							
			75 to 100 Per Cent		50 to 74.9 Per Cent		25 to 49.9 Per Cent		24.9 Per Cent or Less	
			No.	Value	No.	Value	No.	Value	No.	Value
$1,000,000,000 and more	32	$55,2	3	$3,8	3	$3,8	11	$21,0	15	$26,7
$500,000,000 to $1,000,000,000	50	35,8	4	3,0	7	5,7	18	12,8	21	14,3
$100,000,000 to $500,000,000	182	44,4	15	3,2	37	8,8	62	14,8	68	17,5
Less than $100,000,000	176	8,2	21	1,0	54	2,1	67	3,3	34	1,7
Total	440	143,6	43	11,0	101	20,4	158	51,9	138	60,2

Note. Because of excessive duplication in the total value of shipments reported for certain industries, only 440 of the 452 industries appear above. The remaining 12 industries are distributed below according to concentration ratio computed on the basis of value added by manufacture.

Industry Size (Value Added by Manufacture)	Number of Industries	Value added by manufac.	75 to 100 Per Cent		50 to 74.9 Per Cent		25 to 49.9 Per Cent		24.9 Per Cent or Less	
			No.	Value	No.	Value	No.	Value	No.	Value
$1,000,000,000 and more	6	$8,4	—	—	1	$3,6	5	$4,9	—	—
$500,000,000 to $1,000,000,000	1	6	—	—	1	6	1	1	—	—
$100,000,000 to $500,000,000	4	5	2	$0,17	1	22	1	—	—	—
Less than $100,000,000	1	0.3	1	3	—	—	—	—	—	—
Total	12	9,53	3	0,20	3	4,40	6	4,95	—	—

Source. Census of Manufactures, 1947.
Note. Dollar amounts in millions; figures have been rounded out.

A game of economic survival as formulated in Chapter 10 includes explicitly the possibility of the eventual liquidation of a firm. An indication of the corporate birth and death rate can be obtained from the study of William Leonard Crum. As an example, we note that of the 491.2 thousand corporations active in 1946 [6] there were 418.7 thousand surviving (i.e., corporations which were born before 1946 and were still legally active). Table 20 shows the age structure of the corporate population of those firms. [7]

Crum notes that his corporate birth and death figures are based upon legal definition. It is possible for a firm to be incorporated several years before it engages actively in business and that it may cease to carry out trade several years before it gives up its charter.

In the study by Crum he shows that from the second year on the probability of survival during any year varies directly with the age of the corporation and that at the death rates of 1946 half of the corporations could expect to survive between nine and ten years. [8]

R. G. Hutchinson, A. R. Hutchinson, and Mabel Newcomer in a study of 10,000 businesses in Poughkeepsie, New York, 1843–1936, found that over this period 30 per cent of the entrants failed within a year. The highest death rate was related to the trades with lowest entry capital requirements. Corporations fared better than other concerns. Thus 31 per cent lived to be older than ten years, but only 22 per cent of all concerns survived this time. [9]

Successful entry and the ability to survive depends heavily upon the strength of a firm to withstand early losses. Among the newly chartered corporations in 1946 of those which were completely new enterprises 49.7 per cent operated at a loss in their first year; 23.9 per cent which were successors to active businesses also ran at a loss. [10] In manufacturing these percentages were 57.2 and 27.2, respectively. [11]

Oligopoly to a greater or lesser degree appears to be the dominant form in American industry. The 500 largest (by sales) manufacturing firms for which information is available had a sales total of 140.8 billion dollars in 1954, [12] an amount equal to 38.9 per cent of the gross national product. [13] There are many different measures of concentration [14] used to indicate the presence of monopolistic elements in an economy. Using the Bureau of Census' classification of industries, the percentage of output by the largest four or eight firms in the United States has been used. The study of monopoly power submitted to the Judiciary Committee of the House of Representatives gives the 1947 concentration ratios for the largest four, eight, twenty, and fifty firms in 452 industries. [15] A summary of the findings is reproduced in Table 21.

The various measures of oligopolistic concentration are for the most part one-dimensional characterizations of the markets and may be sufficient to indicate areas in which neither the theories of competition (pure competition, Chamberlinian large group theory, and other non-co-operative static theories described in Part One) nor monopoly apply. However, as is well known, [16] a one-dimensional measure is not sufficient, in general, to characterize the many factors that tend to limit the form of competition possible within a given market structure.

3. MEASURES OF INTERDEPENDENCE

In Chapters 9, 10, and 11 we constructed a general model of a market as a game of economic survival. In order to discuss the possibilities of competition or collusion we had to examine first the interlocking of the strategy spaces of the various firms and to be able to specify the payoffs associated with all possible policies. The strategy spaces and the payoffs were determined by long- and short-run market manufacturing and financial conditions considered in conjunction with each other. Here we tentatively suggest five different types of "rule of thumb" measures of *vulnerability*, some of which are associated *damage exchange rates*. These proposed measures are directly related to the theoretical construct of a game of economic survival. After we have defined them, their relevence to the definition and measurement of competition or collusion will be discussed.

(1) *Short-run market vulnerability* is a measure of the amount of damage that can be done to a firm by short-run market action of an opponent or by a shift in a market parameter. It is related to the nature and size of inventory positions, the immediate effect of price changes, advertising maneuvers, and style shifts upon imme-

diate profits. A different measure can be given for each variable considered. Thus the short-run market vulnerability with respect to price is measured by the loss of profit to a firm caused by a price cut of an opponent.

The revenue of firm i in the single period t is given by the market matrix $R_{i,t}(a; s_1, s_2, \ldots, s_n)$ where a is a random variable (i.e., it is the move controlled by the exogenous features of the market), and the s_j, $j = 1, 2, \ldots, n$ are the strategies of the players in this single-period subgame. The short-run market vulnerability of firm i with respect to an action by firm j is given by

$$\frac{\Delta R_{i,t}}{\Delta s_j}.\text{[17]}$$

The short-run market damage exchange rate is given by

$$\frac{\Delta_j R_{i,t}}{\Delta_j R_{j,t}},$$

where the Δ_j indicates that the increment is defined with respect to a change in s_j.

(2) *Short-run financial vulnerability* relates to current asset and liability position, to the nature of the firm's capitalization, especially the leverage present, to the credit rating of the firm, and to the state of the money markets. It is given by the ratio of the largest amount of money that a firm can lose in a single period (determined by the short-run market vulnerability) to the amount of losses that force bankruptcy or possibly take-over or other financial reorganization.

(3) *Long-run market vulnerability* depends upon the structure of overhead costs, flexibility of product-variation, and the state of long-run demand. The long-run market vulnerability of firm i against a change in strategy by firm j for τ periods is given by

$$\frac{\sum_{t=0}^{\tau} \Delta R_{i,t}}{\Delta S^j}$$

The long-run market damage exchange rate is given by

$$\frac{\sum_{t=0}^{\tau} R_{i,t}}{\sum_{t=0}^{\tau} R_{j,t}}.$$

Practically, this measure is not very satisfactory, since we face considerable difficulty in specifying what is meant by an incremental change in strategy by player j. However, at least in theory it is possible to calculate the resulting revenues over a number of periods caused by the employment of any set of strategies. The simple example in Chapter 10: 5 shows this.

(4) *Long-run financial vulnerability* depends upon the total assets and credit that a firm can muster in a struggle for survival. It can be measured by the ratio of the largest amount of money that a firm could stand to lose over a specified number of periods to the amount of losses that the firm is able to sustain before it is forced into liquidation or some other form of reorganization. This is not quite adequate because the amount that a firm can lose over several periods is, in general, determined by the time path through which it converts frozen or fixed assets into liquid assets available to avoid short-run disaster.

(5) *Control vulnerability* depends upon the way stockholdings are fractionated, the size of the stock issue, and the debt structure. It is measured by the size of resources required by an "invading group" to capture the corporation through gaining stockholding allies, bying in the open market, exerting pressure through credit control, or fighting for proxies, using an optimal combination of these tactics. A short- and long-run control vulnerability can be defined. The first is the cost to an invading group on the assumption that no countermeasures are taken. The second is the cost to an invading group on the assumption that defenders attempt to prevent the capture.

The indices described are suggested merely as a means of examining the strategy spaces and revenues of a group of firms. If the firms are at an efficient point equilibrium, the short-run damage exchange rate will be unfavorable to a firm that cuts price. The financial vulnerabilities play a role in an economy in which only long-term individual financial considerations may overrule technological efficient allocation conditions. If we are able to measure the strategic vulnerabilities of firms or groups of firms, it then becomes possible to form estimates of the varieties of $\{k_i\} - \{r_j\}$ stability that are consistent with the state of the market. It is the strategic interconnection of firms and the behavior exhibited under various conditions of this interconnection that form a central part of the theory and measurement of oligopolistic power.

4. THE AUTOMOBILE INDUSTRY [18]

4.1. DESCRIPTION OF THE AUTOMOBILE INDUSTRY

In this and the succeeding section we present a brief sketch of two industries up until the end of 1955 in order to indicate the relationship between the theoretical construct of a game of economic survival, the measures of interdependence suggested, and the type of empirical investigation envisioned as necessary to reconcile our knowledge of market forms more closely with a theory of oligopoly.

The automobile industry has an oligopolistic structure with three major and two minor firms and an amount of foreign competition. Its products reach the consumer via many thousands of distributors.

The nature of the industry has changed considerably since its early days. At the turn of the century automobile manufacturers contracted with other firms for most of their parts and, in the main, merely did the assembling. Because of this system capital requirements were small, [19] and entry was correspondingly easy. In 1899 there were fifty-seven producing establishments in the industry, and by 1904 this number had increased to 121. [20] As the industry grew, the more successful firms began to integrate, and the numbers thinned.

At present the diversification and complexity of the corporate structure of the remaining firms is considerable. Although the mere counting of the number of corporations controlled by a single business entity does not necessarily supply information about the diversity of its activities, it may serve as a crude index of diversification and may suggest natural subdivisions of a large corporation. In some cases more or less semi-independent sections are organized as divisions with no separate corporate existence.

The consolidated financial statement of General Motors includes approximately seventy corporations. It controls several hundred other corporations. In some cases the control is split with another large corporation. For instance, it owns 50 per cent of the Ethyl

Gas Corporation, with Standard Oil of New Jersey owning the other 50 per cent, and $33\frac{3}{10}$ per cent of the International Freighting Corporation, with du Pont owning the rest. [21] In 1955 91 per cent of its sales, exclusive of defense contracts, were automobiles and trucks.

American Motors consists of Hudson and Nash and about twenty other companies, including Kelvinator. Sixty-seven per cent of its sales in 1955 were automobiles. Ford Company's diagram of corporate structure has about forty companies, including 50 per cent of the Humboldt Mining Company, the Fordson Coal Company, and Ford Tractor and Equipment Sales Company of Canada. [22] Over 90 per cent of its sales were automobiles and trucks. Chrysler is split into divisions rather than many separate corporations, except for a few subsidiaries such as the Chrysler Corporation of Canada. However, its business is diversified.

Even Kaiser Motors, which has now gone out of the automobile business, did so by ceasing to make utility vehicles and becoming part of Kaiser Industries Corporation, which operates directly through controlled corporations or partially through minority stockholding in the sand and gravel, engineering, construction, aluminum, chemical, steel, and cement businesses. [23]

In 1955 General Motors sold over 50 per cent of all the automobiles sold in the United States, 80 per cent of the buses, 43 per cent of the trucks, a considerable proportion of the diesel locomotives and refrigerators, 20 per cent of all wheel-type farm tractors, as well as other defense material. Chrysler sold approximately 17 per cent of all cars sold, around 9 per cent of the trucks, as well as medium tanks, guided missiles, air conditioning, marine engines, Oilite powdered metal products, and Cycleweld adhesives.

With the exception of Ford, the control of the automobile firms appears to lie with the officers. The stock issues are large and the holdings fractionated. In the Ford Company the Ford family controls 40 per cent of the votes, hence just about all the power. [24] Table 22 indicates the size of the stock issues and number of stockholders. Du Pont owns about 23 per cent of General Motors. Leaving out antitrust considerations, it is the only financial concentration in a position to capture control of General Motors if it wished to do so. The largest individual shareholder of Chrysler in 1955 held $1\frac{15}{100}$ per cent.

Table 22

Control Structure

	Shares	Stock-holders	Control
General Motors	276,000,000 common 1,800,000 pfd. 5 per cent 1,000,000 pfd. 3.75 per cent	600,000	Directors and officers
Ford	53,500,000 common	310,000	Ford Family
Chrysler	8,700,000 common	88,000	Directors and officers
American Motors	5,700,000 common	55,000	Directors and officers
Studebaker-Packard	6,400,000 common	110,000	Directors and officers

The long-term debt structure is not very important in this industry. Most financing has utilized earnings or the sale of common stock.

The ratio between current assets and current liabilities has varied between 1.7 and 4 for the firms. The two smallest companies have tended to have the worst ratios. They are also heavily dependent on bank loans.

As automobiles are a consumer durable, demand depends upon the size and age distribution of previous stocks as well as upon prices and income levels. It has been variously estimated that the price elasticity for automobiles in the United States is between −0.5 and −1.0. [25] Even given a 200- to 300-dollar cut in automobile prices, it appears to be highly unlikely that more than 8,500,000 cars can be sold per annum for several years to come.

Little is known for certain about the relative efficiencies of the various firms in the automobile industry. The industry is of the break-even type. Heavy overhead costs must be met, and therefore profits are very sensitive to volume. Table 23 gives the production figures for thema in line of automobiles for four of the companies.

The mere presence of high rates of profits for the larger firms does not establish a criterion to measure and compare inherent manufacturing efficiencies.

Styling and advertising are important components of competition in the automobile industry. A wrong guess by a small firm can

Table 23

Production

(In millions of popular cars)

	Chevrolet	Buick	Ford	Plymouth	Studebaker
1951	1.118	0.404	0.902	0.623	0.233
1952	0.878	0.321	0.775	0.475	0.173
1953	1.477	0.485	1.181	0.663	0.190
1954	1.414	0.531	1.396*	0.472	0.085
1955	1.830	0.781	1.764*	0.815	0.112

*Includes Thunderbirds

spell disaster. The demand fluctuations for Studebaker and Chrysler products appear to be heavily related to styling and "sales competition" rather than price. [26] There are no estimates available of the cross-elasticities of demand between different makes of automobiles. Product differentiation and consumer loyalty obviously play a major role in automobile demand. However, in the low-priced range it appears reasonable to assume that a price cut of over 100 dollars by Chevrolet would seriously eat into the markets of the other firms if it went unanswered.

An indication of the importance of the automobile industry to the economy is given by the following figures: In 1955 there were approximately 51,000,000 passenger cars and 10,000,000 trucks and buses in the United States. [27] The Automobile Manufacturers Association calculated in 1953 that 700,000 businesses could be classified as automotive. Among these were 50,000 new- and used-car retailers, 17,000 used-car dealers, 60,000 general repair establishments, 188,000 gasoline stations, and 210,000 for-hire trucking firms. These amounted to approximately one sixth of all the firms in the United States. In that year automotive retailer sales (dealers, parts, and gasoline) amounted to 44 billion dollars. The 1954 employment figure in highway transport industries was placed at 9,800,000. [28]

Production and financial information for five years of operation is given in the following tables:

Table 24

Production

(in millions of automobiles)

	Total	General Motors	Ford	Chrysler	American Motors	Studebaker-Packard	Kaiser
1951	5.3	2.27	1.17	1.229	0.254*	0.298†	0.100
1952	4.3	1.78	1.00	0.953	0.228*	0.225†	0.075
1953	6.1	2.80	1.54	1.246	0.212*	0.268†	0.022
1954	5.6	2.88	1.69	0.776	0.011	0.113	0.005
1955	7.9	3.99	2.24	1.464	0.162	0.182	0.005

*American Motors was formed in 1954 as a combination of Nash Kelvinator and Hudson Motors.

†Studebaker-Packard was formed in 1954 as a combination of Studebaker and Packard.

Table 25

Production

(in millions of trucks and buses)

	Total	General Motors	Ford	Chrysler	American Motors	Studebaker-Packard
1951	1.42	0.562	0.320	0.169	N	0.052
1952	1.21	0.453	0.235	0.162	O	0.059
1953	1.20	0.476	0.315	0.105	N	0.032
1954	1.04	0.412	0.303	0.107	E	0.015
1955	1.25	0.499	0.374	0.116		0.019

Table 26

Sales

(in millions of dollars)

	General Motors	Ford	Chrysler	American Motors	Studebaker-Packard
1951	7,466	2,742	2,547	582*	682†
1952	7,549	2,640	2,601	573*	879†
1953	10,028	4,211	3,348	672*	930†
1954	9,824	4,062	2,072	400	650†
1955	12,443	5,594	3,466	441	480

*Estimated, exact data not published.

†Studebaker-Packard was formed in 1954 as a combination of Studebaker and Packard.

Table 27

Assets

(in millions of dollars)

	General Motors	Ford	Chrysler	American Motors	Studebaker-Packard
1951	3,672	1,469	758	279*	265†
1952	4,001	1,584	914	321*	228†
1953	4,405	1,758	898	340*	294†
1954	5,130	1,895	1,035	267	246
1955	6,176	2,585	1,363	260	230

*Estimated, exact data not published.
†Studebaker-Packard was formed in 1954 as a combination of Stude-baker and Packard.

Table 28

Net Profit

(in millions of dollars)

	General Motors	Ford	Chrysler	American Motors	Studebaker-Packard
1951	506	126	72	15*	24†
1952	559	117	79	21*	25†
1953	598	166	75	4*	13†
1954	806	228	19	−11	−26
1955	1,189	437	100	−7	−30

*Estimated, exact data not published.
†Studebaker-Packard was formed in 1954 as a combination of Stude-baker and Packard.

Table 29

Dividends

(in millions of dollars)

	General Motors	Ford	Chrysler	American Motors	Studebaker-Packard
1951	350	35	65	—	—
1952	349	35	52	—	—
1953	349	52	52	—	—
1954	437	90	39	4	0
1955	592	175	35	0	0

Table 30

Income Retained

(in millions of dollars)

	General Motors	Ford	Chrysler	American Motors	Studebaker-Packard
1951	143	92	7	—	—
1952	197	82	27	—	—
1953	236	114	23	—	—
1954	357	138	−20	−15	−26 .
1955	584	262	65	− 7	−30

4.2. COMPETITION IN THE AUTOMOBILE INDUSTRY

The description in subsection 4.1 provides the information for setting up a crude model of the automobile market as a game of economic survival. Although insufficient detail has been given to merit setting up a completely formal model, we can relate this information to the general structure of the game given in Chapter 10: 3.2 and use the indices of vulnerability to estimate the type of competition in the automobile industry.

(1)   There are five major *players* (the domestic firms), several minor players (foreign competition, primarily German and British), and apparently no firms-in-being or potential entrants, since there does not appear to be a financial and engineering group available with the necessary ante.

(2)   The *personal moves* of the players which are of importance in this industry include advertising, styling, innovation, pricing, production and inventory scheduling, the payment of dividends, and investment (labor-union and industry bargaining is highly important to all firms).

(3)   The *chance moves* involve probabilities of technical success in research and innovation, the vagaries of consumer taste, and the fluctuations in national income.

(4)   The *positional payoffs* are determined by the distribution of the corporate net income, as are the *corporate asset positions*.

(5)   The *bankruptcy conditions* are determined by the various firms' ability to lose money and still be able to meet their obligations. Both Studebaker-Packard and American Motors barely

have a quarter of a billion dollars each; hence even under the most optimistic assumption that they could afford to lose all they could still be driven into bankruptcy or merger in one or two poor years.

(6) The *liquidation* or *ruin values* depend upon the degree of specialization of the equipment being sold. The two small automobile companies could realize their best values if they sold out to the others. Such a sale to General Motors or Ford would probably be declared illegal. At the end of 1955 General Motors evaluated its real estate, plants, and equipment at 4,354 million dollars, less 2,001 million for depreciation. In order to evaluate its liquidation worth we would have to calculate the effect of such a sale on the market.

(7) The *information conditions* are such that at the end of every year the firms are completely informed of most of the moves made by their opponents, although they may lack information about some of the long-term development and planning actions. As an outsider's guess, we may assume that they are equally and fairly well informed about each other's costs and that they are equally adept or inept at "crystal-ball gazing" at outside events or factors exogenous to the industry.

(8) *The utility function and motives for maximization:* We note in Chapter 10: 3.3 that the profit maximization motive suggested by the simple static theory of the firm is not adequate in a dynamic corporate setting. Without having to resort to complex psychological theories, it is not difficult to observe that even if all directors and officers were motivated solely by monetary goals the institutional structure of a large corporation is such that the corporate goal, although, in general, it will be positively correlated, with immediate money income, will involve many other considerations. The aims of a corporation are sometimes stated generally in terms of duties towards stockholders, employees, consumers, and even the government.

A direct relation between the welfare of the salaried employees and the net income of the firm may come about through a fixed bonus scheme. Thus the General Motors bonus plan calls for at most 12 per cent of net earnings after deducting 5 per cent on net capital. This amount must not exceed the amount paid out as dividends. [29]

The automobile industry has been very heavily self-financing, as can be seen by the small size of long-term debt as well as the size of retained earnings (see Table 30). This may relate to the cyclical nature of the industry, since a heavy debt structure would magnify the variance in yearly earnings. Thus it appears that the lessening of revenue fluctuation is taken into consideration in the aims of the firms. We continue the discussion of motivation later is this Chapter.

Competition between the automobile firms can proceed along several lines. As we have already noted, advertising, styling, innovation, investment, production and inventory scheduling, and pricing all may enter as components of a strategy. Using the measures suggested in section 3, we examine the payoffs associated with some of the strategies available to the firms.

There are at least two types of policy which would, if adopted by General Motors, spell doom to American Motors and Studebaker-Packard and could possibly ruin even Chrysler. General Motors could cut prices drastically. A 300 dollar cut across the board would appear to be sufficient; [30] or a larger cut, say 400 dollars, off Chevrolet might be more effective. Alternatively, it could take a gamble and introduce nine-month or even six-month styling in order to take away product acceptance from other cars. As the cost of setting up new production lines is very high, the three smaller firms would be unable to counter with the same tactics.

The effectiveness of the latter policy would depend upon consumer reaction to an increased tempo of change in styling and might misfire on the company attempting it. [31] The effect of a major price cut is easier to predict. A very rough index of the ability of the firms to compete via price can be obtained by dividing profits by the number of automobiles and trucks sold. This leaves out of consideration other product diversification and the different profitability of various automotive lines; however, it supplies a crude estimate of the ability to maneuver in the automobile market. This calculation is in Table 31.

An evaluation of the payoffs resulting from the employment of the strategies noted can be obtained by examining the vulnerability criteria. The *short-run market vulnerability* of Studebaker-Packard and American Motors is such that a 300 dollar price cut by General Motors would certainly keep them operating in the red unless they happened to capture a style market. If the cross-

Table 31

Profit* per automotive unit

	General Motors	Ford	Chrysler	American Motors	Studebaker-Packard
1951	522	316	108	75	180
1952	674	280	244	121	191
1953	503	329	148	19	187
1954	500	249	24	deficit	deficit
1955	608†	371	142	deficit	deficit

*Profit before income tax.
†Includes overseas production.

elasticity of demand between different makes of automobiles were moderately high, then on the assumption of a market for around 8,000,000 automobiles Ford could meet the price cut of General Motors and still make a profit. If Chrysler met the price cut and maintained only its market share (even in a slightly expanded market), then it would probably operate in the red. If it did not meet the price cut and if market cross-elasticity were high enough to reduce its market share by 50 per cent or more, it would operate in the red. *Short-run market vulnerability* for all firms is unlikely to be larger than one per automobile [32] and is probably not smaller than 0.5 per automobile for the small firms, i.e., a 100 dollar price cut by General Motors should cause a drop in profit of at least 50 dollars per automobile for the small companies.

As leverage is low in the automobile industry, the dangers of *short-run financial vulnerability* are not important to the three larger firms. Studebaker-Packard, which lost 14.3 million dollars in the first three months of 1956, could be forced out within a year. Its danger level is at best of the order of 100 million dollars. However, even without action by General Motors or Ford, a downturn in the market would be sufficient to wipe out the two smaller firms. In Chapter 10: 6 we note that if there are random elements present, a stationary state may remain in equilibrium only with some probability. A "run of bad luck" against a particular firm might weaken it sufficiently to render it unable to enforce an equilibrium it had previously been able to maintain. As the small firms become poorer, their credit ratings deteriorate; hence their financial vulnerability increases cumulatively.

Unless a small company is able to protect itself by successful product differentiation sufficient to offset even major price cuts, then in the automobile industry *long-run market vulnerability* is high, since there is little chance to retrench and cut down overhead.

We have seen from Table 22 that the financial structure of the automobile industry is such that "takeovers" and raids on the three large firms are virtually impossible. [33] Voting control is fractionated and common stock predominates. The directors and officers are in control of the automobile companies. With the exception of Ford, no members of a controlling group hold a significant amount of stock.

At best the short-run damage exchange rate via price competition for General Motors is not better than ten for one sustained by the small firms. Even if cross-elasticities were infinite between the products, if the other firms met a price cut on, say, just Chevrolet, the difference in volume would cause General Motors by far the greater absolute loss.

In order to demonstrate the effect of different corporate goals upon the various strategies we assume two different (and highly simplified) sets of motivation for the directors of General Motors. We first assume that they wish to maximize the discounted (expected) value of the monetary income of General Motors. Second, we assume that their only interest is to see that the public is offered automobiles at as cheap a price as is consistent with paying stockholders a "fair" return from investment and employees, including officers, a "reasonable incentive" rate of remuneration.

In the first case, in which we assume that the directors are interested in maximizing expected monetary income to the corporation, they can compute two different types of income streams. The first is one in which they maximize their expected discounted income subject to the restraint that the other firms are able to survive. The second income stream consists of two parts, the profits made in carrying out a policy designed to put its competitors out of business and the extra profits obtained after it has been successful in this policy. There are several reasons why an all-out price war would not be fought. It would take so long to drive Chrysler out of the market that at a discount rate of 4 or 5 per cent the profits foregone could never be recouped unless the price of automobiles were doubled after the market struggle. Even then it is fairly certain that General Motors could not put Ford out of business, no matter what strategy were utilized. Another reason why a market fight would not be employed is that public opinion and legal action would be taken against General Motors long before Chrysler were bankrupted. Furthermore, in a cyclical industry even General Motors might be loath to expand its capacity to a size sufficient to cope with the whole industry demand. [34] Thus, if profit maximization is the motivation, a strategy of heavy price cutting will not be adopted.

In the second case, in which we assume that the directors wish to serve the public, they may feel that a 5 per cent return to capital is a "fair" yield to stockholders. The 1955 stockholders' equity was 4,255 million dollars; hence approximately 213 million dollars would be required for dividends. Even if a bound of one million dollars per annum were taken as a "reasonable incentive" rate for an officer, [35] General Motors still appears to be in a position to indulge in price cuts which only Ford could survive with a high degree of certainty. The antitrust division could then descend upon General Motors with a Sherman Act accusation of attempting to monopolize which would in fact be based upon the motivation of the directors of General Motors to sell automobiles as cheaply as possible. Thus even though "public service" were the motivation, the directors of General Motors could not cut prices heavily for fear of the antitrust laws.

4.3. Numbers and Stability in the Automobile Industry

Entry of new firms, exit or merging of existing firms, and competition by means of many different weapons characterize the state of a market. The cost of entry into the automobile industry is so large that it appears reasonable to assume that there are no firms-in-being. Joe S. Bain has estimated that at present the capital requirements for a minimum optimal firm in the automobile industry, exclusive of shakedown losses, is of the order of 250 to 500 million dollars. [36] This estimate is based on a range running between 5 and 10 per cent of the volume of the low-price field (Ford, Chevrolet, and Plymouth). He has also suggested that about 250 million dollars more would be needed for shakedown losses in order to give a firm an even chance of becoming established.

Even without any aggressive tactics on the part of the larger firms, mere chance fluctuations are sufficient to ruin the two smaller firms. Possibly the number of competitors could be preserved if the small firms merged with strong outside corporations. [37]

Given the present economic background of the automobile industry, we must expect that there will be no wide divergence in pricing policies, even with no explicit co-operation between the directors of the firms. High competition in styling, innovation, efficiency, and advertising can go on. The more approximately constant sum are the effects of a competitive weapon, the stronger the competition will be. In other words, weapons which fight for market share in which one firm's gain is approximately the other firm's loss will be used extensively. When one firm puts out an innovation the probability that an opponent can retaliate with an equally effective innovation before the costs have been at least covered is by no means as great as the probability that a price cut can be replied to fast enough to make it unprofitable. As the techniques of advertising and styling become more and more routine, the effectivity of one firm's threat to take action against another is greater and the employment of these weapons becomes more jointly detrimental; hence we must eventually expect a limitation on the percentage of expenditure in these areas.

It is evident, using the criterion of Chapter 11, that the market is not $\{0\} - \{1\}$ stable; hence it is not competitive in the pristine sense. As the threat of counteraction by General Motors is sufficiently large to make any sizeable downward pricing action by a group of all the other firms unprofitable, General Motors is the dominant firm with respect to price in the sense of Chapter 11: 1.3.2.

Healthy competition does not necessarily mean the preservation of unhealthy competitors. However, in an oligopolistic market with few large firms efficiency becomes difficult to define. Inherently, American Motors might be far more efficient than Ford, but in any emergency it would fail first. [38] Although competition via increased technical efficiency and innovation may remain high, there is little that can be said a priori about the optimality of resource utilization in the automobile industry because of the size and structure of the firms and the importance of financial conditions to survival in an imperfect market.

5. THE TOBACCO INDUSTRY

5.1. A BRIEF SUMMARY OF THE HISTORY OF THE TOBACCO INDUSTRY, 1890–1911

A detailed study of the tobacco industry has been made by W. H. Nicholls [39] and R. B. Tennant. [40] Here only a few salient features of the history of the parent trust of the major cigarette companies are noted.

The American Tobacco Company was formed from five companies in 1890, after a trade war conducted by James B. Duke, and controlled more than 90 per cent of the cigarette production in the United States. In 1891 it started to buy up producers of smoking tobacco, snuff, and plug tobacco. Between 1894 and 1898 it engaged in a battle with the independent plug manufacturers. The "Plug War" was carried out by selling certain fighting brands below cost. Battle Ax was used in this manner. [41]

In the five years of war the American Tobacco Company's profits from plug sales were

Table 32

Profits ($1000)

1894	110
1895	−913
1896	−1378
1897	−890
1898	−942

The substantial profits made from cigarettes more than offset these losses. The independent plug manufacturers did not have the resources to carry on the war indefinitely, and peace was concluded with the formation of the Continental Tobacco Company in 1898.

In June 1898 the Union Tobacco Company was formed. It purchased the National Cigarette Company of New York, most of the stock of Blackwell's Durham Tobacco Company, and obtained an option on Liggett and Myers. These holdings combined with a strong financial backing enabled the Union Tobacco Company to command a high price when its interests were bought out by American in 1899.

By 1900 American and Continental Tobacco controlled 93 per cent of the cigarette production, 62 per cent of the plug tobacco, 59 per cent of the smoking tobacco, and 80 per cent of the snuff. [42] In 1901 they turned to the cigar business and to the British cigarette market. The latter exploit ended in a truce between the alliance of the British interests, consisting of thirteen major British manufacturers banded together in the Imperial Tobacco Company, and the American and Continental Tobacco forces. Later the two groups joined together to form the British-American Tobacco Company to further their interests in other parts of the world.

Continental and American had cemented their alliance in 1901, when the Consolidated Tobacco Company was formed, and held a majority of the common stock of both companies. In 1904 this holding company structure was abandoned, and all three corporations merged into the American Tobacco Company. Nicholls notes that,

This single company was the culminating corporate entity of some 250 formerly separate concerns and combinations in the tobacco business. [44]

In 1907 Sherman Act proceedings were brought against the company. The judgement of May 1911 [43] held that the American Tobacco Company was a monopoly in violation of the Sherman Act, and in November 1911 a dissolution decree resulted in the corporation being split into sixteen companies.

By 1910 the Tobacco Trust had control of 86 per cent of the cigarette production, 76.2 per cent of the smoking tobacco, 84.9 per cent of the plug, 96.5 per cent of the snuff, 91.4 per cent of the little cigars, and 79.7 per cent of the fine-cut tobacco. [45]

The four major successor companies, American, Liggett and Myers, P. Lorillard, and R. J. Reynolds, were given approximately 80 per cent of all lines except cigars. American and Liggett and Myers obtained the largest shares (about 60 per cent between them). Except for plug tobacco, Reynolds' share was insignificant.

5.2. THE CIGARETTE INDUSTRY TODAY

The cigarette industry today is dominated by three of the four major companies formed by the split in 1911, with the fourth company, Lorillard, and two newcomers, Philip Morris and Brown and Williamson, being the only other competitors of substantial size. In the course of competition Reynolds fought its way into the cigarette market, starting in 1913 with the introduction of Camel cigarettes and competing in pricing and advertising. American Tobacco countered with Lucky Strikes in 1917, Liggett and Myers boosted Chesterfields in 1918, and Lorillard followed with Old Golds in 1926. In the predepression era advertising increased in importance as a method of competition. [46] During the depression the successor firms kept their prices high, with Reynolds leading a price increase on June 23, 1931. Because of this pricing policy independent firms were able to make large inroads into the cigarette market. In 1931 the four successor companies had 97.59 per cent of the cigarette production; by 1939 their share of the market was down to 73.65 per cent [47]. Although in 1933 the major companies cut prices, the independents had been able to establish themselves, but possibly the short-run gains of the early 1930's were not sufficient to offset the losses due to successful entry. By 1946 the percentage of the four successors was again over 80 per cent. This production, together with the two large independents, accounted for 97.9 per cent of the cigarette output.

Competition in the industry is characterised by a heavy stress on advertising and product differentiation. This has run the gamut from slogans to king-sized, corktipped, filtered, mentholated, or oval-shaped cigarettes. Machinery for the production of cigarettes is fairly well standardized, and, although no data is available, it appears safe to assume that the costs of production of cigarettes of similar quality and size are approximately the same to any producer who uses the machines at the same intensity. In 1949 95 per cent of the cigarette production was carried out in twenty-one plants. [48] The major blocks to entry are the sizes of advertising expenditures and the cost of carrying a sufficiently large inventory necessary to allow the tobacco to age. (See Table 34.)

Each firm produces a variety of products. American Tobacco Company produces Lucky Strike, Pall Mall, Herbert Tareyton, Filter Tip Tareyton, and eight other brands of cigarettes. It produces Half and Half, Blue Boar, and Genuine "Bull" Durham smoking tobaccos, as well as approximately twenty other brands and six brands of chewing tobacco. Its cigar brands include La

Corona and El Roi-Tan. [49] Reynolds' products include Camel,
Winston, and Cavalier cigarettes, Prince Albert, Stud, and George
Washington smoking tobaccos, as well as other smoking tobaccos
and several brands of chewing tobacco. [50] Liggett and Myers makes
sixty-three different kinds of cigarettes and smoking and chewing
tobaccos, including Chesterfield and L. & M. Philip Morris sells
Marlboro, Parliament, Dunhill, Spud, English Ovals, Virginia
Rounds, Player's Navy Cut, and Philip Morris cigarettes, as well
as smoking tobaccos and Benson and Hedges cigars. [51] Lorillard
produces Old Gold, Kent, Embassy, Murad, and Helmar cigarettes,
several smoking and chewing tobacco brands, and little cigars. [52]
The products of Brown and Williamson include Avalon, Kools,
Raleigh, Viceroy, and Wings.

The consumer is reached via many thousands of distributors
who in turn deal through approximately 1,500,000 retail outlets.
This introduces numerous difficulties in the study of the effect of
pricing and other moves among the manufacturing firms.

5.3. CONTROL

In their book [53] Berle and Means included a statement of control
of the 200 largest corporations in 1929. At that time they listed
American, Reynolds, and Liggett and Myers as controlled by the
legal device of nonvoting common stock. [54] The holdings of power
in Lorillard were believed to be widely distributed. [55]

The Temporary Natural Economic Committee report shows that
in 1938 the twenty largest stockholders held 20.5 per cent of
American, 35.9 per cent of Liggett and Myers, and 59.7 per cent of
Reynolds common stock, [56] although Tennant has noted that
several of the large holders were banks, brokers, and insurance
companies. [57] The 1954 share structure of the firms is given in
Table 33. Control is presumed to be with the directors and officers
only because no evidence to the contrary is in the possession of
this writer.

There is a considerable overlap between directors and officers.
American has eight directors out of nineteen who are officers;
Liggett and Myers, six out of twelve; Philip Morris, five out of
ten; Lorillard, seven out of thirteen; and at Reynolds almost all
directors are officers or counsel. [58]

Table 33

	Shares	Stockholders	Control
American Tobacco Company	6,513,000 common	81,000	Directors
	528,000 pfd.	7,000	and officers
Reynolds Tobacco Company	396,000 common	79,000	Directors
	9,604,000 common class B		and officers
	490,000 pfd. 3.6 per cent	12,000	
	260,000 pfd. 4.5 per cent		
Liggett and Meyers	3,912,000 common		Directors
	225,000 pfd. 7 per cent cum.	44,000	and officers
Philip Morris	2,887,000 common		
	180,000 pfd. 4 per cent		Directors
	124,000 pfd. 3.9 per cent	28,000	and officers
Lorillard	2,853,000 common		Directors
	98,000 pfd. 7 per cent cum.	28,000	and officers
Brown and Williamson	Wholly owned subsidiary of British-American Tobacco Co. Ltd.		

5.4. MAXIMIZATION AND CONTROL

As the officers are not major stockholders, their personal fortunes are not necessarily highly correlated with the size of the dividends declared (see Tennant for a discussion of bonus plans.) [59] In fact, since this is an industry which needs heavy financing because of inventory loads and tobacco taxes, there is an incentive to retain earnings in order to attain greater long-run strategic flexibility without complete dependence on outside financing. In the last ten years the percentage of earnings paid out in dividends has varied from almost 100 per cent down to less than 50 per cent.

As a crude first approximation it appears that the directors attempt to maximize long-run expected income to their firms, subject to bounds on risk and to the necessity of paying out sufficiently large dividends to make their stock attractive at prices above book value.

.5.5. ASSET STRUCTURE

The long-term debt structure is large in the cigarette industry, and preferred stock also plays an important role in the financial structure. This gives a leverage to the earnings of the common shares. This particular capital structure of the industry appears to be caused mainly by the need for large inventories of tobacco. Table 34 shows that in the years 1948–1954 inventories have made up approximately 90 per cent of current assets. This table also lists the ranges in the percentages of longterm debt and preferred stock equity to ownership and long-term debt. The first set of figures is the ratio of current assets to current liabilities. These serve as an index of short-run vulnerability.

Table 34

Cur- rent	American Tobacco	Reynolds	Liggett and Myers	Philip Morris	Lorillard
(1)	3.15– 4.61	3.96– 5.17	3.56– 7.53	2.23– 3.24	2.30– 5.23
(2)	88.97–91.06	91.21–91.84	90.05–93.16	88.71–91.30	83.61–88.34
(3)	35.20–41.20	25.38–35.78	31.67–40.81	17.96–29.50	28.40–40.01
(4)	10.11– 8.50	15.86–17.89	5.76– 6.66	16.39–20.72	7.54–12.13

  (1) Assets/liabilities
  (2) Inventories/current assets
  (3) Longterm debt
  (4) Preferred issues

An index of the importance of the tobacco industry and the major firms in it is given by their net sales in the national market. Table 35 shows the net sales for five of the six largest firms for the period 1951–1955 (in units of 1000 dollars).

Table 35

	American Tobacco	Reynolds	Liggett and Myers	Philip Morris	Lorillard
1951	942,552	814,217	539,947	305,804	188,447
1952	1,065,738	881,424	603,081	306,698	214,508
1953	1,088,380	876,189	586,499	314,895	253,933
1954	1,068,579	814,274	548,862	294,902*	231,047
1955	1,090,845	866,426	546,965	283,219*	228,268

*Philip Morris Incorporated and Benson & Hedges Consolidated.

Table 36

	American Tobacco	Reynolds	Liggett and Myers	Philip Morris	Lorillard
1951	734,480	577,886	479,794	253,586	135,485
1952	783,154	591,641	488,288	265,025	160,844
1953	798,870	598,609	497,229	240,305	173,991
1954	775,364	617,636	491,309	255,131*	184,210
1955	801,725	611,641	458,592	261,593*	186,366

*Philip Morris Incorporated and Benson & Hedges Consolidated.

The total assets of the firms in the same period are shown in Table 36 (in units of 1000 dollars).

5.6. THE DEMAND FOR TOBACCO

Although the per capita demand for cigars and other forms of tobacco has fallen in the last fifty years, the per capita demand for cigarettes has risen almost without break. In 1954 there was a slight decline over 1953. The "cancer scare" appeared to be strong enough to change temporarily the secular trend in the consumption of cigarettes. Table 37 gives the per capita consumption of tobacco products in the United States for the years 1945–1954. [60]

Table 37

Per Capita Consumption
(in pounds)

	Cigarettes	Cigars	Tobacco	Total
1945	7.76	1.23	2.10	11.09
1946	8.75	1.36	1.58	11.69
1947	8.76	1.29	1.51	11.76
1948	9.13	1.31	1.46	11.90
1949	9.15	1.16	1.44	11.75
1950	9.16	1.18	1.42	11.76
1951	9.64	1.18	1.31	12.13
1952	9.94	1.25	1.25	12.48
1953	10.03	1.26	1.19	12.48
1954	9.48	1.23	1.15	11.86

Tennant gives a multiple regression of per capita consumption on real national income and on "time" (i.e., a trend factor). This is done for the years 1913–1945. He obtains [61]

$$X_1 = -0.446 + 0.460X_2 + 0.00156X_3,$$

where X_1 is the logarithm of consumption in hundredths of a pound- X_2 is the logarithm of income in dollars, and X_3 is the year of obser, vation numbered according to its last two digits.

This gives an income elasticity of $+0.460$ for tobacco.

It is suggested that the price elasticity of cigarettes is low, [62] although no formal verification is given.

5.7. ADVERTISING AND DEMAND

From his study Tennant concludes that we may be nearly certain that the advertising elasticity of total cigarette demand is very small, [63] although no attempt has been made to impute any of the long-run trend in tobacco consumption to advertising.

The elasticity of demand for different cigarette brands depends heavily upon the size and success of individual advertising campaigns. The company reports list selling, advertising, and administrative expenses together. In 1955 these amounted to approximately 10 per cent of the total net sales of Liggett and Myers; 6 per cent of the sales of Reynolds, and 10.5 per cent for Philip Morris. Nicholls presents a table of advertising expenditures for the six main firms for the years 1939–1949 [64] and Tennant shows change in market share between Camel, Lucky Strike, and Chesterfield. The considerable fluctuation in market share contrasts with the fairly steady increase in the over-all demand for cigarettes. [65]

The 1955 report of the American Tobacco Company notes that.

Trade estimates of national advertising expenditures again indicated, as they have for the last fifteen years, that your Company's traceable advertising costs per pack of cigarettes are substantially lower than the industry average. [66]

It appears that advertising efficiency grows with size, hence advertising expenditures are a factor working to the disadvantage of the small-sized firm. However, no formal study of the fluctuation of individual brand sales has been made.

5.8. STRATEGIES AND PROFITS

Both Nicholls and Tennant present an analysis of the price behavior of the firms in the market for cigarettes. The pricing policy has for the most part been one of follow the leader, with Reynolds instigating the majority of the changes, American next, and Liggett and Myers, the least. Both upward and downward price changes have been followed with a few exceptions. Although the price increase in the early 1930's may have helped to make 1930, 1931, and 1932 exceptionally profitable years, it appears to have been a tactical blunder. This can be seen by the plummeting of profits in the following years, due to the loss of market shares to new firms and the drastic price cuts to stem the growth of new entries in the cigarette industry. Table 38 gives the net income figures for five companies in the period 1936–1955 as well as net income calculated as a percentage of net worth.

These firms maintain almost the same percentage of inventory to current assets, and their buying tactics in the tobacco markets appear to be similar.

5.9. INDICES OF VULNERABILITY, STABILITY, AND STRATEGIES.

In section 3 we noted five different indices for the measurement of strategic interlinkage between firms.

The *short-run market vulnerability* of all firms in the cigarette industry is high. Since they all have approximately the same product line, if any firm wished to cut prices across the board and its reductions were not met, it appears that the cross-elasticity between different brands is high enough that the other firms would lose more revenue than if they met the cut. If they met the cut, then the damage exchange rate would be proportional to the volume of trade done, i.e., it might cost a very large firm several dollars of lost profits to cause a dollar loss to a small firm if it had to take action on a national basis. On the other hand, the damage exchange rate might be better if the small firm were confined to a regional market.

The *short-run financial vulnerability* of the six largest firms does not appear to be of great importance to fraternal warfare between them. They all have sufficient resources to weather several bad

Tabel 38

Net Income Before Dividends and Rate Earned on Net Worth, Less Good Will

	Net Income (millions of dollars)					Net Income (as percentage of net worth)				
	American Tobacco	Liggett & Myers	Reynolds	Lorillard	Philip Morris	American Tobacco	Liggett & Myers	Reynolds	Lorillard	Philip Morris
1936	20.1	24.2	29.3	3.5	2.4	12.0	17.3	20.6	8.2	31.2
1937	26.2	21.4	27.6	2.3	3.6	15.8	15.1	19.6	5.4	25.5
1938	25.4	20.6	23.7	4.0	5.7	15.6	14.2	16.8	9.3	34.4
1939	26.4	20.7	25.6	3.8	6.6	16.2	13.9	17.7	8.9	25.0
1940	27.7	20.3	25.5	3.9	7.4	16.9	13.4	17.2	8.7	25.1
1941	23.3	17.9	23.2	3.4	7.4	14.7	11.7	15.2	7.5	15.8
1942	22.3	16.8	19.9	3.9	7.8	13.5	10.1	12.8	8.5	15.8
1943	22.5	16.7	18.6	3.6	6.9	13.2	9.9	11.7	6.9	11.1
1944	19.9	14.8	17.8	3.6	6.8	11.7	9.2	11.0	6.9	10.5
1945	19.7	14.9	19.7	3.5	6.1	11.4	9.1	9.3	6.7	10.5
1946	29.9	18.4	28.0	3.5	5.0	16.1	10.9	12.7	6.5	9.0
1947	33.8	22.9	32.1	5.5	6.0	13.6	13.1	13.9	10.0	7.1
1948	43.9	29.3	34.6	5.6	6.0	16.3	15.8	12.9	9.9	8.6
1949	45.7	29.6	40.5	6.8	12.5	15.7	12.7	14.0	11.6	16.3
1950	41.7	29.1	40.3	6.7	15.3	13.6	12.0	13.2	10.7	18.3
1951	33.1	21.8	32.1	5.1	16.7	10.5	9.0	10.2	7.7	13.9
1952	34.1	21.4	31.9	5.7	12.6	9.0	9.0	10.0	8.4	10.2
1953	41.2	23.0	34.1	7.2	11.3	10.5	9.3	10.2	9.2	9.0
1954	43.1	22.2	44.8	6.3	12.4*	11.0	9.0	13.0	8.0	9.1*
1955	51.7	26.7	53.2	6.6	11.5*	12.2	10.3	14.2	8.1	8.0*

years, hence there is no payoff to be gained by indulging in fight-to-the-death struggles. The short-run financial vulnerability of a new entrant would be great unless he could come in with sufficient resources to take high losses for several years and establish a market via pricing and advertising in order to gain product acceptance.

Long-run market vulnerability is hard to characterize, since it contains a large random component due to the unpredictability of the success of advertising campaigns and innovation. The successes of Reynolds after World War I and the recent successes and failures of Philip Morris and of Lorillard would have been hard to predict.

In a market even with a secular increase in demand but with rising costs of, production small firms may have a high long-run market vulnerability. This could be caused by a policy which leaves the competitive products of the major firms at prices such that the small firms are unable to raise prices without losing markets and are forced to work on diminishing margins as costs rise. This appears to be the policy followed by the major firms to limit the inroads of the economy brands during the 1930's. Such a policy has long-run profit maximization justification if the costs of containment are less than the costs of possible loss of markets owing to the permanent establishment of new firms.

The long-run financial vulnerability of the major firms with the possible exception of Lorillard appears to be small. In order for ruin conditions to play a role the attacking firms would have to wait so long that the war costs would be more than the expected value of future extra profits, even if antitrust legislation did not interfere. This is not the case for minor firms. If a sufficiently low ceiling is established by the major firms, then random fluctuations may be enough to take care of small competitors (see Chapter 11: 4.1).

The costs of carrying inventory, the dependence upon debt financing, the costs of prepaid tobacco tax, and the flat-rate feature of the tax regardless of the final price of the cigarettes, as well as the apparent increasing returns to scale in advertising are all factors which work in the favor of large established firms in the cigarette industry.

Control vulnerability is not important for the large firms. The capture of a large firm would take a considerable amount of money nuder the present capital structure. Even if this were possible, given the state of the antitrust laws, any merger among the six largest firms would probably be declared illegal. For the small firms this is not so. Thus it is not surprising that the American Tobacco Company acquired the American Cigarette and Cigar Company on December 31, 1953, and that Philip Morris consolidated with Benson & Hedges.

The form of strategy that approximates the behavior of the major firms in the cigarette industry can be described as follows:

Firm i accepts a price $p_{i,t}$ in the tth period for its mth product and a range of advertising expenditures $A_{i,t} \leqslant a_{i,t} \leqslant \bar{A}_{i,t}$ for its mth product, provided the other major firms charge certain equivalent prices for comparable products and keep their advertising expenditures within given ranges. If any major firm j inaugurates a price increase, then the decision to meet the increase depends upon the state of information of i at that time. If the increase is met and no other firms meet the increase, and if business falls off as a result, then the old price will be resumed. If firm i initiates a price raise and is not followed sufficiently within a specified time, it will resume its previous price. If any major firm cuts prices, the ith firm will meet this cut if it observes that its market will be sufficiently affected to make it more profitable to do so. If any firm exceeds some bound in advertising expense, and this apparently has an important effect on the market of i, the campaign will be met. If any marginal firm or small competitor begins to take more than some percentage of the market (determined by the costs of fighting a containing action at that level, the ith firm will cut prices and/or increase advertising on the relevant products or, depending upon financial and legal conditions, attempt to absorb the competitor.

If we consider this type of strategy as a threat strategy, then in the terminology of Chapter 11 it appears that price in the cigarette industry is stable against downward cuts (given the present state of demand) if each of the big three were to use this type of strategy against any violator or group of violators (i.e., the subset consisting of the largest three firms is sufficient to deter price cuts by any other firm or group of firms). The fluctuation in demand for brands has been so considerable that any stability will be of the conditional type described in Chapter 10: 6.3.

5.10. CONCLUSIONS

A brief general sketch of the cigarette industry has been given in order to show the relationship between the game theoretic models of Chapter 10 and empirical investigation. Because of lack of information it was not possible to evaluate the effect of different policies upon the payoffs to the firms. However, even without doing so, it is fairly evident that because of the high state of information and common technology, the ease of retaliation, the difficulties in hiding price cuts or other major policy changes, and the large investment of the firms the conscious parallelism which results from following the type of strategy outlined is highly probable and needs no co-operative mechanism to bring it about.

The variability in demand for specific brands or types of cigarettes is large enough to be an important source of danger to a small firm. Hence advertising and product variation present a formidable barrier to entry. Possibly the biggest threat to any change in the industry structure (barring any great change in the over-all demand for cigarettes) would be caused by the success of a brand of an already existing small cigarette firm which had established a small specialized market and was not immediately financially vulnerable to demand fluctuations for or price cuts affecting other types of cigarettes.

As there does not appear to be very much scope for technological improvements in the manufacture of cigarettes (as compared with the manufacture of automobiles or other durables), the oligopolistic pressures to avoid intensive price competition force competition to be channeled into advertising and product variation. In consumer durable industries the desire to avoid price competition may switch the competitive forces to technological research and new methods. In the cigarette industry, under its present structure, the social disadvantages of next-to-no price competition are hardly counteracted by dynamic innovation features. This appears to be caused by the combination of an oligopolistic structure with the technological conditions in the production of cigarettes.

Although we have attempted to link theory and investigation for two industries, considerably greater detail is required Possibly after the simulation of several complex models of industries we will be able to validate economic theories of solution to n-person games.

NOTES

[1] A. D. H. Kaplan, *Big Enterprise in a Competitive System* (Washington: The Brookings Institution, 1954), pp. 64–65.

[2] *Loc. cit.*

[3] *Op. cit.*, p. 117.

[4] *The Structure of the American Economy* (Washington: U.S. Government, Pristing Office June 1939), National Resources Committee Report, Charts I and II opposite p. 158 and p. 162.

[5] Compiled from *Fortune*, July 1955 Supplement, and Annual Report of the Ford Motor Company, 1955.

[6] W. L. Crum, *The Age Structure of the Corporate System* (Berkeley: University of California Press, 1953), Chapters VI and VII.

[7] *Ibid.*, p. 146.

[8] *Ibid.*, p. 148.

[9] A. R. Hutchinson, and M. Newcomer, "A Study in Business Mortality," *American Economic Review*, **28** (1938) pp. 497–514.

[10] W. L. Crum, *op. cit.*, p. 119.

[11] *Op. cit.*, p. 120.

[12] Compiled from *Fortune*, July 1955 Supplement, and Annual Report of the Ford Motor Company, 1955.

[13] *Survey of Current Business*, U.S. Department of Commerce, **XXXVI**. (July 1956), p. 11.

[14] See G. Rosenbluth, "Measures of Concentration," in *Business Concentration and Price Policy* (Report of a Conference of the National Bureau of Economic Research) (Princeton: Princeton University Press, 1955), pp. 57–95.

[15] *Study of Monopoly Power*, hearings before a Subcommittee of the House Committee on the Judiciary, the 81st Congress, first session, Part 2-B, p. 1454.

[16] See the comment of J. S. Bain, in *Business Concentration and Price Policy*, p. 139.

[17] The strategy s_j will, in general, be multidimensional, involving price, production, advertising, and many other factors. Further specification is needed in order to be able to define an incremental change in s_j. In some cases, in which we limit the strategy of a player to a single variable, such as price, the meaning of a small change is clear.

[18] Part of the material in this section has appeared in M. Shubik, "A Game Theorist Looks at the Antitrust Laws and the Automobile Industry," *Stanford Law Review*, July 1956.

[19] L. H. Seltzer, *A Financial History of the American Automobile Industry* (Cambridge: Houghton Mifflin, 1928), pp. 20–21.

[20] *Ibid.*, p. 19.

[21] Moody, Industrials (1955).

[22] Ford Motor Company, Annual Report (1955).

[23] Kaiser Motor Corporation, proxy statement (February 9, 1956).

[24] L. S. Shapley, and M. Shubik, "A Method for Evaluating the Distribution of Power in a Committee System." American Political Science Review, **XLVIII** (September 1954), pp. 787–792.

[25] G. C. Chow, "Demand for Automobiles in the United States, a Case Study in Consumer Durables," Ph.D. thesis (Chicago: University of Chicago Press, September 1955); D. B. Suits and Janosi "The Demand for Automobiles in the United States" (a report to the Ford Motor Company, 1955); M. J. Farrell, "The Demand for Motor-Cars in the United States," *Journal of the Royal Statistical Society*, Series A (General), **117**, Part 2, 1954.

[26] See, for instance, Chrysler Corporation, Annual Report (1955), p. 12.

[27] Automobile Facts and Figures (1955).

[28] *Ibid.*

[29] General Motors Corporation, Annual Report (1955), p. 53.

[30] A 300 dollar price cut at the factory level would mean a larger price cut to the consumer after the percentage of dealer's mark-up and the reduction in taxes are added.

[31] One of the selling points of Volkswagen is the *infrequency* of style change.

[32] For instance, at the worst a firm can meet a price cut of an opponent and thereby maintain the same share of the market as before (on the assumption that income effect is negligible).

[33] The two small firms lie within the range of raid feasibility.

[34] W. Adams, *The Structure of American Industry* (New York: Macmillan, rev. ed. 1954), p. 315.

[35] The highest remuneration paid by the Ford Motor Company in 1955 was $321,000 to the Chairman of the Board of Directors and to the President. See Ford Motor Company, prospectus (1956).

[36] J. S. Bain, "Barriers to New Competition" (Cambridge: Harvard University Press), pp. X, 329.

[37] For example, if firms such as Sperry-Rand and Curtiss-Wright merged with the smaller firms, they would have the necessary resources to have a chance to regain a larger portion of the automobile market.

[38] A crude measure of efficiency is the cost of production of a specified number of automobiles of a comparable type, given the same input costs for the materials.

[39] W. H. Nicholls, *Pricing Policies in the Cigarette Industry* (Nashville: Vanderbilt University Press, 1951), pp. XIX, 444.

[40] R. B. Tennant, *The American Cigarette Industry* (New Haven: Yale University Press, 1950).

[41] *Op. cit.*, p. 28.

[42] W. H. Nicholls, *op. cit.,* p. 27.

[43] *Loc. cit.*

[44] U.S. v. American Tobacco, 221 U.S. 106, 31 S.Ct. 632, 55L. Ed. 663 (1911).

[45] W. H. Nicholls, *op. cit.*, p. 31.

[46] *Op. cit.*, Chapter VI.

[47] *Op. cit.*, p. 91.

[48] *Op. cit.*, p. 17.

[49] American Tobacco Company, Annual Report (1955).

[50] Reynolds Tobacco Company, Annual Report (1955).

[51] Philip Morris Company, Annual Report (1955).

[52] P. Lorillard Company, Annual Report (1955).

[53] A. A. Berle, and G. C. Means, *The Modern Corporation and Private Property* (New York: Macmillan, 1933), pp. 95–116.

[54] *Ibid.*, p. 98.

[55] *Ibid.*, p. 113.

[56] U.S. Temporary National Economic Committee, "The Distribution of Ownership in the 200 Largest Non-Financial Corporations," *Monograph No. 29* (Washington: U.S. Government Printing Office, 1940), pp. 391–392.

[57] R. B. Tennant, *op. cit.*, pp. 100–103.

[58] Tobacco Company Reports (1955).

[59] R. B. Tennant, *op. cit.*, 103–106.

[60] U.S. Department of Agriculture, *Tobacco Statistics* (Washington: U.S. Government Printing Office, 1955).

[61] R. B. Tennant, *op. cit.*, p. 119.

[62] *Ibid.*, p. 144.

[63] *Ibid.*, p. 142.

[64] W. H. Nicholls, *op. cit.*, p. 160.

[65] R. B. Tennant, *op. cit.*, pp. 163–172.

[66] American Tobacco Company, Annual Report (1955).

Economic analysis, social policy, and law

In our worship of the survival òf the fit under free natural selection we are sometimes in danger of forgetting that the conditions of the struggle fix the kind of fitness that shall come out of it; that survival in the prize ring means fitness in pugilism, not for bricklaying nor philanthropy; that survival in predatory competition is likely to mean something else than fitness for good and efficient production; and that only from a strife with the right kind of rules can the right kind of fitness emerge.

J. B. Clark [1]

1. PREAMBLE

In this chapter we relate the preceding economic analysis to the areas of social goals, public policy, and law. What are the basic features of "competition" that society wishes to preserve? If we make the heroic assumption that society via the Congress knows what they are, then do the antitrust laws convey this information to the courts? Can economic theory and empirical findings give objective meaning to the legal, social, and semieconomic phrases used to describe various states of competition and collusion? If it can, does it also provide a method of analysis which can be used in the design of the law and of corrective procedures within the scope of the law?

2. THE ANTITRUST LAWS

The main antitrust laws of the United States consist of the Sherman and Clayton Acts, the Federal Trade Commission Act, and the Robinson-Patman Act. [2] The initial sentiment behind the Sherman Act was that of a philosophy of freedom, and the basis of the act was found in the common law. [3] The central core of sections 1 and 2 of the Sherman Act was a policy against "undue limitations of competitive conditions." [4] Unfortunately, the concepts of competition, monopoly, attempt to monopolize, and conspiracy to monopolize turned out to be by no means as simple as they may have appeared at that time. It was left to the judges to interpret what they meant. Thus Justice Harlan interpreted the clause forbidding "restraint of trade" to mean every restraint of trade, whether "reasonable" or "unreasonable." Later, Justice McReynolds supported this view.

It was said ... that McReynolds' concept of competition, as it was required by the law to be carried on, was that of a fight to the death with knives in the dark in a cabin in his Tennessee mountains! [5]

In the Standard Oil and American Tobacco cases, with White as Chief Justice, the courts followed the interpretation that the Sherman Act ruled only against "unreasonable" restraints of trade.

What determines "reasonableness"? The law has to act as a means to put public policy into effect in the light of economic fact. A reasonable restraint is one whose effect is condoned by public policy on the presumption that its effect is objectively known and understood. It is possible for a law to be passed that the area of the circle of unit radius be fixed at 3 instead of π. For some purposes this crude distortion of the facts will work, for others it will fail. Similarly, generations of justices are at liberty to give legal preciseness to economic terms or to set legal precedents to guide the enforcement of antitrust on the presumption that the rulings of the court will fulfill the aims of society. Whether they do so or not depends upon a knowledge of the aims of society and the relationship between the legal acts and economic reality.

Broadly speaking, the reasons for the antitrust laws are to see that bargaining conforms to the community's sense of fairness and to preserve checks and balances between the competitive forces in an economy. [6] The scope of the laws includes cases involving trade associations, vertical and horizontal integration of firms, price discrimination, tie-in sales, base point systems, mergers, patents, exclusive dealings, and many other manifestations of market control. Behind all of these specific manifestations of antitrust problems there lies a single conceptual basis. As Morris Adelman has put it.

> Until and unless we decide that the real problem is market control and how much and what kind we ought to permit, the situation will remain confused. [7]

In attempting to deal with the host of cases confronting it, the courts have advanced several lines of reasoning with varying success. The *Northern Securities* case provides an example in which a direct *per se* ruling was made and conformed both to the social spirit of the Sherman Act and to the economic facts. Mr. Justice Harlan stated that,

> The mere existence of such a combination and the power acquired by the holding company as its trustee constitute a menace to, and a restraint upon, that freedom of commerce which Congress intended to recognize and protect, and which the public is entitled to have protected. [8]

Unfortunately, although it is sufficient for the public good that a *per se* ruling and the economic facts are in agreement, it is not necessarily true that this will always be so. The door was left open for a greater recognition of economic reality in the decisions under the "rule of reason" which were introduced in the Standard Oil [9] and American Tobacco [10] cases. The rule of reason approach amounts to making vague the basis for legal action that a *per se* approach attempts to make precise. But possibly it is preferable to be vague about situations whose social and economic features are not completely understood than to be committed to a line of action, which, though well defined and easy to apply, evidently fails to reflect the intent of public policy.

With the growth of the modern oligopolistic economy, the need for detailed economic understanding of the problems of antitrust has grown. Thus the test of percentage control of the market applied by Justice Learned Hand in the Alcoa case, [11] even if it were based on a faulty economic analysis as some claim [12], at least was based on recognition that control of the market is the central issue in appraising a charge of monopolization and that the question of how this control was achieved is largely irrelevant. The *Alcoa* approach has dominated the decision of monopoly cases, including the recent du Pont cellophane decision. [13] Although the results of the recent cases have not been consistent, their reasoning has always explicitly adopted market-control criteria. It is probably safe to say that the *Alcoa* test of market control has supplanted the completely uneconomic reasoning of the U. S. Steel decision, [14] in which market structure was ignored and the inquiry was addressed to the *manner* in which U. S. Steel acquired and used its power. To this extent, at least, economic tests have come to dominate an area of legal decision.

This recognition of danger in a market structure was further supported in the Supreme Court's ruling in the appeal of the American Tobacco Company. [15] The initial ruling in the American Tobacco Company case represented an attempt to deal with a situation for which the law is not prepared even today. The concept of conscious parallelism or implicit collusion is a prime example of a construct that flies in the face of economic logic. Although few economists would disagree that the cigarette industry was a candidate for antitrust action, the fiction of conscious parallelism does not deal with the problem of the control of such an oligopolistic industry. This doctrine has apparently been rejected in Theater Enterprises, Inc., vs. Paramount Film Distributing Corporation [16] and the Justice Department's decision to drop the action against the "Big Four" meat packers apparently reflects the view that a conspiracy case cannot be made on evidence of parallel action alone. [17]

A revision of the antitrust laws may be useful, especially if section 2 of the Sherman Act were changed to enable the prosecution of cases against oligopolistic market forms which are deemed to be economically unhealthy and/or socially undesirable. However, since the laws contain so many undefined words and vague concepts, the reading into them of more economic analysis might suffice.

3. ECONOMIC THEORY AND THE MARKET

The myriads of special words used to describe and qualify competition contain a mixture of social, legal, and economic meanings. Among the many used are perfect competition, pure competition, imperfect competition, monopolistic competition, fair competition, workable competition, cutthroat competition, and predatory competition. Monopoly, bilateral monopoly, oligopoly, and oligopsony are also used to describe market forms or market behavior. The weapons and general nature of the economic struggle have produced a crop of new words. In the dynamic economy we have dynamic competition or innovation competition, as well as competition through advertising and product variation. In the corporate economy the body social and politic is protected by the broad sweep of countervailing power. [19]

The competitive economy is not only beset with good and evil adjectives but may also fall prey to control, collusion, combination, and other organized deviations from competition. The classical competitive economy of the heyday of the "dismal science" may also be blessed with the coming of Utopia in which competition is modified by co-operation, mutual help, and other forms of good joint action.

The method of analysis developed in this book attempts to provide a way in which we can examine and separate the contents in the words used into that which is socio-political sentiment and that which can be given a more or less precise objective economic meaning. Using the methods of game theory we turn to the task of producing our Devil's dictionary.

We base our discussion of the formulation of an economy or a market as a *game of economic survival*. This, at least theoretically, gives us a method for describing completely all alternative paths of action available to all participants. It is a notation for counting or arranging all patterns of behavior. An exhaustive examination of these patterns enables us to establish categories of competition or co-operation and collusion in a market.

The meaning of competition in its various forms found in law and economics is different from that found in competitive games played between two individuals or teams. The formalization given for two-person, constant-sum games enables us to give precise meaning to competition as a form of pure opposition of interests. The general class of *strictly competitive games* is one in which there is no point in the two players entering into communication or co-operation because their interests are diametrically opposed. Any increase in the welfare of one player implies a decrease in the welfare of his opponent. The word opponent serves here better than the word competitor. If we assume that utilities or values are comparable, then the loss of a dollar or a utile by one implies a gain of a dollar or utile by the other. In such a situation the most that a player can enforce is the maximin value of his payoff, i.e., the value he can obtain on the assumption that his opponent will do him as much damage as possible. In a strictly competitive game (or a game of pure opposition) there is no operational way in which co-operative or non-co-operative and competitive behavior can be distinguished.

Almost all situations in an economy must be portrayed by nonzero-sum games. The fortunes of the players are not usually diametrically opposed. Very simple static or one-period market models have been constructed in the chapters of Part One. They illustrate the nonzero-sum character of an economic struggle. Two different types of solution have been suggested for the static nonzero-sum games. They are called the *co-operative* and *non-co-operative* solutions. They can be modified further, depending upon whether or not side payments or bribes and kickbacks can be made between the players. The *co-operative* solution assumes that players will jointly maximize their profits and then split them up in a manner which guarantees each individual at least as much as he can guarantee himself. It assumes that there is an environment in which agreements are honored and that no policing to enforce co-operative action is needed. The *non-co-operative* solution is concerned with equilibrium points. An equilibrium point has the property that if any single player observes the strategies of all his competitors he is not motivated to change his strategy. There may be no dynamic path by which players in a game lasting for more than one period can reach an equilibrium point. The equilibrium may be unstable through time if it is exposed to any random shocks or perturbations. It may also be unstable if more than one player, i.e., a group of two or more players, jointly decide to change their strategies. The mathematical definition of an equilibrium point was given in Chapter 4: 2. We restate it briefly here: An n-tuple of strategies S is an *equilibrium point* if and only if for every i

$$H_i(S) = \max H_i(S; \eta_i) \qquad \text{for } i = 1, 2, \ldots, n,$$

where H_i is the payoff function of the ith player and η_i is any strategy for the ith player. Even such a solution has an element of what we might wish to call "co-operation" in it. When the number of players is few, as we have seen in Chapters 4, 5, and 7 it yields the Cournot, Edgeworth, and Chamberlin large-group solutions. These are in some sense more "co-operative" than the purely competitive equilibrium and much more co-operative than the cutthroat tactics used to inflict losses on an opponent.

A co-operative and a non-co-operative solution can coincide if the joint maximum happens to be an equilibrium point. In the first of the two game matrices shown the joint maximum and equilibrium point coincide; in the second they do not.

Game 1	Game 2

$$\begin{bmatrix} 10, 10 & 5, 8 \\ 8, 5 & 3, 3 \end{bmatrix} \qquad \begin{bmatrix} 10, 10 & 2, 15 \\ 15, 2 & 3, 3 \end{bmatrix}$$

We have shown in Chapter 6 that by giving economic form to a non-co-operative game and making assumptions about homogeneity of product and about the number of competitors *pure* and *perfect competition* can be portrayed as non-co-operative game solutions. Apart from the dubiousness of the economic assumptions made for pure competition, the competitive market solution has all the weaknesses of the non-co-operative game solution. How an equilibrium is to be attained is not indicated. In an economy marginal cost pricing (if it can be defined, i.e., if there are no discontinuities, indivisibilities, boundary conditions, etc.) offers an optimal way in which resources can be allocated to satisfy a given demand. However, in an economy viewed as a closed system this essentially technological criterion does not carry with it any welfare implication stronger than Pareto optimality.

As we have already noted in Chapters 2, 7, and 10, there are really two theories contained in Chamberlin's *monopolistic competition*, the large-group and the small-group theory. The large-group theory of *monopolistic competition* and the broad area which is defined as *imperfect competition* appear to be a natural extension of the older work of Cournot, Edgeworth, and others, who had models of duopoly and pure and perfect competition for which they advanced solutions which were non-co-operative equilibrium points. The Chamberlinian analysis extended the strategy space to be considered in market models. Product variation and advertising were introduced, but conceptually there is no difference between the behavior of the Cournot duopolists and the Chamberlinian monopolistic competitors. A host of imperfections has been noted in the literature, such as location, trademarks, and patents. We noted in Chapter 7 that the inclusion of these imperfections under the term of monopolistic or imperfect competition leads us to conclude that monopolistic competition stands for a theory of non-co-operative behavior equivalent to the theory of Cournot, combined with a list of more realistic factors and imperfections that change the position of the final equilibrium point.

The Chamberlinian small-group theory, as we have already noted in Chapter 7: 2.1 and Chapter 10, is conceptually different. It reflects the difficulties faced in a discussion of oligopolistic markets. In order to cope with these difficulties it is not sufficient to examine static or single-period markets. In Chapters 9 and 10 we developed a model of a market as a *game of economic survival*. In this model corporate and financial structure and long-run profit considerations are noted explicitly. A theory of solution for the two-person game and a suggestion for a theory for the *n*-person game are given in Chapters 10 and 11, respectively. They were constructed of a blend of the non-co-operative equilibrium theory and some considerations of an implicit co-operative agreement to limit the actions of the players. The limitations put on the threat strategies suggested in Chapter 10 are nothing but a manifestation of an expectation of a certain level of co-operative behavior on the part of one's competitors. The second example given earlier in this section shows a game whose equilibrium point is minimal for both players. In the single-period game there is an incentive to break any agreement with a competitor to accept the joint maximum. If this game is played over many times, the equilibrium point will still be at $(3, 3)$ per period for any finite number of plays. However, if the players do not know when the game will end and they have to "live with each other" for many periods, then the threat of retaliation by one player if the other breaks an implicit or explicit agreement to maximize jointly may be sufficient to enforce the agreement as a non-co-operative equilibrium. The enforce-ability of some way of dividing the spoils depends upon the strength of the opponent's threat. The literature on dynamic duopoly models and oligopoly always discusses explicit paths of action and reaction. Here we divide all actions and reactions (which can be regarded as time paths traced out by the employment of two strategies) into broad categories, depending upon the costs to the players. A threat that is suicidal to the threatener and hardly costs his opponent anything is not a threat as plausible as one which can kill the opponent at little cost. In theory, a threat that is very costly may be a legitimate strategy. However, we assume that in most economic situations it is possible to place restrictions upon the violence of retaliations and fighting that will take place. This amounts to limiting the strategy space of the players in such a manner that some of the more jointly minimal outcomes are avoided. The Chamberlin and "kinked oligopoly curve" writings on competi-tion between few firms are equilibrium point solutions of this variety, i.e., the equilibrium is enforced by the knowledge that a very plausible form of retaliation will be sufficient to deter any firm from departing from the equilibrium. When there are more than two firms in a market the concept of retaliation or threat becomes vague, inasmuch as the plausibility of the act of firm B in response to a move by firm A depends upon the effect on the others as well as the effect on A. In Chapter 11 we attempted to resolve this difficulty by formulating $\{k_i\} - \{r_j\}$ stability for equilibria enforced by threats. This introduces another co-operative factor into the equilibrium theory. We examine a market form on the assumption that a group $\{k_i\}$ of k firms is willing to use jointly a certain threat action against a group $\{r_j\}$ or r firms which wishes to take joint action to disturb the market. We noted that there will be many equilibria which can be enforced by many different combinations of "policing" firms. However, even though it may not usually be theoretically possible to obtain a one-to-one identification between an equilibrium observed and the particular $\{k_i\} - \{r_j\}$ stability structure maintaining it, it at least enables us to attach direct economic meaning to *trade ethics* as a manifestation of co-operative behavior. The larger the number k has to be in order to maintain an equilibrium, the larger the implicit or explicit agreement to take policing action.

Cutthroat competition is a term used to describe the dynamics of adjustment in a market in which, possibly because of sick or declining industry or depression conditions, the asset and ruin features of economic survival become critical. If side payments and/or mergers are not allowed or do not take place for other reasons, then the game of economic survival model becomes one of almost pure opposition; the profitable survival of every player is inversely correlated with the profitable survival of any opponent.

Predatory competition and *market domination* take place when the maximization conditions for one firm are such that, in the first case, long-run profits are made greater by ruining an opponent than by letting him survive, and, in the second case, long-run profits are made greater by ruining an opponent if he tries to take more than a certain share of the market (see Chapter 10: 5.2).

Fair and *workable competition* are socio-political and legal concepts which may or may not have considerable economic content, depending upon who uses them. [20,21] A discussion of the concept of "fairness" is given in Appendix B.

We have observed that it is difficult and often of little use to make the dichotomy between competition and collusion. Our economic analysis here has adopted a different approach. Stress has been laid upon being able to describe the strategic interlinkage between competitors. Given a description of the strategy spaces of the players and of their payoffs, we have attempted to give meaning to different degrees of competition, co-operation, or collusion in terms of the ability of players or groups of players to enforce the maintenance of certain outcomes upon other players or groups of players. The analysis has avoided including value judgements. What constitutes fair or workable competition cannot be answered objectively; this depends upon social policy. However, it is the belief of this writer that in order to make social policy effective it is necessary that the objective background of the analysis of competition in the markets be understood.

4. COMMENTS ON SOCIAL POLICY AND ECONOMIC ANALYSIS OF MARKETS

Broadly speaking, social policy in the control of industry is aimed at preventing "biting, kicking, and gouging." In the United States the goals are to preserve and promote the "American private competitive enterprise system." [22] In England the goals were "fair shares for all." Despite political differences, certain common problems have been recognized in most countries and solved in more or less the same ways. Thus distinctions are drawn between public utilities, transportation, and manufacturing industries, and social control is usually different between them. However, within the manufacturing and distribution industries many problems of social control are posed. Does competition call for the preservation of competitors? On the one hand, it may be good to let the less efficient firms die, but, on the other hand, does the survival of only one or two firms present a better alternative to society? Are bigness and/or power in themselves an implicit threat or evil? What sort of fitness should be encouraged for the survival of the fittest? Should it be inherent manufacturing superiority, better integration of multiproduct corporations, superior "firepower" in advertizing campaigns, more financial resources and better credit facilities in order to weather any crisis or fight, or better research and more innovations?

The work in Chapter 10 indicates some of the features of control and ability to survive which are related to financial size and integration. Since we have very little information on the relative efficiencies of different firms in various industries, we do not know in general how much the growth of different-sized firms has been shaped by technology, manufacturing efficiency, finance, or corporate structure. In the new economics the automatically self-regulating mechanisms of the "best of all possible worlds" no longer appear to guarantee that the "right type of fitness" will be rewarded. However, the economist can indicate to the framer of social policy what sort of fitness is likely to survive in the different markets.

If economic analysis is to be regarded as an applied science or art, then the final test comes in application. Application in the realm of social policy calls for an explanation and clarification of concepts of competition and control, and this has been the major program of this book.

NOTES

[1] J. B. and J. M. Clark, *Control of Trusts* (New York: Macmillan 1914), p. 200.

[2] *Antitrust Laws With Amendments*, 1890–1951 (Washington: U.S. Government Printing Office, 1953).

[3] G. H. Dorr, "Philosophy of the Sherman Law" *Proceedings of the American Bar Association*, August 1955, pp. 15–33.

[4] C. I. Thompson, "A Policy Against Undue Limitations on Competitive Conditions," *Proceedings of the American Bar Association*, August 1, 1955, pp. 34–63.

[5] G. H. Dorr, *op. cit.*, p. 21.

[6] J. B. Dirlam and A. E. Kahn, *Fair Competition* (Ithaca, Cornell University Press, 1954), p. 16.

[7] M. Adelman, "Effective Competition and the Antitrust Laws," **61**, *Harvard Law Revue*, (1948), p. 1317.

[8] Northern Securities Company v. United States, 193 U.S. 197, 24 S.Ct. 436, 48 L.Ed. 679 (1904).

[9] Standard Oil Company of New Jersey v. United States, 221 U.S. 1 (1911).

[10] American Tobacco Company v. United States, 221 U.S. 106 (1911).

[11] Aluminum Company of America v. United States, 148 F. 2d 416 (1945).

[12] W. Adams, "The Aluminum Case: Legal Victory—Economic Defeat," *American Economic Review*, **41** (1951), p. 915.

[13] E.I. du Pont de Nemours & Company v. United States, 118 F. Supp. 41 (1953).

[14] United States Steel Corporation v. United States, 25 U.S. 417 (1920).

[15] American Tobacco Company et al., v. United States, 328 U.S. 781 (1946), 66 S.Ct. 1125, 90 L.Ed. 1575.

[16] Theater Enterprises, Inc., v. Paramount Film Distributing Corporation, 346 U.S. 537, 540–541 (1954).

[17] See United States v. Armour and Company, Civil No. 48–C–1351,

N.D. Ill., Septemper 15, 1948, *dismissed without prejudice by stipulation*, CCH Trade Reg. Rep.

66,117 (March 17, 1954). See generally Attorney General's National Committee To Study The Antitrust Laws, Report 36–42 (1955); Rahl, *Conspiracy and the Antitrust Laws*, 44 Ill. L. Rev. 743 (1950); Note, *Conscious Parallelism—Fact of Fancy?* 3 Stan. L. Rev. 679 (1951).

[18] Temporency National Economic Committee, "Competition and Monopoly in American Industry," *Monograph 21* (1940), pp. 1–12.

[19] J. K. Galbraith, *American Capitalism* (Cambridge: Houghton Mifflin, 1952).

[20] Milton Handler, "Unfair Competition," *Iowa Law Review*, **XXI**, No. 2. (January 1936), 175–262.

[21] J. M. Clark, "Towards a Concept of Workable Competition," *American Economic Review*, **XXX**, No. 2 (June 1940), 241–256.

[22] S. C. Oppenheim, *Cases on Federal Antitrust Laws, Trade Regulation*, American Casebook Series, Warren A. Seavey, gen. ed. (St. Paul: West Publishing Co., 1948), pp. 88–99.

Appendix A

U TILITY THEORY

In several of the examples discussed in this book we have assumed that individuals, when faced with alternatives involving risk, maximize the expected utility of their gain (see Chapter 5: 4.4.1 for example). If a person has a linear utility for money, then he will maximize his expected money income. Although use is occasionally made of the simplifying assumption of a linear utility for money, we point out that it is not necessary to almost all of the theory in this book, and in Chapter 10: 2 we discuss goals for the firm other than the maximization of expected money income. Nevertheless, in situations involving randomization it is important to know that, at least conceptually, utility is measurable in order to be able to assign values to prospects involving risk.

The trend in the treatment of utility in economic theory during the 1920's and 1930's was away from earlier ideas [1] of a linear measure to that of only an ordering [2]. This gave rise to the indifference curve analysis. [3] With the work done in the theory of games there has come a new view of the measurability of utility, if choice under risk is considered. The new approach does not ignore complementarity as did Jevons and Gossen to a greater and Frisch [4] and Fisher [5] to a lesser extent; but is has pointed out that, under certain very plausible assumptions involving probability mixes of utilities a utility index defined to within an arbitrary linear transformation can be obtained from any indifference map.

Von Neumann and Morgenstern note that little needs to be added to the indifference curve analysis in order to obtain a numerical utility. The additional assumption is obtained by considering probability combinations of goods. For example, if a man is offered one dollar for certain or a choice of three or 0 dollars with a fifty-fifty chance of each and he states that this choice is a matter of indifference to him, then they say that the utility of three dollars is twice as much as that of one dollar (if we regard the utility of 0 dollars as 0). If he had been indifferent when the chance of gaining three dollars was 0.75, then the utility of three dollars would be 1.5 that of one dollar. In brief, the axiomatic development of this utility measure, as given in the *Theory of Games and Economic Behavior*, is outlined here: [6]

3.6.1. We consider a system U of entities u, v, w .... In U a *relation* is given, $u > v$, and for any number α, $(0 < \alpha < 1)$, an operation

$$\alpha u + (1 - \alpha)v = w.$$

These concepts satisfy the following axioms:

(3:A) $u > v$ *is a complete ordering of* U. This means: write $u > v$ when $v < u$.

(3:A:a) For any two u, v one and only one of the three following relations holds:

$$u = v \qquad u > v \qquad u < v.$$

(3:A:b) $\qquad\qquad u > v \qquad v > w$, imply $u > w$.

(3:B) *Ordering and Combining*

(3:B:a) $\qquad u < v$ implies $\qquad u < \alpha u + (1 - \alpha)v$

(3:B:b) $\qquad u > v$ implies $\qquad u > \alpha u + (1 - \alpha)v$

(3:B:c) $\qquad u < w < v$ implies the existence of an α with

$$\alpha u + (1 - \alpha)v < w$$

(3:B:d) $\qquad u > w > v$ implies the existence of an α with

$$\alpha u + (1 - \alpha)v > w.$$

(3:C) *Algebra of Combining*

(3:C:a) $\qquad\qquad \alpha u + (1 - \alpha)v = (1 - \alpha)v + \alpha u$

(3:C:b) $\qquad \alpha(\beta u + (1 - \beta)v) + (1 - \alpha)v = \gamma u + (1 - \gamma)v$

where $\qquad\qquad\qquad \gamma = \alpha\beta.$

These axioms imply the existence of a correspondence between the entities u and the numbers $v(u)$ such that

$$u > v \text{ implies } v(u) > v(v)$$

and
$$v(\alpha u + (1 - \alpha)v) = \alpha v(u) + (1 - \alpha)v(v).$$

We stress that once these axioms have been granted, the measurability properties follow; therefore, criticism of this utility measure must be aimed at the choice of axioms. In the last few years a considerable literature has sprung up on the economic, psychometric, and axiomatic problems of utility measurement. Luce and Raiffa present a detailed survey of the major problems encountered. [7]

NOTES

[1] For a historical survey, see George J. Stigler, "The Development of Utility Theory, I and II," *The Journal of Political Economy*, **LVIII** (August and October 1950), pp. 307–327 and pp. 373–396, respectively; also E. Kauder, "Genesis of the Marginal Utility Theory," *The Economic Journal*, **LXIII** (September 1953), pp. 638–650.

[2] P. A. Samuelson, *Foundations of Economic Analysis* (Cambridge: Harvard University Press, 1948), pp. 92–95.

Samuelson has given the mathematical forms of the early assumptions on the utility function. Gossen suggested, from empirical observation, a function of the form

$$U = K + (a_1 x_1 + b_1 x_1{}^2) + (a_2 x_2 + b_2 x_2{}^2) + \ldots$$

where the x_i are quantities of goods and K is an arbitrary constant.

Jevons later generalized this to be

$$U = V_1(x_1) + V_2(x_2) + \ldots$$

where V_i is that part of an individual's utility function influenced by the ith good.

Edgeworth pointed out that in order to take care of complementarity one needed

$$U = \varphi(x_1 \ldots, x_n)$$

where φ is a general function whose value depends on all goods.

Pareto felt that it was not necessary to consider utility as a cardinal magnitude, and Samuelson summarizes this by writing the utility function as

$$U = F[\varphi(x_1 \ldots x_n)] \qquad F'(\varphi) > 0$$

where φ is any one cardinal index of utility.

[3] See, for instance, J. R. Hicks, *Value and Capital* (London: Oxford University Press, 1939).

[4] R. Frisch, "New Methods of Measuring Marginal Utility," *Beiträge zur Ökonomischen Theorie*, No. 3 (Tubingen, 1932).

[5] I. Fisher, "A Statistical Method for Measuring 'Marginal Utility' and Testing the Justice of a Progressive Income Tax," in *Economic Essays in Honor of John Bates Clark*, published on behalf of the American Economic Association (New York: Macmillan, 1927).

[6] J. von Neumann, and O. Morgenstern, *Theory of Games and Economic Behavior* (Princeton: Princeton University Press, 3ed. ed., 1953), p. 26.

[7] R. D. Luce, and H. Raiffa, *Games and Decisions* (New York: Wiley, 1957), Chapter I.

Appendix B

WELFARE, "FAIR DIVISION," AND GAME THEORY

1. GAME MODELS AND WELFARE ECONOMICS

The meaning of the social welfare function [1] and the compatibility of different individual desires with a social welfare function constitute, in a general way, the study of welfare economics. The problem of individualistic maximization against any machinery for making social choice, including the possibility of the overthrowing of the machinery, belongs to the study of game theory. Arrow notes that, [2]

... once a machinery for making social choices from individual tastes is established, individuals will find it profitable, from a rational point of view, to misrepresent their tastes by their actions, either because such misrepresentation is somehow directly profitable, or, more usually, because some other individual will be made so much better off by the first individual's misrepresentation that he could compensate the first individual in such a way that both are better off than if everyone really acted in direct accordance with his tastes. Thus, in an electoral system based on plurality voting, it is notorious that an individual who really favors a minority party candidate will frequently vote for the less undesirable of the major party candidates rather than "throw away his vote." Even in a case where it is possible to construct a procedure showing how to aggregate individual tastes into a consistent social preference pattern, there still remains the problem of devising rules of the game so that individuals will actually express their true tastes even when they are acting rationally. The problem is allied to the problem of constructing games of fair division, in which the rules are to be such that each individual, by playing rationally, will succeed in getting a preassigned fair share.

It has often been pointed out [3] that the rules of the game, or the mechanism for making a choice, may themselves enter into the values or utility measure of the individual. Thus, free enterprise becomes a force of good in itself to the "rugged enterpriser." We will not pursue this important feature of economics but will limit ourselves for the most part to an investigation of the expected returns to individuals in situations in which the rules of the game are given and in which no intrinsic desirability is attached to the nature of the mechanism given by the rules.

The result of any game may not be very desirable to many of the players, but the rest may be in a position to enforce the outcome. The importance of this manifests itself in situations in which a group of individuals is in a position to "beat the system." For instance, they may be able to lie about their needs for a rationed commodity and thus obtain more than their "fair" ration.

Methods and principles of "fair division," [4] and games designed to enforce fair division provide simple examples which demonstrate several features of the problems faced in developing a theory of economic imputation of wealth. Such egalitarian (or unegalitarian) slogans as "equal pay for equal work," "fair shares for all," can be scrutinized to see how clearly it is possible to define the essence that lies behind these sentiments and to see if systems can be designed which will guarantee the properties of "fairness" desired.

Although we will not carry the investigation any further at this time, the study of the design of fair division games is closely connected to several general problems in organization theory: for example, the design of self-policing systems and the design of decentralized decision-making systems which guarantee that the optimizing behavior of the submit will be optimal for the whole.

2. METHODS AND PRINCIPLES OF "FAIR DIVISION"

> "Equity and 'fairness of division' are charming in the pages
> of Herbert Spencer and delighted Dugald Steward with the
> appearance of mathematical certainty; but how would they be
> applicable to the distribution of a joint product between
> cooperaters?"
>
> F. Y. Edgeworth [5].

The concept of *fair division* is closely related to that of symmetry. If two individuals whose attributes are the same are involved in a division among a symmetric set of joint prospects, then intuitively we feel that the division should be symmetric. By a joint prospect we mean a pair of numbers (a, b) in which a denotes the amount that the first player obtains and b the amount that the second obtains. A symmetric set of joint prospects is such that if the prospect (a, b) is contained so is the prospect (b, a).

The concept of "fairness" is illustrated by a division mechanism which is impartial to the names of the players. Thus if I and II have all the same attributes, except name, and they commit the same crime, they will be given the same punishment.

Two individuals jointly find 100 dollars; how should they divide it? One of them is a milionaire and the other a pauper; what constitutes a "fair division" of the money? A problem such as this is beset with sociological and psychological overtones. If the individuals were in "roughly the same" class, financial condition, age group, etc., one might suggest 50 dollars apiece, i.e., assuming that they are able to make change. If they cannot, then they could randomize with a 50–50 chance for the 100 dollars or nothing. A not unreasonable result is that the fastest and/or strongest takes all. Given the utility functions of the individuals, there are a number of different basic problems of division that we can examine.

In this section some simple problems of fair division are noted. It is always easy to construct a situation in which the application of any suggested method of division produces a result which we might wish to reject as undesirable. This does not necessarily provide sufficient reason for rejecting the method. It merely limits its applicability. In the applied science of arbitration it may be possible to devise a method of settlement which applies between labor unions and corporations but not between private individuals. As such, its use is limited but nevertheless substantial.

Example 1.1 Two individuals must divide 100 dollars between themselves; their utilities are independent of each other's wealth and are defined only up to a complete ordering. An addition of an amount of any good, *ceteris paribus*, is assumed to add utility. If nothing more is known, then no criterion of "fairness" is suggested. Of all possible ways of dividing the 100 dollars there is certainly no way that is most preferred by the "society." This is seen trivially, if we regard a "state of society" as a vector $(100 - x, x)$; then if P_i is a preference relation, [6] for player i, given any two states of society, $(100 - x, x)$ and $(100 - x', x')$; if $(100 - x, x)P_I(100 - x', x')$, then $(100 - x', x')P_{II}(100 - x, x)$, hence never $(100 - x, x)P(100 - x', x')$, where P is the society's preference relation. All divisions are Pareto optimal.

A well-known method of fair division is found in the custom of letting one of two participants divide while the other chooses. The only specific property that this method has is that it guarantees to each individual a share that is, in his own estimation, as large or larger than that of the other claimant. How weak a condition this is is seen in the division of 100 dollars between a millionaire and a pauper. The 100 dollars will be split in two lots of 50 dollars. N. Steinhaus [9] mentions that custom has the older of the partners divide while the younger chooses. This, of course, introduces more "unfairness" into the "fair division" method if the players know each other's preference system and the item to be divided is not homogeneous. Consider as an example that I and II have a cake to divide. I is to cut. The cake consists of sponge and one cherry. I knows that II prefers the cherry to all of the sponge, hence he offers him those two alternatives. We suppose that I is indifferent to any pieces of the cake of the same size. If II had cut, then he would have divided the cake into two sections of $\frac{1}{2} + \epsilon$ and $\frac{1}{2} - \epsilon$ in size, with the cherry in the latter portion. Randomization to determine which man divides would remove this asymmetry.

Example 1.2. Individual utility scales are linear in the sense of von Neumann and Morgenstern but are not directly comparable, i.e., we cannot state that one prospect is worth "twice" as much to I as to II.

We may set up this problem as a two-person bargain. When we have only two individuals bargaining, either is in a position to block trade completely. For this reason it appears natural to single out the no-trade point as the position of *status quo* from which a fair division should be calculated. As the individuals are assumed to have linear utility scales which are not comparable, this means that if we assign a utility function of U_I to player I, a new function $U_I' = aU_I + b$ in which a and b are arbitrary constants would serve equally well. We are in a position to assign any two numbers to the utilities of the *status quo* to each player. It is convenient to call the utility values of the prospect of no trade $(0, 0)$, although it is not necessary to do so. Four assumptions are needed from which we can deduce the Nash "fair division." [8]

Assumption 1. We can pick a natural position of *status quo* in a two-person bargain: this is the no-trade position.

Given two utility functions U_I and U_{II} for the two individuals, we can obtain a graph of the utilities of all possible prospects. This gives us a convex graph, as indicated (the convexity indicates

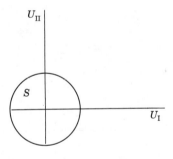

Figure 48

that for any two prospects with different utilities, there will always be other prospects whose utility values lie on a straight line connecting the two). We call the set of all pairs of utilities (i.e., points in Figure 48) which the players can obtain, S. Let $c(S)$ represent a solution point in S.

Assumption 2. If a (we use a as an abbreviation for the pair $\vec{a} = (a_1, a_2)$) is a point in S such that there exists another point

β in S with the property

$$U_I(\beta) \geqslant U_I(a) \text{ and } U_{II}(\beta) \geqslant U_{II}(a), \text{ then } a \neq c(S).$$

This is the condition of Pareto optimality. It states that at the final bargain no point will be considered if both players can improve their position by choosing another bargain.

Assumption 3. If the set T contains the set S and $c(T)$ is in S, then $c(T) = c(S)$.

The third assumption states that if two individuals agree that $c(S)$ is a fair bargain if they are restricted to bargains in S, then if they are faced with a bigger set of possible bargains T which contain S, if they decide $c(T)$ is a fair bargain and $c(T)$ lies in S, then $c(T) = c(S)$. In other words, the addition of irrelevant alternative bargains makes no difference to the choice of a final fair settlement.

A set S is symmetric if there exist utility operators U_I and U_{II} such that when (a, b) is contained in S (b, a) is also contained in S. In other words, the graph becomes symmetrical with respect to the line $U_I = U_{II}$. This is indicated in Figure 49.

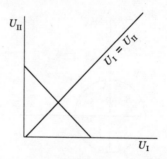

Figure 49

Assumption 4. If S is symmetric and U_I and U_{II} display this, then $c(S)$ will be a point of the form (a, a).

This assumption specifies the symmetry nature of "fairness." For instance, it implies that the fair division of 100 dollars between two individuals who must divide the money between themselves or obtain nothing will be 50 dollars to each if their utility functions for money are of the same shape.

We can show that the four conditions require that the solution be a point of the set S where the product $(U_I - c)(U_{II} - d)$ is maximized, where (c, d) are the co-ordinates assigned to the no-bargain point. Since these may be chosen arbitrarily, we can take them to be $(0, 0,)$ in which case the solution will be the point at which $U_I U_{II}$ is maximized.

We assume that S is a set such that among all the elements of the form (U_I, U_{II}) there will be some for which the product $U_I . U_{II}$ attains its maximal value. [9] The convexity of S implies that there will be only one maximal element of the form $U_I U_{II}$.

We fixed one degree of freedom when we called the no-bargain point $(0, 0)$. However, we can still multiply the utility scales of the individuals by any arbitrary positive factor. We can pick two such factors so that the above-mentioned point is transformed into the point $(1, 1)$. Since this involves only the multiplication of the utility scales by constants, $(1, 1)$ will now be the maximum of $U_I U_{II}$.

We observe that for no points of the set will $U_I + U_{II} > 2$, since if there were a point of the set with $U_I + U_{II} > 2$, at some point on the line segment between $(1, 1)$ and that point there would be an element of the set with a value of the utility products greater than $(1, 1)$. This can be seen in Figure 50. If P is the point whose co-ordinates sum to more than 2, then Q will have a greater value than $(1, 1)$, since it lies above the equilateral hyperbola passing through $(1, 1)$.

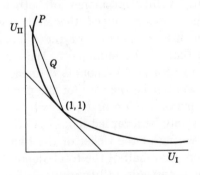

Figure 50

We can now construct a square which has one side on the line $U_I + U_{II} = 2$ and which completely encloses the set of alternatives. If we consider the set of alternatives to be the square region instead of the older set, $(1, 1)$ is the only point satisfying assumptions 2

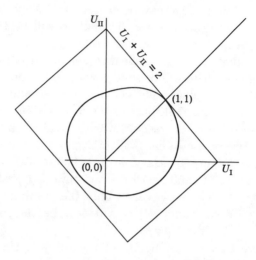

Figure 51

and 4. However by assumption 3 (1, 1) is also the solution to the original set of alternatives. This completes the proof.

Some idea of the result of a "fair division" according to this method can be seen if we apply it to the problem of division of 100 dollars between a millionaire and a pauper. On the assumption that the marginal utility for money of both individuals is non-increasing in the relevant ranges, then it is not unreasonable to expect that the utility function of the pauper will have more curvature than that of the millionaire. We may expect that the millionaire's utility for small amounts of money is approximately linear, but this will not be the case for the pauper.

The point of maximization of $U_\mathrm{I}U_\mathrm{II}$ will be such that the millionaire will certainly be awarded more than 50 dollars. The "fairness" of this favoring of the richer of the two can be interpreted that it takes more than half of the total amount of money to yield to him the same increase in utility in his own units as the pauper receives in his units from the remainder. Max Woodbury has suggested a modification of the Nash procedure which takes into account different bargaining abilities. Instead of maximizing $(U_\mathrm{I}U_\mathrm{II})$, Woodbury considers maximizing $(U_\mathrm{I}{}^{a_\mathrm{I}}U_\mathrm{II}{}^{a_\mathrm{II}})$, in which a_I and a_II are parameters representing bargaining power.

Example 1.3. Utilities are assumed to be measurable and comparable. For the first time equality of two amounts of utility accruing to different individuals can be defined. This assumption has usually been regarded as undesirable. However, it is made here in order to point out that even under such a strong assumption "fairness" presents difficulties for a simple division among two individuals. Several "fair division" rules can be suggested. They will be examined in application to the division problem previously considered. Let the utility functions of the two individuals be those of the pauper and millionaire referred to. However, now no multiplication by a constant is allowed on one scale if it is not done on the other, for the actual "utiles" are comparable. We get a utility diagram as indicated in Figure 52. A natural criterion of "fairness of division" would be that the money be divided in such a manner as to maximize utility subject to the side condition that the

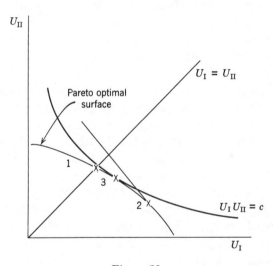

Figure 52

utility given to both sides be equal. In other words, $U_I + U_{II}$ maximal subject to $U_I = U_{II}$. This yields the point labeled 1; the richer of the two gets most of the money. Another method would be to divide the money in such a manner as to maximize the utility derived from it by society. This method will give nearly all the money to the poorer of the two. The point 2 is obtained by finding the point at which the tangent to the Pareto optimal surface has a slope of -1. This is easily seen if we express the curve as $U_{II} = f(U_I)$ we must maximize $U_I + f(U_I)$, hence $f'(U_I) = -1$. If we maximize the product $U_I U_{II}$ we obtain a division that lies between the divisions by the other two methods, as shown at point 3. Again, the richer of the two gets more than half the money.

The problems so far have been concerned with two persons, a homogeneous good to be divided, and complete knowledge. Modifications of these conditions must be discussed.

In a more general form the type of fair-division problem we have dealt with has been known as the "cake problem." By using money and assuming diminishing marginal utility of money, problems of complementarity and the necessity of having to consider a solution involving the use of probabilities were avoided. Complementarity problems were avoided by having the 100 dollars be perfectly homogeneous and infinitely divisible. In examples 1.2 and 1.3 the use of prospects involving probabilities was not necessary because the utility space was already convex, owing to the infinite divisibility of money taken and the fact that both individuals had a nonincreasing marginal, but always positive, utility for money.

Possibly one of the earliest fair-division problems with complementarity involved was that of King Solomon, the two women, and the baby. Two halves of a dead baby are usually worth less to its mother than the whole live baby (although there are always exceptions in economics). Another example of complementarity interfering with division is provided by the story of Saint Martin and the Beggar. Saint Martin cut his coat in half and gave one half to the beggar. Had he offered the beggar a gamble with $\frac{1}{2}$ probability for the whole coat and $\frac{1}{2}$ of getting nothing, the story would not have been so good a parable as it is now, but it would have made a somewhat better welfare theory.

That complementarity can cause the outcome to involve a chance decision can be seen in an attempt to apply fair division methods to the sharing of a painting. Consider two art lovers who ask a judge to divide a Rembrandt between them with no side payments allowed. Their utility map for certain "anticipations" or "prospects" is as indicated. Unless they consider some sort of randomization, they will both get a relatively worthless piece of canvas as a fair share, as shown in Figure 53.

The possibility of extending the three division problems to n-person cases is now considered.

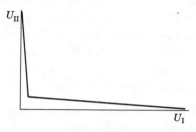

Figure 53

Example 2.1. Given only an ordering on each individual's utility for parts of a "cake," the "divide-and-choose" method can be generalized for n persons. One player cuts what he considers to be a fair share. He then offers it to the others. If no one wants it, he keeps it, and the division is then performed for $n - 1$ persons. If many players want it (thereby indicating that it is worth more than $1/n$ of the cake to them), then each is given an opportunity to diminish the size of the slice and offer it around. The last person to diminish the size of the slice gets it unless there is a tie, which occurs when two or more want it but will accept nothing less as a fair share. In this case they can randomize to see who gets it. Everyone will get at least $1/n$ of the cake in his own valuation if complementarity is ignored and diminishing marginal utility of cake is assumed. A more complete discussion than presented here is given by Hugo Steinhaus. [10]

Example 2.2. The Nash axioms can be generalized for n players, and the mode of action suggested is maximization of $\Pi_i U_i$ in which $i = 1, 2, \ldots, n$. There is a feature of the Nash treatment of the n-person situation which causes trouble if it is looked at either as a bargaining problem or as a fair-division problem. This is the selection of the no-bargain point by a method which does not take into account the underlying effect of the coalition structure available to the players. In the two-person game an individual could threaten not to co-operate and block the "society" (which consists of two people) from obtaining anything. Each player is in a position to enforce no trade; hence we may regard the no-trade point as a plausible and naturally defined initial point from which to work out a fair division. Hildreth has used this feature of the Nash bargaining mechanism, generalized to n persons, in his construction of a theory of social welfare. [11] He accepts as the initial point the no-trade position. This amounts to assuming that each individual has an absolute veto on the rest of society. In a two-person situation if one individual is not satisfied with a division he can refuse to trade. In an n-persons case $(n > 2)$ this usually does not block other trading or distribution of welfare from taking place.

Example 2.3. Given comparable utilities, then any of the solutions given in example 1.3 can be generalized. A general statement of the problem of cutting equal shares in a manner which is maximal, subject to this constraint, has been suggested to the writer by E. Calabi and is given here.

Let A be a topological space.

Let m_i, $(i = 1, 2, 3, \ldots, n)$ be a set of n measures on A, each continuous with respect to the topology of A, and such that $m_i(A) = 1$.

Problem. Partition A into n subsets $A_1, A_2, A_3, \ldots, A_n$ such that

$$m_1(A_1) = m_2(A_2) = \ldots = m_n(A_n) = \max$$

(of all partitions *of* A).

3. "FAIR-DIVISION" GAMES

So far, the division problem has been considered under conditions of complete information. As mentioned before, in game situations people will lie if it is to their advantage, especially if they know that the work entailed in finding out even a rough approximation of their true utilities in a given situation is costly and difficult to perform.

The first modification is of a nature that changes "fair division" into a game. Let us assume that the referee or social service agency knows absolutely nothing about the individual utilities of the players; however, it tells them that it trusts them and asks each of them to submit a document containing the relevant information about his preferences. After all the documents have been submitted (privately), the referee will apportion the wealth or welfare in accordance with one of the criteria already discussed. A game has thus been formulated in which the strategy of the players is a statement about a preference system. Each player must work out how to lie in a maximal manner. In this model the referee has no criterion for judging the truth of any statement and merely believes what he is told. In most cases it would be desirable to consider that he has some discernment. This is discussed later. We assume for the moment that each player knows the preference systems of the others.

Example 3.1. We assume that utility is measurable, that there are n players or "recipients" who know each other's preference system. There is a referee or a "donor" who distributes funds according to some convention based upon the information he receives from the recipients. We further assume that the referee has no information concerning the preference functions of the players, except that they are bounded (i.e., there is a number which is the largest that he will believe concerning any player's claim). If we further assume that each player must state his claimed "need" in integers of utiles or dollars and that no coalition or side payments are allowed, then we can represent the whole problem by a non-co-operative matrix game. If the awards of the donor are positively correlated with the size of an individual's claim, then this game has a unique equilibrium point which is determined by every player telling the biggest lie that will be believed.

The proof of this is obvious. Suppose that there were n players. The strategies available to any player i are the numbers 1, 2, 3, ... M_i, in which M_i is the largest amount that the donor will believe as a demand from player i. Given the strategies of the others as fixed, then a player may always improve by naming a larger number than he has previously named; hence every player will name the largest number he is permitted to name.

In example 3.1 the referee or donor was assumed to be a mere mechanism with no specified utility function of his own. In many situations involving governmental or social policy a welfare problem of the following type is faced. A central governmental agency wishes to allocate funds to a group of subagencies in such a manner that some general program is maximized. The central agency has only a vague idea of the requirements of its subagencies if they are to fulfill the program. The various subagencies may know about each other's needs (this may come about through technical meetings in which discuss common problems). In order to specify the problem completely we need to assign utility functions to the recipients and a utility function to the referee. An example of the aims of the donor can be seen in a foreign-aid program. The country giving the aid will usually have some humanitarian, political, or military evaluation scheme worked out to measure the success of its program.

We would like to set up a problem to determine how the players lie to this referee. The information restrictions put on already eliminate consideration of a von Neumann and Morgenstern type of game. In order to specify the problem more completely it is necessary to consider the discernment of the donor in being able to judge lies. A specification might be obtained by introducing a criterion for the donor's discernment and a cost of information. The problem can best be described as being dynamic in nature, possibly involving statistical decision. Its relevance can be seen in the following situation. The disbursement board of a donor country says:

If country X applies for aid and asks for an amount below a certain sum, then we regard this as a reasonable statement of needs. Even if they are lying, they are probably not lying very much, and we believe that in this instance an investigation will cost more than it is worth. If X asks for more than this sum, then we will investigate before we give.

A whimsical example of the importance of fooling the donor in an incomplete information situation was suggested by a member of the British government some time ago. In essence, he felt that Great Britian could get economic aid if it paid its Communist Party to start a small amount of guerrilla warfare in northern Scotland.

The "cake" or "fair division" problems and the modifications illustrate, even at this comparatively simple stage, four fundamental factors which appear to be present in most economic problems as major determinants.

They are wants of the individual decision-making units; control of physical factors by players; the information state of each player; and the cost of information or more generally the cost of the choice-mechanism employed.

The preceding problems have been formulated not only in an attempt to highlight some of the aspects of "fair division" but also to help show the relationship between welfare economics and game economics. The relationship is not unlike that between the turf committee and an individual jockey. The committee attempts to define an aggregative concept of "sportmanship", to lay down the codes of racing, and to devise methods of keeping the game "fair and honest." The jockey may decide what he, as an individual, is after and attempt to win it without running afoul of the committee. In the very long run the individual playing the game may also participate in writing the codes; however, in a shorter run the individual can take the rules as given.

Criteria of "fairness" are intimately connected with our intuitive concepts of symmetry and equality. An examination of fair division emphasizes the extreme difficulties entailed in attempting to get more than some very general rules without specifically adding ethical content.

NOTES

[1] See P. A. Samuelson, Foundations of Economic Analysis (Cambridge: Harvard University Press, 1948). pp. 219–253.

[2] K. J. Arrow, *Social Choice and Individual Values* (New York: Wiley, 1951), p. 7.

[3] *Ibid.* F. H. Knight has stressed this point in *The Ethics of Competition and other Essays* (New York: Harper, 1931).

[4] For a historical discussion of division problems, see G. Th. Guilbaud, "Les problèmes de partage," *Economie Appliquée*, I (1952), pp. 93–137.

[5] F. Y. Edgeworth, *Mathematical Psychics* (London: C. Kegan Paul, 1881), pp. 18–19.

[6] See, for instance K. J. Arrow, *op. cit.*, p. 34.

[7] Hugo Steinhaus, "The Problem of Fair Division" (abstract, *Econometrica*, XVI (January 1948), pp. 101–104.

[8] J. F. Nash, Jr., "The Bargaining Problem," *Econometrica*, XVIII (April 1950), pp. 155–162.

[9] This will be so if the set S is compact. See J. F. Nash, Jr., *op. cit.*

[10] Hugo Steinhaus, *loc. cit.*

[11] C. Hildreth, "Measurable Utility and Social Welfare," *Cowles Commission Discussion Paper, Economics*, No. 2002 (1950).

Appendix C

NOTES FOR THE TEXT

CHAPTER 4, SECTION 2, PAGE 62

In general we can describe the payoffs in a two-person non-zero-sum game involving two strategies for each player by two 2 x 2 matrices:

$$
\begin{array}{cc} a_{11} & a_{12} \\ a_{21} & a_{22} \end{array} \qquad \begin{array}{cc} b_{11} & b_{12} \\ b_{21} & b_{22} \end{array}
$$

If there is a mixed strategy equilibrium point, then the expected value of the payoff obtained by using either of his pure strategies, given his opponent's mixed strategy, must be the same to any player. If this were not true, one would yield more than the other; hence the player would not use a mixture of both strategies, in which case there would be no mixed-strategy equilibrium.

Let the mixed strategy employed by player 1 be $\xi = (\zeta_1, \zeta_2)$ and by player 2 be $\eta = (\eta_1, \eta_2)$; where $\zeta_1 + \zeta_2 = 1$ and $\eta_1 + \eta_2 = 1$ and $\zeta_1, \zeta_2, \eta_1, \eta_2 < 0$.

Suppose that the value or payoffs obtained by each player at the equilibrium were, respectively, V_1 and V_2. Then in order to solve for the equilibrium point we would have two sets of three equations in three unknowns each:

$$
\begin{aligned}
a_{11}\eta_1 + a_{12}\eta_2 &= V_1 & b_{11}\zeta_1 + b_{21}\zeta_2 &= V_2 \\
a_{21}\eta_1 + a_{22}\eta_2 &= V_1 & b_{12}\zeta_2 + b_{22}\zeta_2 &= V_2 \\
\eta_1 + \eta_2 &= 1 & \zeta_1 + \zeta_2 &= 1
\end{aligned}
$$

These can be solved immediately by simple algebra.

CHAPTER 4, SECTION 3.6.2, PAGE 74

The N.S.P. threat point and the no-side-payment settlement point (see Figure 10) form a solution if the line joining these two points has a slope that is the negative of the slope of the tangent to the settlement point on the Pareto optimal surface and if the profit curves obtained by holding either player's strategy constant at his threat strategy, while the strategy of the other is varied, lie, respectively, above and below this line (i.e., they are tangent at the threat point). The latter condition amounts to stating that if one player is using his optimal threat, the other only can obtain more profit than he gets by playing his threat strategy by increasing his opponent's profit more than proportionally.

The settlement point must satisfy the Pareto optimality condition which is given by the Jacobian:

$$\begin{vmatrix} \dfrac{\partial P_1}{\partial q_1} & \dfrac{\partial P_2}{\partial q_2} \\[2ex] \dfrac{\partial P_1}{\partial q_2} & \dfrac{\partial P_2}{\partial q_2} \end{vmatrix} = 0.$$

We note that the optimal threat point must also satisfy this condition as the profit curves traced out by holding one player's strategy fixed at his threat strategy are tangent at the threat point. The slope of the tangent at the settlement point is given by

$$\frac{\partial P_2/\partial q_1}{\partial P_1/\partial q_1} = \frac{\partial P_2/\partial q_2}{\partial P_1/\partial q_2},$$

and the slope of the line joining the settlement point and the threat point is given by

$$\frac{P_2{}^S - P_2{}^T}{P_1{}^S - P_1{}^T},$$

where $P_1{}^S$, $P_2{}^S$, and $P_1{}^T$, $P_2{}^T$ are the payoffs to the players at the settlement point and the threat point, respectively. The slope of this line must be the slope of the two curves at the threat point, so, defining

$$\frac{\partial P_2/\partial q_i}{\partial P_1/\partial q_i} = D_i,$$

we obtain the equations

$$- D_1{}^S = -D_2{}^S = \frac{P_2{}^S - P_2{}^T}{P_1{}^S - P_2{}^T} = D_1{}^T = D_2{}^T.$$

These four equations in four unknowns, $q_1{}^S$, $q_2{}^S$, $q_1{}^T$, and $q_2{}^T$ were solved by approximation.

CHAPTER 5, SECTIONS 4.1 AND 4.4.1, PAGE 105

The computation of the probability density functions for the strategies is beyond the scope of this study. However, there is a way in which a price game may be solved which gives rise to several problems concerning the nature of equilibrium points.

The price game as dealt with in Chapter 5: 4 permitted each player to use an infinite number of strategies. Any price was available as a strategy. We can restrict the actions of the players (in a realistic manner) by permitting only a finite number of prices. Thus a player may not be allowed to cut prices in units finer than one cent or one mil. If we do this, we can write down the payoff matrices for the players, and the problem of finding the equilibrium points involves the solution of two sets of simultaneous equation systems:

$$\sum_j P_1(p_{1i}, p_{2j})\zeta_j = V_1 \text{ and } \sum_i P_2(p_{1i}, p_{2j})\eta_i = V_2,$$

in which the p_{1i} and the p_{2j}, the prices charged by the first and second players, respectively, range over some bounded interval. The η_i and the ζ_j are the probability weightings used by the first and second players, respectively. These equations play the same role as the integral equations in Chapter 5: 4.3.

The payoffs for continuous price variation, as given in Chapter 5: 4.1 were approximated in section 4.4.1 by a price grid. In the game with a finite number of strategies we have to specify how the market is divided when the prices of the players are equal. In the continuous game the probability that the players picked the same price was negligible (actually of measure zero); hence we could ignore the value of the payoffs obtained at equal price. In the finite game there is a finite probability that the players will pick the same price; hence we have to know the value of their payoffs when they do so. This necessitates the specification of a convention to decide how the market is shared when the players' production oversaturates the demand at the price they both wish to charge.

A game with each player possessing only a finite number of strategies is in many ways a more realistic economic model than a game with an infinite number of strategies. In some cases it is easier to handle continuous models, and no violence is done to the economic analysis in so doing. Here this may not be true. If the players have different scales of fineness, this will influence the equilibrium; for instance, one player may be able to change production rates only in lots of a thousand and prices in multiples of one cent, whereas his opponent can change production by units of a hundred and prices by the mil. In a general discussion of the theory of the firm these details may not be very important. However, it is of interest to note that they arise naturally in an attempt to construct mathematical models of the market form. The importance of this type of phenomenon, i.e., discreteness and different scales of fineness, appears to be great when introduced into individuals' preference scales. [1]

CHAPTER 5, SECTION 4.3, PAGE 102

At a mixed strategy equilibrium point the probability mixture used by player i must be such that the payoff obtained by player j by using any one of his active strategies is the same. If this were not true, some of the active strategies of player j would be dominated and would therefore not be used. The same condition applies to the probability mix used by player i against player j. This is proved here for games with a finite number of pure strategies.

A two-person, nonzero-sum game may be represented by $||a_{ij}||$, $||b_{ij}||$, $i = 1, 2, \ldots, n$; $j = 1, 2, \ldots, m$, $i\epsilon S_1$, the set of strategies for the first player, and, similarly, $j\epsilon S_2$.

Consider the pair of strategies (ζ, η) which form an equilibrium point.

Theorem. Given $\boldsymbol{\eta}$, any active pure strategy $i \epsilon S_1$ used in $\boldsymbol{\zeta}$ will yield the same payoff to player 1 as any other active strategy.

Proof. The selection of $\boldsymbol{\zeta}$, given $\boldsymbol{\eta}$, involves a choice of the maximum element or a linear combination of maximal elements out of a set of n elements of the form

$$\sum_{j=1}^{m} a_{ij}\eta_j$$

Any active strategy i yields a payoff

$$\sum_{j=1}^{m} a_{ij}\eta_j = v_i.$$

Let v^* be the maximum of v_i and let $\bar{S}_1$ be the set of active strategies employed by the first player, $\bar{S}_1 C S_1$. The value of $\boldsymbol{\zeta}$ is $\sum_{i \epsilon S_1} \zeta_i v_i$ where $\sum_{i \epsilon S_1} \zeta_i = 1$. If any $v_i < v^*$ where $i \epsilon \bar{S}_1$, we can increase $\sum_{i \epsilon S_1} \zeta_i v_i$ by dropping this strategy and re-normalizing; hence all active strategies employed by player 1 must yield v^*.

CHAPTER 5, SECTION 4.3, PAGE 103

A proof that the values of the Bertrand game cannot lie above those determined by the highest of the low points of the Bertrand-Edgeworth cycle is as follows:

Consider the player whose opponent has no finite amount of probability at the top end of his range. If he plays his highest strategy, he will always be high man; hence, if this strategy is to give him the value of the game, the average of all possible payoffs to him as the other player varies his price must equal the value of the lower end of the range. However, if the range starts above the lower end of the Bertrand-Edgeworth cycle for the first player, this cannot be so because it holds only when the other player names the price at the bottom of the range. Otherwise all other payoffs are lower, hence the average of all payoffs is lower. Therefore the lower end of the strategy range must be below the lower cycle point of the first player.

CHAPTER 5, SECTION 4.4.1, PAGE 105

The problem of maximization with price discrimination is closely related to tariff and international trade problems. For instance, if the firms in section V.4.4.1 were able to separate all their customers into different markets, they would be able to reduce consumer surplus to zero. In doing so they would charge different prices to all customers and make a profit of

$$\int_0^{1.3286} (10 - q)\, dq - 0.9161\gamma_1(0.9161) - 0.41250\gamma_2(0.4125)$$

$$= 10q - \frac{q}{2}^2 \bigg|_0^{1.3286} - 3.6 - 1.9 = 13.3 - 0.8 - 3.6 - 1.9 = 7.$$

CHAPTER 6, SECTION 1.4, PAGE 123

The following was proof communicated by L. S. Shapley that if in a class of Bertrand games without pure strategy equilibrium points there exists a mixed strategy equilibrium point then the lower end of the strategy spectrum must lie above the efficient point.

Given a symmetric n-Person Bertrand game,
p_0 = efficient point price,
e_1 = efficient point value to first player,
$a(p)$ = profit to first player if his price p is lowest,
$b(p)$ = profit to first player at price p if all others are at p_0,
$c(p)$ = profit to first player at price p if all others just undercut him.

Then $a(p_0) = b(p_0) = c(p_0) = e_1,\ a'(p_0) > 0$

and $a'(p) \geqslant b'(p) \geqslant c'(p).$

If $b'(p_0) < 0$, then the efficient point is a pure strategy equilibrium Suppose $b'(p_0) > 0$. Let n be an integer greater than

$$2 - \frac{c'(p_0)}{b'(p_0)}.$$

Consider the prices

$$p_1 = p_0 + \epsilon$$
$$p_2 = p_0 + \epsilon^2$$
$$.$$
$$.$$
$$.$$
$$p_n = p_0 + \epsilon^n$$

where ϵ is a positive number less than 1, whose order of magnitude will be specified later. Let the first player use the mixed strategy which plays p_i with probability $A\epsilon^{-i}$, in which $A = 1/\sum\limits_{i=1}^{n} \epsilon^{-i}$. The worst that can occur is to have all his opponents undercut at one of the p_i. If they undercut at p_k, his profit is

$$P_1 = \sum_{i=1}^{k} A\epsilon^{-i}[c(p_k) + (\epsilon^i - \epsilon^k)b'] + \sum_{i=1+k}^{n} A\epsilon^{-i}a(p_i),$$

if we assume ϵ to be so small that second derivatives of a, b, and c can be ignored, leaving $a'(p)$, $b'(p)$, $c'(p)$ constant in the range from p_0 to p.

Then

$$P_1 = e_1 + \sum_{i=1}^{k} A\epsilon^{-i}[\epsilon^k c' + (\epsilon^i - \epsilon^k)b'] + \sum_{i=k+1}^{n} A\epsilon^{-i}\epsilon^i a'$$

$$= e_1 + kAb' - A(b' - c')[1 + \epsilon + \ldots + \epsilon^{k-1}] + (n - k)Aa'$$

$$\geqslant e_1 + A[nb' - b' + c' - (b' - c')\frac{\epsilon - \epsilon^k}{1 - \epsilon}], \text{ using } a' \geqslant b'$$

$$P_1 > e_1 + A[b' - \epsilon(b' - c')\frac{1 - \epsilon^{k-1}}{1 - \epsilon}], \text{ using } n > 2 - \frac{c'}{b'}$$

$e_1 >$ for ϵ sufficiently small.

The first player has a mixed strategy which guarantees him *more* than e_1. Therefore, any equilibrium point must give him more than e_1. The lower end point p' of the range of pure strategies in the symmetric equilibrium point must therefore be *greater* than p_0, since the value of that equilibrium point is $a(p')$, and $a'(p) > 0$.

CHAPTER 6, SECTION 2.3, PAGE 130

In order to compute the various equilibrium points that are consistent with a market in which entry is possible it is necessary to examine the solutions to many different equation systems.

Let n be the total number of firms and firms-in-being i.e., possible entrants.

$$p = \phi(\sum_{i=1}^{n} q_i) \qquad i = 1, 2, \ldots, n.$$

Call the set of all firms N. Consider N divided into a set A of active firms and a set B of firms-in-being:

$$A \cup B = N$$
$$A \cap B = \theta.$$

A set of active firms A' exactly saturates the market if the array of production rates $\mathbf{q}$ satisfying the system

$$\frac{\partial(pq_j - \gamma_j q_j)}{\partial q_j} = 0 \qquad \text{for all } j \epsilon A'$$

$$q_j > 0$$

and $\qquad\qquad q_k = 0 \qquad \text{for all } k \epsilon B'$

is such that $P_j = pq_j - \gamma_j q_j < 0$ for all $j \epsilon A'$; but there exists no $\mathbf{q}$ such that the system

$$\frac{\partial(pq_j - \gamma_j q_j)}{\partial q_j} = 0 \quad \text{for all } j \epsilon A' \cup \{b\}$$

$$q_j > 0$$

$$q_k = 0 \qquad \text{for all } k \epsilon B' - \{b\}$$

$$P_j = pq_j - \gamma_j q_j \geqslant 0 \qquad \text{for all } j \epsilon A' \cup \{b\}$$

is satisfied. $\{b\}$ is the set consisting of any single firm from B'.

In general, there exist many sets of the type A' which exactly saturate the market. Unless there is a discernable special structure to the costs of the firms, such as in the example in Chapter 6: 2.3, the process of finding them appears to involve testing all pairs of sets A, B.

CHAPTER 7, SECTION 2, PAGE 147

The following is an example of demand conditions in a duopolistic market with transportation costs present. This example
was communicated by Roy Radner.

Consider an indefinitely large number of consumers distributed
uniformly along an interval $0 \leqslant t \leqslant T$ and two producers of a
homogeneous commodity, one at each end of the interval. Let the
density of demand for the commodity at point t, when the delivered
price at t is p, be given by

$$\delta(p) = \begin{cases} b & p < 0 \\ b - ap & 0 \leqslant p \leqslant b/a \\ 0 & b/a \leqslant p \end{cases}$$

where both b and a are positive.

Let the cost of transportation per unit of commodity per unit
of distance be one, and let the prices, "delivered at the factory,"
of the two producers be p_1 and p_2, respectively. Thus for a consumer
at point t, the delivered price from producer 1 is $(p_1 + t)$, and the
delivered price from producer 2 is $(p_2 + T - t)$.

Assuming that at each point consumers want to buy from the
producer whose delivered price is lowest and that the density of
demand at that point for the cheaper producer's product is given
by the function δ (the density of demand for the other producer
being zero), the total demands $\phi_i(p_1, p_2)$ for the products of the
two producers, as functions of their factory prices, are given by
(for $0 \leqslant p_i \leqslant b/a - T$)

$$\phi_1(p_1, p_2) = \begin{cases} b - a\left(p_1 + \dfrac{T}{2}\right) \\ \dfrac{1}{8T}(p_2 - p_1 + T)(4b - aT - 3ap_1 - ap_2) \\ 0 \end{cases}$$

$$0 \leqslant p_1 \leqslant p_2 - T$$
$$p_2 - T \leqslant p_1 \leqslant p_2 + T$$
$$p_2 + T \leqslant p_1$$

and similarly for ϕ_2.

A graph of $\phi_1(p_1, p_2)$ as a function of p_1, for a typical fixed value of p_2, is shown in Figure 54.

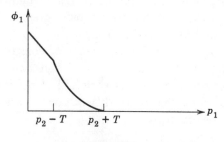

Figure 54

Now make the further assumption that producer 2 has set an upper bound $\bar{q}_2$ on the quantity he will sell. If $\phi_2(p_1, p_2) > \bar{q}_2$, then some consumers who would prefer to buy from producer 2 will not be able to do so and will have to buy from 1, if at all. If, from among those consumers who want to, those who actually do buy from 2 are chosen at random up to the point at which 2's supply is exhausted, then a graph of the "reconstituted" demand ψ_1 for the product of 1, as a function of p_1, for typical fixed values of p_2 and $\bar{q}_2$ is shown in Figure 55.

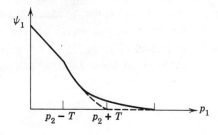

Figure 55

The dotted curve shows that part of the demand curve shown in Figure 55 does not coincide with the "reconstituted" demand.

CHAPTER 7, SECTION 5.1, PAGE 156

Strictly speaking when we wrote $q_1 = \psi(p_1, p_2)$ in Chapter 5: 5.1 we should have written $q_1 = \psi(p_1, p_2|q_2)$. This expression includes the possibility that because of a restriction on output of the second player the amount sold by the first player may depend upon a boundary maximization. If there is no limitation to the amount that the second player offers to the market at any price, then of course, this capacity effect is not observed. It is precisely this effect that causes the "kinks" in Radner's example given in the notes to Chapter 7: 2. In general, a capacity limitation will cause a discontinuity in the profit function of a player and will therefore make Stigler's suggested analytic solution invalid.

When we introduce product differentiation into a Cournot duopoly model, all the difficulties encountered in the price models occur. Formally, we can write down the payoffs as

$$P_1 = q_i \zeta_i(q_1, q_2) - C_i(q_i),$$

in which $p_i = \zeta_i(q_1, q_2)$. However, even if these relations can be defined and are unique, it is likely that they are not differentiable in relevant ranges.

CHAPTER 10, SECTION 6.3., PAGE 248

In calculating the probability of absorption of a particle in a random walk with three transition probabilities, one of which is the probability of remaining stationary, we can replace the three probabilities by two which specify motion to the left or right. Thus the probability of absorption for a particle which moves n units to the right with a probability of $\frac{1}{2}$, $2n$ units to the left with a probability of $\frac{1}{4}$, and remains stationary with a probability of $\frac{1}{4}$ is equivalent to the probability of absorption for a particle which moves n units to the right with a probability of $\frac{2}{3}$ and $2n$ units to the left with a probability of $\frac{1}{3}$.

Let $P(X)$ be the probability of absorption for a particle starting at X, then

$$P(X) = \tfrac{1}{3}P(X - 2n) + \tfrac{2}{3}P(X + n).$$

By changing units we can consider an equivalent walk with steps of two to the left and one to the right.

$$P(X) = \tfrac{1}{3}P(X - 2) + \tfrac{2}{3}P(X + 1).$$

Let $\qquad\qquad P(X) = \alpha^x.$

$$\tfrac{2}{3}\alpha^{x+1} - \alpha^x + \tfrac{1}{3}\alpha^{x-2} = 0.$$

or $\qquad\qquad 2a^3 - 3a^2 + 1 = 0,$

which has roots of $\alpha = 1$, 1, and $-\tfrac{1}{2}$.

The most general form of

$$P(X) = A_0 + A_1 X + A_2(-\tfrac{1}{2})^X.$$

(1) $\qquad\qquad As P(X) \leqslant 1 \qquad A_1 = 0.$

(2) $\qquad\qquad P(X) > P(X + 1)$ implies that

$$A_0 - A_2(-\tfrac{1}{2})^X - A_0 + A_2(-\tfrac{1}{2})^{X+1} \geqslant 0,$$

or $\qquad\qquad A_2(-\tfrac{2}{3})\,(-\tfrac{1}{2})^X \geqslant 0 \qquad \text{for all } X,$

therefore $\qquad\qquad A_2 = 0$

(3) $\qquad\qquad P(0) = 1 = A_0 + A_2,$

therefore $\qquad\qquad A_0 = 1,$

hence $\qquad\qquad P(X) = 1.$

NOTES

[1] J. von Neumann, and O. Morgenstern, Theory of Games and Economic Behavior (Princeton: Princeton University Press, 3rd. ed., 1953), pp. 614–616.

BIBLIOGRAPHY

Adams, W., "The Aluminium Case: Legal Victory—Economic Defeat," *American Economic Review*, **41** (1951), p. 915. **13,12***

— — —, *The Structure of American Industry* (New York: Macmillan, rev. ed., 1954), p. 315. **12,34**

Adelman, M., "Effective Competition and the Antitrust Laws," *Harvard Law Revue*, **61** (1948), p. 1317. **13,7**

Allen, R. G. D., *Mathematical Analysis for Economists* (New York: Macmillan, 1938), p. 110. **5,7**

Aluminum Company of America v. United States, 148 F 2d 416 (1945). **13,11**

American Tobacco Company, Annual Report (1955). **12,49. 66**

American Tobacco Company v. United States, 221 U.S. 106 (1911). **13,10**

American Tobacco Company et al., v. United States, 328 U.S. 781 (1946), 66 S.Ct. 1125, 90 L.Ed 1575. **13,15**

Antitrust Laws with Amendments, 1890–1951 (Washington: U.S. Government Printing Office, 1953). **13,2**

Arrow, K. J., "Alternative Approaches to the Theory of Choice in Risk-Taking Situations," *Econometrica*, **XIX** (October 1951), 404–437. **8,24**

— — —, *Social Choice and Individual Values* (New York: Wiley, 1951), p. 7 and p. 34. **B,2-3, 6**

Arrow, K. J., T. Harris, and J. Marschak, "Optimal Inventory Policy," *Econometrica*, **XIX** (July 1951), pp. 250–272. **5,13**

Automobile Facts and Figures (1955). **12,27**

* Boldface numbers indicate, respectively, chapter number and end-of-chapter reference: for example, Chapter 13, Note 12.

Bain, J. S., in *Business Concentration and Price Policy*, p. 139.   **12,16**

— — —, "Barriers to New Competition" (Cambridge: Harvard University Press).   **12,36**

Bean, Louis, H., "The Farmer's Response to Price," *Journal of Farm Economics*, **XI** (July 1929), pp. 368–385.   **8,20**

Bellman, R., "The Theory of Dynamic Programming," *Proceedings of the National Academy of Science*, **38** (1952), pp. 716–719.   **10,19**

Berle, A. A., and G. C. Means, *The Modern Corporation and Private Property* (New York: Macmillan, 1933), pp. 95–116.   **12,53-55**

Bertrand, J., "Théorie mathématique de la richesse sociale" (review), *Journal des Savants* (Paris: September 1883), pp. 499–508.   **5,1**

Bishop, R. L., "Elasticities and Market Relationships," *American Economic Review*, **XLII** (December 1952), pp. 779–803.   **2,24**

Blackwell, D., and M. A. Girshick, *Theory of Games and Statistical Decisions* (New York: Wiley, 1954).   **7,1**

Bonar, James, ed., *Letters of David Ricardo to Thomas Robert Malthus, 1810–1823* (Oxford: Clarendon Press, 1867), p. 18.   **8,1**

Brems, H., *Product Equilibrium under Monopolistic Competition* (Cambridge: Harvard University Press, 1951), p. 166, p. 168, p. 172, p. 173.   **2,25**

Bronfenbrenner, M., ' Applications of the Discontinuous Oligopoly Demand Curve," *Journal of Political Economy*, **XLVIII** (1940), pp. 420–427.   **5,5**

Burns, A. R., *The Decline of Competition* (New York: McGraw-Hill, 1936), pp. 280–328.   **7,12**

Chamberlain, Edward H., *The Theory of Monopolistic Competition* (Cambridge: Harvard University Press, 6th ed., 1950), p. 3, Chapter IV, VI, p. 10, p. 44, p. 52, p. 60, pp. 89–94, pp. 74–81, pp. 81–100, 100–110, p. 204.   **1,1. 2,1-16. 2,21. 5,3. 7,3. 7,5. 8,12**

Chow, G. C., ' Demand for Automobiles in the United States, a Case Study in Consumer Durables," Ph. D. thesis (Chicago: University of Chicago, Press, September 1955).   **12,25**

Chrysler Corporation, Annual Report (1955), p. 12.   **12,26**

Clark, J. B. and J. M., *Control of Trusts*, (New York: Macmillan, 1914), p. 200.   **13,1**

Clark, J. M., *Studies in the Economics of Overhead Cost* (Chicago: University of Chicago Press, 1923), p. 417.   **8,14**

— — —, ' Towards a Concept of Workable Competition," *American Economic Review*, **XXX**. No. 2 (June 1940), pp. 241–256.   **13,21**

Coase, R. H., "The Problem of Duopoly Reconsidered," *Review of Economic Studies*, **II** (1934–1935), pp. 137–143.   **5,12**

Conklin, L. R., and H. T. Goldstein, "Census Principles of Industry and Product Classification, Manufacturing Industries," in *Business Concentration and Price Policy* (Princeton: Princeton University Press, 1955), pp. 15–56.   **6,12-13**

Courant, R., *Differential and Integral Calculus*, **I** (London: Blackie & Son, 2nd. ed., 1942), p. 479.   **4,14**

Cournot, Augustin A., *Researches into the Mathematical Principles of the*

Theory of Wealth (New York: Macmillan, 1897), pp. 79–80, p. 84.   **4,9. 6,1**

Crum, W. L., *The Age Structure of the Corporate System* (Berkeley: University of California Press, 1953), Chapter VI, Chapter VII, p. 119, p. 146, p. 148, p. 120.   **12,6-8. 9-10**

Dirlam, J. B., and A. E. Kahn, *Fair Competition* (Ithaca: Cornell University Press, 1954), p. 16.   **13,6**

Dorr, G. H., "Philosophy of the Sherman Law," *Proceedings of the American Bar Association, August* 1955, pp. 15–33.   **13,3. 5**

E. I. du Pont de Nemours & Company v. United States, 118 F. Supp. 41 (1953).   **13,20**

Edgeworth, F. Y., *Mathematical Physics* (London: C. Kegan Paul, 1881), pp. 20–25, pp. 18–19.   **3,10. B,5**

— — —, *Papers Relating to Political Economy*, I (London: Macmillan, 1925), pp. 111–142, p. 120, p. 118.   **5,2. 5,14. 5,17**

Enke, Stephen, "On Maximizing Profits," *American Economic Review*, XLI. No. 4 (September 1951), p. 578.   **8,11**

Estes, W. K., "Individual Behavior in Uncertain Situations: An Interpretation in Terms of Statistical Association Theory," in R. M. Thrall, C. H. Coombs, and R. L. Davis, eds., *Decision Processes* (New York: Wiley, 1954).   **11,3**

Everett, H., "Recursive Games" (Princeton: Princeton University, 1954), Mimeographed.   **10,1**

Ezekial, Mordecai, "The Cobweb Theorem," *The Quarterly Journal of Economics* (February 1938), pp. 255–280.   **8,20**

Farrell, M. J., "The Demand for Motor-Cars in the United States," *Journal of the Royal Statistical Society*, Series A (General), **117**. Part 2 (1954).   **12,25**

Feller, W., *An Introduction to Probability Theory and its Applications*, I (New York: Wiley, 1950), p. 282–288.   **10,2**

Fellner, William, *Competition Among the Few* (New York: Knopf, 1949), p. 51, p. 53, Chapter 7, pp. 169–174.   **1,2. 9,16**

Flood, M. M., "On Game-Learning Theory and Some Decision Making Experiments," R. M. Thrall, C. H. Coombs, and R. L. Davis, eds., in *Decision Processes* (New York: Wiley, 1954).   **11,3**

Fisher, I., "A Statistical Method for Measuring 'Marginal Utility' and Testing the Justice of a Progressive Income Tax," in *Economic Essays in Honor of John Bates Clark* (New York: 1927).   **A,5**

Ford Motor Company, Prospectus (1956).   **12,35**

Frisch, R., "New Methods of Measuring Marginal Utility," *Beiträge zur Ökonomischen Theorie*, No. 3 (Tubingen, 1932).   **A,4**

Galbraith, J. K., *American Capitalism* (Cambridge: Houghton Mifflin, 1952).   **13,19**

General Motors Corporation, Annual Report (1955), p. 53.   **12,29**

Glicksberg, I. L., "A Further Generalization of the Kakutani Fixed Point

Theorem, with Application to Nash Equilibrium Points," *Proceedings of the American Mathematical Society*, **III** (February 1952), pp. 170–174.   **4,5**

Guilbaud, G. Th., "Les problèmes de partage," *Economie Appliquée*, **I** (1952), pp. 93–137.   **B,4**

Guthmann, H. G., and H. E. Dougall, *Corporate Financial Policy* (New York: Prentice-Hall, 2nd. ed., 1948), p. 21.   **8,4**

Handler, Milton, "Unfair Competition," *Iowa Law Review*, **XXI**. No. 2, (January 1936), pp. 175–262.   **13,20**

Hausner, M., *Games of Survival* (Santa Monica: The Rand Corporation, February 12, 1952), *RM*-776.   **10,1**

— — —, *Optimal Strategies in Games of Survival* (Santa Monica: The Rand Corporation, February 18, 1952), *RM*-777.   **10,1**

Hicks, J. R., *Value and Capital* (London: Oxford University Press, 1939).   **A,3**

Hildreth, C., "Measurable Utility and Social Welfare," *Cowles Commission Discussion Paper, Economics*, No. 2002 (1950).   **B,11**

Hotelling, H., "Stability in Competition," *The Economic Journal*, **XXXXI** (March 1929), p. 41.   **1,3**

Hurwicz, L., "Some Specification Problems and Applications to Econometric Models" (abstract) *Econometrica*, **XIX** (July 1951), pp. 343–344.   **8,23**

Hutchinson, A. R., and M. Newcomer, "A Study in Business Mortality," *American Economic Review*, **28** (1938), pp. 497–514.   **11,5**

Jacoby, O., *Poker* (New York: Doubleday, rev. ed., 1948). p. 42.   **1,6**

Jannaccone, P., *Prezzi e Mercati* (Torino: Einaudi, 1951), Chapters I and II.   **3,14**

Kaiser Motor Corporation, proxy statement (February 9, 1956).   **12,23**

Kaldor, N., "Mrs. Joan Robinson's Economics of Imperfect Competition" (review), *Economica* (new series), **I** (August 1934), pp. 335–341.   **3,2**

Kaplan, A. D. H., *Big Enterprise in a Competitive System* (Washington: The Brookings Institution, 1954), pp. 64–65, p. 117.   **12. 1-3**

Karlin, Samuel, "On a Class of Games," in H. W. Kuhn and A. Tucker, eds., *Contributions to the Theory of Games*, **II** (Princeton: Princeton University Press, 1953), pp. 159–172.   **6,9**

Kauder, B., "Genesis of the Marginal Utility Theory," *The Economic Journal*, **LXIII** (September 1953), pp. 638–650.   **A,1**

Knight, F. H., *Risk, Uncertainty and Profit* (London: London School Reprints of Scarce Works, No. 16, 1933), p. 197.   **8,9**

— — —, *The Ethics of Competition and Other Essays* (New York: Harper, 1931).   **B,3**

Koopmans, T. C., "Efficient Allocation of Resources," *Econometrica*, **XIX** (October 1951), pp. 455–465.   **4,11**

Kuhn, H. W., "Extensive Games and the Problem of Information," in *Contributions to the Theory of Games*, **II**,   **9-2-3**

— — —, "Lectures on the Theory of Games" (reproduced lecture notes) (Princeton, 1953), p. 102.   **9,7**

Lange, Oscar, *On the Economic Theory of Socialism* (Minneapolis: University of Minnesota Press, 1938). **4,12**

P. Lorillard Company, Annual Report (1955). **12,52**

Luce, R. D., χ—Stability: A New Equilibrium Concept for n-Person Game Theory," *Mathematical Models of Human Behavior*, (Stanford: Dunlop and Associates, 1955). pp. 32–44. **11,1**

Luce, R. D., and H. Raiffa, *Games and Decisions* (New York: Wiley, 1957), Chapter 1. **1,4. 3,7. A,7**

Marschak, J., "Rational Behavior, Uncertain Prospects and Measurable Utility," *Econometrica*, **XVIII** (April 1950), p. 114, p. 138. **1,7. 2,28**

Mayberry, J. P., J. F. Nash, and M. Shubik, "A Comparison of Treatments of a Duopoly Situation," *Econometrica* **XXI**, (January 1953), pp. 141–154. **2,26. 4,6. 18**

McKinsey, J. C. C., *Introduction to the Theory of Games* (New York: McGraw-Hill, 1952), especially Chapters 1, 2, 5, 6, 15, 16, 17 and 18. **1,4-5**

Milnor, J. W., "Games Against Nature," in R. M. Thrall, C. H. Coombs, and R. L. Davis, eds., *Decision Processes* (New York: Wiley, 1954), pp. 49–59. **8,25**

Milnor, J. W., and L. S. Shapley, *On Games of Survival* (Santa Monica: The Rand Corporation, August 10, 1954), *RM*–1320. **10,6**

Morgenstern, O., "Demand Theory Reconsidered," *Quarterly Journal of Economics*, **LXII** (February 1948), p. 168. **5,8**

— — —, "Perfect Foresight and Economic Equilibrium," (translation), *Zeitschrift für National Ökonomie*, **VI**. Part 3 (1935). **8,10**

Moody's Industrials (1955). **12,21**

Nash, J. F., Jr., "The Bargaining Problem," *Econometrica*, **XVIII** (April 1950), pp. 155–162. **3,12**

— — —, "Non-Cooperative Games," *Annals of Mathematics*, **LIV** (September 1951), pp. 286–295, p. 287. **1,9. 4,3**

— — —, "Two-Person Cooperative Games," *Econometrica*, **XXI** (January 1953), pp. 128–140. **3,13**

National Resources Committee. *The Structure of the American Economy*, (Washington: U.S. Government Printing Office, June 1939), I and II opposite p. 158 and 162. **12,4**

Nicholls, W. H., *Pricing Policies in the Cigarette Industry* (Nashville: Vanderbilt University Press, 1951), p. 17, p. 27, p. 31, p. 91, p. 160, Chapter VI. **12,39. 27. 43. 45-48**

Northern Securities Company v. United States, 193 U.S. 197, 24 S.Ct. 436, 48 L.Ed. 679 (1904). **13,8**

Oppenheim, S. C., *Cases on Federal Antitrust Laws, Trade Regulation*, American Casebook Series, Warren A. Seavy, gen. ed. (St. Paul: West Publishing Co., 1948), pp. 88–89. **13,22**

Papandreou, A. G., "Market Structure and Monopoly Power," *American Economic Review*, **XXXIX** (September 1949), pp. 883–897. **6,14**

Pâreto, V., *Manuel d'économie politique* (Paris: Girard, 2nd. ed., 1927), Chapter VI, Appendix. **3,8. 7,6**

376   Strategy and Market Structure

Peisakoff, M. P., *More on Games of Survival* (Santa Monica: The Rand Corporation, June 20, 1952), *RM*–884.   **10,1**

Philip Morris Company, Annual Report (1955).   **12,51**

Raiffa, H., "Arbitration Schemes for Generalized Two-Person Games," in H. W. Kuhn and A. W. Tucker, eds. *Contributions to the Theory of Games,* **II** (Princeton: Princeton University Press, 1953), pp. 361–387.   **3,16**

Redfield, J. W., "Elements of Forecasting," *Harvard Business Review,* **XXVIII.** No. 6 (November 1950).   **8,4**

Reynolds Tobacco Company, Annual Report (1955).   **12,50**

Robinson, Joan, *The Economics of Imperfect Competition* (London: Macmillan, 1950), p. 21.   **2,19. 2,31**

Rosenbluth, G., "Measures of Concentration," in *Business Concentration and Price Policy* (Report of a Conference of National Bureau of Economic Research) (Princeton: Princeton University Press, 1955), pp. 57–95.
                        12,14

Rothschild, K. W., "The Degree of Monopoly," *Economica* (new series), **IX** (1942), pp. 21–39, 214–239.   **5,11. 6,14**

Samuelson, P. A., *Foundations of Economic Analysis* (Cambridge: Harvard University Press, 1948), pp. 36 and 60, Chapter V, pp. 92–95, pp. 219–253.
                        5,23. 7,9. A,2. B,1

Savage, L. J., *The Foundations of Statistics* (New York: Wiley, 1954), Chapter II, p. 30.   **8,21. 8,27**

Scitovsky, T., "Economic Theory and the Measurement of Concentration," in *Business Concentration and Price Policy* (Princeton: Princeton University Press, 1955), pp. 101–118.   **6,14**

Schumpeter, J. A., *The Theory of Economic Development* (Cambridge: Harvard University Press, 1934), Chapter IV.   **10,16**

Seltzer, L. H., *A Financial History of the American Automobile Industry* (Cambridge: Houghton Mifflin, 1928), pp. 20–21.   **12,19**

Shackle, G. L. S., *Expectations in Economics* (Cambridge: Cambridge University Press, 1949), p. 3.   **8,23**

Shapley, L. S., "A Duopoly model with Price Competition" (abstract), *Econometrica,* **XXV** (April 1957), pp. 354–355.   **5,20**

Shapley, L.S., and M., Shubik, "A Method for Evaluating the Distribution of Power in a Committee System,"*American Political Science Review,* **XLVIII,** (September 1954), pp. 787–792.

Shubik, M., "A Business Cycle Model with Organized Labor Considered," *Econometrica,* **XX** (April 1952), pp. 234–294.   **3,7**

— — —, "A Comparison of Treatments of a Duopoly Situation, Part II," *Econometrica,* **XXIII** (October 1955), pp. 417–431, p. 424.   **5,15. 5,18**

— — —, "A Game Theorist Looks at the Antitrust Laws and the Automobile Industry," *Stanford Law Review,* July 1956.   **12,18**

— — —, "Edgeworth Market Games," *in Contributions to the Theory of Games,* **IV.** R. D. Luce and A. W. Tucker, eds. (Princeton: Princeton University Press, 1958).   **3,6. 8,5**

— — —, "Information, Risk, Ignorance, and Indeterminacy," *Quarterly*

Journal of Economics, **LXVIII** (November 1954), pp. 629–640.   **8,17**

— — —, "Information, Theories of Competition, and the Theory of Games," *The Journal of Political Economy*, **LX** (April 1952), pp. 145-150.   **8,3**

— — —, "The Uses of Game Theory in Management Science," *Management Science*, **II**. No. 1 (October 1955), pp. 40–54.

Shubik, M., and G. L. Thompson, "Games of Economic Survival," **10,9. 17-18**

Slutsky, E., "Sulla Teoria del Bilancio del Consumatore," *Giornale degli Economisti*, **II** (1915), pp. 1–26.

Stackelberg, H. von, *Marktform und Gleichgewicht* (Berlin: Julius Springer 1934), p. 134.   **4,10**

Standard Oil Company of New Jersey v. United States, 221 U.S. 1 (1911). **13,9**

Steinhaus, Hugo, "The Problem of Fair Division" (abstract), *Econometrica*, **XVI** (January 1948), pp. 101–104.   **B,7**

Stigler, George J., "The Development of Utility Theory, I and II," *The Journal of Political Economy*, **LVIII** (August and October 1950), pp. 307–327 and pp. 373–396.   **A,1**

— — —, "The Kinky Oligopoly Demand Curve and Rigid Prices," *The Journal of Political Economy*, **LV** (October 1947), pp. 432–449. **2,23.5,6**

— — —, "Notes on a Theory of Duopoly," *Journal of Political Economy*, **XLVIII** (1940), pp. 521–541, especially p. 535.   **7,14**

— — —, *The Theory of Price*, p. 197.   **8,13**

Suits, D. B. and Janosi, "The Demand for Automobiles in the United States," (a report to the Ford Motor Company, 1955).   **12,25**

Survey of Current Business, **XXXVI** U.S. Department of Commerce, (July 1956), p. 11.   **12,13**

Sweezy, Paul, "Demand under Conditions of Oligopoly," *Journal of Political Economy*, **XLVII** (1939), pp. 568–573.   **2,23. 5,4**

Taeusch, Carl F., *Professional and Business Ethics* (New York: Henry Holt, 1926), pp. 279–284.   **11,4**

Tennant, R. B., *The American Cigarette Industry* (New Haven: Yale University Press, 1950), p. 28, 83, pp. 100–103, 103–106, 119, 144, 142, pp. 163–172, pp. 293–296.   **10,15. 11,7. 12,40-41. 57. 59. 61-53. 65**

Theater Enterprises, Inc., v. Paramount Film Distributing Corporation., 346 U.S. 537, 540–541 (1954).   **13,16**

Thompson, C. I., "A Policy against Undue Limitations on Competitive Conditions," *Proceedings of the America Bar-Association, August* 1, 1955, pp. 34–63.   **13,4**

Thompson, G. L., "Signalling Strategies in *n*-Person Games," in H. W. Kuhn and A. W. Tucker, eds., *Contributions to the Theory of Games*, **II**. p. 268.   **9,10**

Thrall, R. M., C. H. Coombs, and R. L. Davis, eds., *Decision Processes*, (New York: Wiley, 1954).   **11,3**

Tinbergen, J., *Econometrics* translated by Dr. H. Rijken van Olst (Philadelphia: Blakiston, 1951), p. 38.   **9,14**

Triffin, R., *Monopolistic Competition and General Equilibrium Theory* (Cambridge: Harvard University Press, 1940), p. 45, 67, 68.   **2,18. 2,20**

U. S. Department of Agriculture. *Tobacco Statistics*. (Washington: U.S. Government Pointing Office, 1955).   **12,60**

U. S. House of Representationes. Committee on the Judiciary. *Study of Monopoly Power*, hearings before a Subcommittee of the House Committee on the Judiciary, the 81st Congress. first session, Part 2–B, p. 1454.
12,15

U. S. Temporary National Economic Committee. "Competition and Monopoly in American Industry." Monograph No. 21 (Washington: U.S.G.P.O., 1940), pp. 59–63.   **11,2**

U. S. Temporary National Economic Committee, "The Distribution of Ownership in the 200 Largest Non-Financial Corporations," Monograph No.29(Washington:U.S. Government Printing Office, 1940), pp. 391–392.
12,56

United States v. American Tobacco, 221, U.S. 106, 31 S.Ct. 632, 55L. Ed. 663 (1911).   **12,44**

See *United States v. Armour and Company*, Civil No. 48–C–1351, N.D. Ill., September 15, 1948, *dismissed without prejudice by stipulation*, CCH Trade. Reg. Rep.

(March 17, 1954). See generally *Attorney General's National Committee to Study the Antitrust Laws, Report* 36–42 (1955): Rahl, *Conspiracy and the Antitrust Laws*, 44 Ill., L. Rev. 743 (1950) Note, *Conscious Parallelism-Fact or Fancy*[6] 3 Stan L. Rev. 679 (1951).   **8,6**

United States Steel Corporation v. United States, 25 U.S. 417 (1920). **13,14**

von Neumann, J., and O. Morgenstern, *Theory of Games and Economic Behavior*, (Princeton: Princeton University Press, 3rd. ed., 1953), Chapters I, II, III, pp. 86–112, Chapter IV, pp. 169–186, Chapter V, Chapter X, p. 26, 31, 34, 30, 64–66, pp. 112–124, pp. 245–49, pp. 263–4, p. 289, pp. 409–413, p. 526, p. 545, pp. 584–586.   **1,4. 8. 3,5. 9,1.6. A,6. B,1**

Wald, Abraham, "On Some Systems of Equations of Mathematical Economics" (translation), *Econometrica*, **XIX** (October 1951), pp. 368–403. **4,7**

— — —, *Statistical Decision Functions* (New York: Wiley, 1950).   **7,10**

Wold, H., *Demand Analysis* (New York: Wiley, 1953). p. 13.   **9,15**

Whitin, T. M., *The Theory of Inventory Management* (Princeton: Princeton University Press, 1953), Chapter III.   **5,13**

Wilks, S. S., *Elementary Statistical Analysis* (Princeton: Princeton University Press, 1951), p. 98, pp. 106–110.   **5,21**

Zeuthen, F., "Undeterminierte Lohnprobleme," *Archiv für Socialwissenschaft und Sozialpolitik*, **62** (1929).   **3,15**

INDEX OF NAMES

INDEX